About the Author

Robert Brooks Strong is a seventy-eight year old man, who has spent the last forty-five years in mental hospitals because he has always refused to have sex with his mother. There is nothing wrong with his mental health and his whole adult life has been ruined by a corrupt system, presided over by his late mother.

My Journey Back – Book Four
God's Ongoing War with Lucifer

Robert Brooks Strong

My Journey Back – Book Four
God's Ongoing War with Lucifer

Olympia Publishers
London

www.olympiapublishers.com
OLYMPIA PAPERBACK EDITION

A CIP catalogue record for this title is
available from the British Library.

ISBN: 978-1-80439-068-9

This book is, to the best of the author's
knowledge and belief, a true story. Some of the names of the people and places
have been changed to protect their identity.

First Published in 2023

Olympia Publishers
Tallis House
2 Tallis Street
London
EC4Y 0AB

Printed in Great Britain

Dedication

This book is dedicated to my soulmate, Lucy Lawless, of Xena-Warrior Princess fame.

INTRODUCTION

This book is a journal. It is a cross between a diary, a narrative, and a series of letters which I have written and I am here publishing. The letters are principally to my soulmate and lover, Lucy Lawless, but also to my shrink, Dr Twee Dampensquib, as well as other people. Towards the end of the book, I publish a series of letters which I wrote to a list of world leaders, explaining the danger that my late mother, Mrs Dorothy (Dolly) Ayres, who is none other than the vainglorious Archangel Lucifer, presents to the world and what to do about her. By continuing to prolong the agony of her existence she is the main cause of Global Warming and Climate Change.

Back in the 1980s, I was fighting, mentally, with Edward Richard Pitchblack, the Devil Himself, when it occurred to me that the fact that I was successfully defending mankind from Him must mean that this life of mine is, indeed, that of the coming of the Lord God, and that is WHO I AM. That was when I *found myself.*

Lucifer has been the sexual, and therefore the **real** leader of the human race for the last seventy years or so, and the fact that she died in 2006 doesn't alter that fact. Her spirit still exists as a ghost, and continues to wield power in the world.

This book is the story of my ongoing fight with her; a fight which is not over yet.

This book was originally subtitled 'The birth of The Survival Party' which was my idea, and I produced a Manifesto of my political policies that I wish to pursue, but it now seems that my political Party was stillborn. I cannot, at present, foresee any future for The Survival Party, although I still say that my policies are the only ones by which the world will survive the Climate Change crisis.

My late mother, Lucifer, is the one who has stymied my political ambitions, just as she and her followers thwarted my professional ambitions when I was in business in the 1970s. She got her followers to bully me into committing homicide and I have been in mental hospitals ever since then. And all because I refuse to have sex with the old witch, not even mentally.

I wouldn't have sex with her, not even if she was the last woman left in creation. It is not who I am. I am the King of the Gods, not Lucifer's toyboy.

Continuing From the Last Book

Chapter 1

The Conception of the Survival Party

Events and Thoughts from Thursday 11th April 2019

Thursday 11th April 2019. This is the fourth volume of the story of my adult life. The preceding "My Journey" books are a requisite to be read before reading this book. This is the latest in a series of books about my story. I wrote to my soulmate, Lucy Lawless, today as follows: The letter is self-explanatory: - Thursday 11th April 2019

Lucy Lawless,

Dear Soulmate,

My letter to Dampensquib of the 9th April, of which I sent you a copy, is the concluding entry in my journal entitled *My Journey Back – Part Three*. I am now enclosing for you the three preceding pages which are the entries since Friday the 5th April. The manuscript has now been sent to the publishers for approval for publishing. It should be in print in about a year's time. I am just waiting for the final draft of the cover illustration for my approval of *My Journey Back – Part Two,* before I approve it for publishing. It should be published this year. This letter will be the first entry in *My Journey Back – Part Four.*

Last night and again this morning I felt your sincere love very strongly, and I have never been happier than feeling your love. My heart goes out to you in reply, Darling. I love you more than ever even though my libido is suppressed by the filthy drugs which these evil idiots force me to take. I'm sure I'll be free from them soon, when Dolly is ratified. Everybody in the UK and Europe is busting a gut to make that happen as soon as possible.

Take care of yourself, my Love,

I have much more to say to you, but it can wait until we talk, Bless you,

My Queen,

    Yours with Love, Affection and Friendship,

Bob XX

I also wrote today to Paula. She is my grandson, Troy's, mother and one of my son, Christopher's, ex-girlfriends: - Thursday 11th April 2019

    Paula Evans,

Hiya Paula,

    Thanks ever so much for your lovely letter. It was really good to hear from you, and it was good for me to get news concerning Chris and Troy. On the subject of emotions, that is one of the differences between adults and children. When you are a kid, your emotions control you – when you are an adult, you control your emotions. I know that's a lot easier said than done, but it's one of the things that life is all about. Each generation puts the next one through a series of tests to see who is the best at controlling their emotions. Those who are the strongest are the natural leaders of their generation.

    My late father, Frank, myself, Chris and Troy comprise four generations of natural leaders. Chris is discovering that anger is one of the most difficult emotions to control, and Troy is discovering that love is one of the most difficult emotions to control. I'm sure that Chris has got what it takes to be a good man, and that he will be man enough to set Troy a challenge to prove himself when the time comes for Troy to do so.

    Very few people under the age of fifty understand these things. I was forty-nine years old myself before I discovered what it really meant to prove myself.

    On the lighter side, is anyone going to Spain with you apart from your two dogs? I hope you have a good time, and enjoy lots of sangria! My ex-girlfriend used to be known as the girl who ate the pieces of lemon. Little did I know that one day I was to be a lemon that she would eat! Looking back on it now, I can see the funny side of it, but learning to control unrequited love was not easy, especially with two young boys on my hands and a partner who stole my business from me.

    I didn't get any joy from my Tribunal hearing, but I live in hope that things will get better for me. Having a friend like you helps me to keep my spirit up. Do please stay in touch.

Lots of love,

Bob XX

Tuesday 16th April 2019. I had an MDT (Multi-Disciplinary Team) meeting this morning. Dr Dampensquib was there and so was Sophia the social worker, a staff nurse and the secretary. Dampensquib had the report by the second opinion dentist that I had seen last Monday, and he said that I could go ahead with the dental work that I want done. This came as a huge relief to me as I have been waiting and planning for nearly three years to get some dental implants in my upper jaw.

These should enable me to pronounce my words clearly when talking and singing and also to eat properly again. This should also eliminate the problem which I have at the moment of my upper teeth cutting the inside of my top lip.

Dampensquib also spoke about getting me some unescorted leave, and he said he would contact the Ministry of Justice for permission to do this.

Last night there was a huge fire at the Notre Dame Cathedral in Paris, France. Most of the roof was destroyed as well as the spire, but they discovered this morning that most of the inside of the Cathedral was spared and not damaged much, including many priceless artefacts and works of art. Some of the stained-glass windows were destroyed though. The Cathedral dates back to the 12th century and is considered to be the very heart of the city of Paris. It is one of the most famous buildings in the world and has special religious significance to many millions of people. President Emmanuel Macron has sworn that the Cathedral will be rebuilt and hundreds of millions of Euros have already been pledged to help with the reconstruction effort.

Those who pray to "Our Lady" Mary, the mother of Jesus Christ should know that she can't hear them. She has already been reborn in the form of my soulmate, Lucy Lawless. Likewise, Jesus Christ Himself has already been reborn and is living a life as a person, although I don't think he knows yet who he was in his last life. It took me a long time to figure that out for myself, about myself. I want the boy who is now the reincarnation of Jesus Christ to become the Official World Leader when Lucy passes away in about fifty years' time. Between now and then I want to pass on as much of my wisdom as I can to Him. Even though I may have to hurt Him to teach Him what I know, it doesn't mean I don't love him, because I do, and so does Lucy. I made Him a promise two thousand years' ago that I would make Him King of the World one day, to recompense Him for sacrificing Him as I did. I am on course to fulfilling that promise.

I am indeed the Lord God, and I am going to punish mankind for following the false God, my late mother Mrs Dorothy (Dolly) Ayres, who is none other than the vainglorious Arch-demon Lucifer, and her decadent ways. She condones same-sex sexual relationships as socially acceptable. I do not, and I AM GOD, NOT HER. Time will tell which of us is right. I know that I am, but I have to prove this to her. It will be proven when I make her come back to life as an animal, which is what she deserves to be because of her insane obsession with forcing me to have an incestuous relationship with her.

Unfortunately for me, however, is the fact that a large part of the establishment of the International Community follow her, although the vast majority of the ordinary men and women of the world follow me, not her. Most people ignore her propaganda because they know it for what it is – the demented ravings of a pathetic old witch. Like I said, time will tell which of us is right, but I have the weight of three hundred thousand years of history on my side.

When my powers are recognised, I will have the authority to bring about multilateral disarmament of all weapons of mass destruction! Which is the objective of my exercise – a more peaceful and secure world for people to live in.

The whole human race can then live in peace, freedom and security and, hopefully, prosperity, knowing that God is in charge, and is looking after the world, just as I have always done from one lifetime to the next.

People should have learned that same-sex sexual relationships are against God's Will from the Bible story of the cities of Sodom and Gomorrah. The same thing is happening again but on a global scale this time. The human race has left me no choice but to punish them. They should have learned from what I wrote in the Bible, "I am the Lord thy God, and thou shalt have no other Gods before me"

Monday 22nd April 2019. I've written a few letters to Lucy recently which

I will not be publishing, but I wrote to her this morning as follows: -
Monday 22nd April 2019

Lucy Lawless,

Dear Soulmate,

All is well!

I felt us come together at about nine a.m. this morning and I couldn't be happier. I don't have a word for the way I feel, so I've just invented one. The word is, "bobulucydated". It means a special kind of happiness that can't be beaten, and only happens when you and I dance and come together at the same time. It means relaxed, fulfilled, content and extremely happy all at once. That is the best way I can say it, but I know that you know this feeling too.

Yours etcetera

Tuesday 23rd April 2019. All great movements evolve, but they are sparked into being by an idea in the mind of a leader. My idea for The Survival Party was sparked into being by my appreciation of the Extinction Rebellion movement that has made headlines recently. Those people were, no doubt, inspired by the TV series of Sir David Attenborough, who boldly stated on TV that the human race has only got another ten years before it will be too late to save the planet from Global Warming. The Extinction Rebellion people have been taking drastic action to draw to the public's attention the need for imminent change. They are campaigning for the UK to have a zero carbon emissions policy by 2025. Whilst this is an admirable ambition, they haven't said how they plan to go about making it happen, except by disrupting the public.

It seems to me that they should have some idea of what laws they want the government to pass to make this happen, and then campaign for the passing of those laws. So, I think that what is needed is a new political Party with a Manifesto of what laws we want to see passed. This is what gave me the idea for The Survival Party.

My thoughts on this Manifesto are still in the embryonic stage at the moment, but my first thought is to ban the manufacture of vehicles with internal combustion engines immediately, and concentrate on the production of vehicles with electric motors. The government should immediately sponsor research into bigger and better batteries, both for vehicles and for electricity storage and distribution. The government should immediately invest in solar powered power stations and wind powered power stations, so that we can cease producing electricity by burning coal in power stations within twelve months from now. The government should immediately embark upon a programme of installing power points on lamp posts, so that people can charge the batteries of their electric vehicles from these power points. The plugs on electric vehicles could have a fourth pin on which would be encrypted the registration number of the vehicle; this could then be read by the metre supplying the electricity, so that the electricity company would know who to charge for their electricity.

These changes would cause enormous disruption and force huge numbers of people out of their comfort zones, but I say that these measures should be forced through immediately in the interest of the survival of all life on Earth.

Thursday 25th April 2019. The Survival Party is my idea, and I want to be the leader of the Party. The fact that I have a conviction for manslaughter and I have spent the last forty-three years in the custody of psychiatrists doesn't alter the fact that I AM A MAN, AND A NATURAL LEADER OF MEN AND WOMEN. My heart is in the right place and my ideas are sound. I want people to judge me for themselves, and those who want to know the whole truth about me can read the whole story in my autobiographies. They can be accessed from my website. The address is http://www.robert-brooks-strong.olympiapublishers.com/.

I wrote to Lucy again today, as follows: - Thursday 25th April 2019
    Lucy Lawless,

Dear Soulmate,

    I felt bobulucydated again this morning. Thank you for making me feel this way, Darling. I love you.

    I thought you'd like to see the most recent two entries in my latest journal. When I get near a computer with the internet on it, I shall look up the address of Sir David Attenborough and also the leaders of the Extinction Rebellion group, and send them copies of these two journal entries. There is a proverb, 'You can't keep a good man down'. I am living proof of it.

Yours etcetera

I then enclosed copies of the previous two journal entries.

Saturday 27th April 2019. I was having a chat with a man this morning who stated that any moves to help mankind in the battle against Global Warming and Climate Change must be international as the problem is a global one. My point in reply was that although what he said is true, we can make a start, here in Great Britain, and lead the world by example, so that other countries can emulate the success of Great Britain and thereby create a global movement for an International Survival Party.

Sunday 28th April 2019. I wrote to Lucy today, as follows: - Sunday 28th April 2019
Lucy Lawless

Dear Soulmate,
I felt us coming together at about twelve fifteen p.m. (UK time) today, which if I'm right would have been at about one fifteen a.m. (NZ Time) on Monday 29th April for you. It is now three fifteen p.m. as I write this and I'm still enjoying the afterglow and feeling exquisitely bobulucydated. In my mind, I'm lying beside you with my arm around your shoulder and your head nestled against my neck. We are both relaxing and enjoying the afterglow of love-making. As long as we keep believing in each other, we'll make it happen in the flesh before too long. I have a CPA meeting on the 14th May. I want three things from Dampensquib: I want him to apply to the Ministry of Justice for unescorted leave for me to go and do my shopping. I also want WiFi installed on my computer so that I can have internet access, and thirdly I want him to arrange with my dentist for me to go to Dundee for the day to have the dental surgery that I want done. (I plan to have my remaining upper teeth extracted and some dental implants inserted into my upper jaw. This should enable me to speak and to sing and to eat properly).
I'm going to hospital tomorrow to have my eyes looked at by the eye clinic there. I suffer from wet AMD, which stands for 'Age-related Macular Degeneration'. The macular is the central part of the retina at the back of the eye, and with wet AMD one gets fluid on the macular which distorts one's vision. They inject the eye with a chemical compound called

'EYLEA' which disperses the fluid. I have this done about every three months. I have been having it done for eleven years now, and my eyes are largely OK because of it.

Yours etcetera

I then enclosed a copy of Saturday's journal entry for her.

Thursday 2nd May 2019. The government have been taking my thoughts on Climate Change seriously, but not seriously enough. They are talking about making the UK virtually free of carbon emissions by 2050. This will be too little too late to stop the world from overheating by the critical figure of a 1.5° C rise in temperature. They must have the guts to shake people out if their comfort zones. It is already too late for an orderly transition to a clean way of living. I repeat they must stop production of vehicles with internal combustion engines immediately, and not just for vehicles: all manner of devices such as lawn mowers and cement mixers use smelly petrol engines. This has got to stop.

The world is waking up to the need to take measures to counteract Climate Change, but President Trump and his followers are still sleeping. Even those who are awake are only talking about the practical solutions. I think they are leaving the solution to the moral cause of Climate Change to me, but I can't do anything to stop the moral cause of Climate Change whilst the soul of my late mother, Dolly, (AKA Lucifer) still exists. Once that old witch has disappeared, my thoughts on moral matters will be the dominant ones. This is why I say that the public won't get my blessing for Brexit until Dolly has been ratified and I come off the antipsychotic drugs that her stupid followers in the psychiatric profession force me to take.

This is the end of Dolly's era that she has chosen for herself. She could have rested in peace when she died, but she chose not to. She could have accepted my truce terms, but she chose not to. She could have come back to life as a human being again, but she chose not to. She chose to make her life and mine into a fight to the finish, so she left me with no choice but to finish her off by turning her into an animal, such as a rat. She will be happier as a rat than she was as a person; rats have no taboo against incest and that will suit her fine.

I posted a copy of today's journal entry in a letter to Lucy.

Saturday 4th May 2019. I wrote to Lucy again today, as follows: - Saturday 4th May 2019

    Lucy Lawless,

Dear Soulmate,

    A lot has happened to me this week. On Tuesday I noticed pains in my chest, but I didn't think anything of it and I assumed that they would go away on their own. But they got worse on Wednesday, and on Wednesday evening I noticed a rash on my chest. So, on Thursday I reported it to the staff, and on Friday I saw the GP. She took one look at my rash and said, 'You've got shingles!' The rash had spread round the side of my body and up my back. Apparently, when I was a small child, I had chicken pox, and although the chicken pox was cured, it left a trace of the virus in the nerve in my spinal cord. This is not unusual. This virus can be reactivated at any age and this is what has happened to me. It is very painful.

    The GP gave me some antivirus tablets and told me to take one, five times a day for a week. It should all be cleared up by next Friday. She said it may leave me feeling very tired but they can give me something for that. So, I'm quite optimistic that modern medicine is coming to my aid. I was quarantined to my room all day on Friday, so I missed my fortnightly shopping trip and this has left me short of toiletries and a badly-needed haircut.

    On top of that, I'm suffering from constipation. I haven't opened my bowels since Tuesday and I'm feeling all bunged up! I've been written up for some lactulose but they only give me fifteen mils a day which isn't nearly enough. And then on top of it all, the flush in my toilet has stopped working, and the maintenance people can't get it fixed until Tuesday, so I have to use the loo in the communal shower room, which is kept locked so I have to ask the staff to unlock the door for me.

    I think the above discomforts are Dolly's parting shots at me. I hope that's all they are. On the positive side, I was well pleased with the results in the national council elections. The Labour Party and the Conservatives have both done very poorly and the Liberal Democrats and the Greens have both done surprisingly well. I have reason to believe that that's the result of my influence at work. I'm sure that large numbers of people feel the same way I do about our politicians.

    Yours etcetera

Saturday 11th May 2019. I wrote to Lucy again today, as follows: - Saturday 11th May 2019

 Lucy Lawless,

Dear Soulmate,

 I haven't felt fit enough to dance with you for the last week, and I'm still not fit. I'm still bunged up with constipation, and the antibiotics haven't cleared up my shingles yet. I still have a bit of the rash left and I've finished the course of tablets that I was prescribed. I won't get to see the GP again until Tuesday. The workmen mended my toilet flush but it promptly broke again and it won't be fixed until Tuesday.

 I'm enclosing a copy of a letter which I wrote today to Sir David Attenborough. I thought you'd like to know what I'm up to. I post-dated it to Monday as I won't be able to find the man's address until then. I'm relying on my Occupational Therapist to look it up for me on the internet.

 In spite of my woes, I am reminded of you in the words of the song that goes, "… then I look at you, and the world's all right with me". That's how I feel when you send me your loving vibes. You still make my life worth living, and that's worth more than any amount of money. I like to think that my letters have a similar effect on you, so I shall keep on writing to you whether these psychiatric idiots like it or not.

 Keep up the pressure on my late mother. I'm sure she is close to ratification now, but we need you to play a part because Dolly is more afraid of you than she is of me, rightly or wrongly. Make her know that the longer she prolongs the agony of her existence the more you will make her suffer fear. Make her feel it.

 At my CPA on Tuesday, I'm going to say that I will accept a conditional discharge and keep on taking the antipsychotic medication. I will be more able to work at my political career if I am out of hospital. This is a change of attitude on my behalf. Wish me luck on Tuesday.

 Yours etcetera

My letter to Sir David Attenborough is as follows. I enclosed copies of the entries of 23rd, 25th and 27th April in this journal, and also the first paragraph of the entry for the 2nd May: - Monday 13th May 2019

 Sir David Attenborough,

Dear David,

I am writing to invite you to join me as co-founder of a new political Party called, "The Survival Party". The human race is fighting for its survival at the moment, and not just for our own species but of all life on Earth. The enemy is an unsustainable way of living, which has got to change, and soon. The only way forward is to overcome the inertia of people's habits, and this has got to be done politically. Hence the new Party which is called The Survival Party.

I keep a journal which is a cross between a diary, a narrative and a series of letters which I have written. This journal will be the fifth volume of my autobiography. I am enclosing, for your benefit, four recent entries in my journal which will keep you abreast of my current thinking.

I will be happy to correspond with you and tell you about myself if you are interested. Suffice it to say that I am seventy-five years young, and I studied maths at university when I was in my twenties. I have been married twice and I have four sons, only two of whom are alive today.

Please be kind enough to reply and let me know your thoughts on this letter and its enclosures.

Kind regards,

Robert Strong.
As a matter of interest, Sir David never did reply.

Tuesday 14th May 2019. I wrote to Lucy this morning as follows: - Tuesday Morning 14th May 2019
Lucy Lawless,

Dear Soulmate,
It is now two a.m. and I've just got to write to you again as I've just had a realisation that is worth recording. I've just realised WHO my late mother, Dolly, is, historically. Dolly IS the vainglorious Archangel Lucifer. She has tried to oust me, God, from my throne in the Kingdom of Heaven, just like she did before, thousands of years ago, and just like before, I am ending her attempted coup by sending her down into the world of animals, only this time she won't ever be coming back again as a human being. No wonder she chose to fight me to the finish. She had to do that because of WHO SHE IS.

Recent events such as the event labelled 'The End of an Era', namely the abdication of Emperor Akihito of Japan and the coronation of his son as his successor, and also the three-day coronation of the new King of Thailand, lead me to believe that we are winning the endgame in our long fight with Lucifer.

I think that the death yesterday of Doris Day may prove to be the last straw that breaks her back. Two current shows on the BBC also give me confidence that we are winning this endgame, one is called "Brexit – Behind Closed Doors", and the other is by Louis Theroux called "Mothers on the Edge" (pronounced "Mother's on the Edge!"). Dolly is on the edge of defeat and I am already savouring victory. It won't be long now before she ratifies herself.

I'm seeing the GP again this morning as I still have this rash caused by the shingles. I may need some more antibiotics, but I'll leave that decision to the GP. It still hurts a lot in my chest and on my back. I'm still bunged up with constipation, which the shingles doesn't help. Hopefully, the workmen will fix the flush in my loo today.

I felt your sympathy for my woes yesterday. It is always good to feel your love, which you give so generously. You must have received my letter of the 4th May. Your heart still replies. It is so good to know that we are fighting together against all the woes afflicting the world at the moment. I believe that WE WILL PREVAIL.

Yours etcetera

Thursday 16th May 2019. I wrote to Lucy again this evening, as follows: -
Thursday Evening 16th May 2019
Lucy Lawless,

Dear Soulmate,

I have known ever since the 9th June 2017 that the world is using the British Prime Minister, Theresa May, as an allegorical figure for my late mother, Dolly. The media, when they cottoned on, started using Theresa May's demise as Prime Minister as an allegory for Dolly's demise as a human being. Today, Theresa May announced that she will be quitting the job as Prime Minister according to a timetable to be announced after her next attempt to get her Brexit deal through Parliament, which will take place the week beginning the 3rd June. So, in three weeks' time we will know how much longer we will have to wait before Dolly ratifies herself. The pressure for her to do just that is colossal and mounting all the time.

She may prefer to be a duck, rather than a rat, but I want her to become a rat as that is more appropriate. She has been a two-legged rat to me all my life because of her insane incestuous obsession.

I sent my letter off to Sir David Attenborough on Tuesday, and I learned today that the man is ninety years old, so I hope he has enough life left in him to help me with my plans for The Survival Party.

I saw the GP on Tuesday and she said that the shingles is clearing up on its own without the need for any more antiviral tablets. This afternoon I began to notice a reduction in the pain caused by the rash, which is now beginning to clear up. So, hopefully I'll be back to health soon. The constipation is beginning to clear up as well. The lactulose, which I take daily, is beginning to work.

Once Dolly has disappeared, I'll soon get my discharge, my public apology and my compensation from the Royal College of Psychiatrists, as well as coming off the antipsychotic drugs (which will be a great help in coming back to health). AND enough influence to liberate you from your oppressor. All these things will swing into action the instant the old witch disappears, which should be by the end of next month. All our trials will soon be over for good this time.

When I was a boy, I had a girlfriend called June. My brother stole her from me. I always felt that her name was prophetic. I wondered what would happen in June? And in June of which year? Now I know.

I have approved the cover design for *My Journey Back – Part Two*, which is subtitled 'The Arrival of God's Kingdom'. It won't take long now before it is published.

I felt us coming together at ten p.m. (UK Time) on Tuesday, which would have been nine a.m. on Wednesday the 15th for you. I felt beautifully bobulucydated. Thank you, Darling. I love you more and more all the time.

Yours etcetera

Chapter 2

The First Draft of the Manifesto

Events and Thoughts from Saturday 18th May 2019.

Saturday 18th May 2019. I wrote two letters this evening. The first is to my shrink, Dr Twee Dampensquib, and the second is to Lucy. They are as follows: - Saturday Evening 18th May 2019

Dr Twee Dampensquib,
Medical Director,
Alcatraz Island Hospital.

Dear Dr Dampensquib,

I have good reason to believe that the soul of my late mother, Mrs Dorothy Ayres, will come back to life in the body of a rat before 6th June this year, when my next injection of paliperidone is due. If this proves to be the case, and I am pretty sure it will, then I will not want you to waste any time in taking me off the antipsychotic medication.

I will acquire all my late mother's power and influence from the instant that the old witch is ratified, and I will not take kindly to those who procrastinate in obeying my will. I do not want to take any more paliperidone, nor any other neuroleptic drug.

I will expect your cooperation in persuading the Royal College of Psychiatrists to give me the public apology and the compensation that I am demanding from them. You know as well as I do that there has never been anything wrong with my mental health, and so do all the senior members of the Royal College of Psychiatrists. I was driven to homicide and detained for over forty-three years because of WHO MY LATE MOTHER IS and WHAT SHE WANTS – not because there has ever been anything wrong with me.

Forgive me if I sound a little angry, but so would anyone in my circumstances.

Yours sincerely,

Robert Strong.
Cc Lucy Lawless.

Saturday Evening 18th May 2019
Lucy Lawless,

Dear Soulmate,
The Americans, the Canadians and the Mexicans are all talking about the ratification of the removal of trade tariffs on steel imports and exports. I have twisted Xi Jinping's arm into ratifying Dolly, even though he was the last of her followers to agree to the ratification. I told the British and American governments not to invest in Huawei 5G technology until after Dolly has been ratified as I don't trust Xi Jinping until then.
The pressure on Dolly to ratify herself is matched only by the pressure on Theresa May to step down as Prime Minister. Current thinking is that she will present her Brexit deal before Parliament for the fourth time on June 3rd; it won't get passed, and she will then step down immediately. When Theresa goes, so will Dolly. When Dolly disappears, then I will become the next AWL and when that happens, the world will see some changes. This new broom will sweep clean.
Take care of yourself, my Love,
I have much more to say to you, but it can wait until we talk,
Bless you, my Queen,
Yours with Love, Affection and Friendship,

Bob XX.
Cc Dr Twee Dampensquib

Friday 24th May 2019. I wrote to Lucy this evening as follows: - Friday Evening 24th May 2019
Lucy Lawless,

Dear Soulmate,

Theresa May gave her resignation speech today. She is resigning as leader of the Conservative Party two weeks from today, June 7th. But she will stay on as caretaker Prime Minister until the Conservative Party elects a new leader, which will be at the end of July at the latest. I think we can be fairly sure that Dolly will have disappeared by the end of July. The UK newspapers have been screaming at her to clear off for weeks now. I'm fairly sure that she can't take much more pressure before she goes. Theresa May couldn't.

My own woes are easing. I'm not so constipated now because the lactulose does work. The shingles is less of a problem now. My rash is going but not quite gone yet, and the pain is easing off a bit, thank Heaven. The maintenance men still haven't fixed the flush in my toilet yet, so I'm still using the loo in the communal shower room.

I haven't felt like dancing for a while. Partly because of my illness but mainly because of the antipsychotic drug that these bastards force me to take. Not for much longer now, I think. Your loving vibes still make me very happy though. Keep them coming. I still love you as much as ever.

I produced a Manifesto for the Survival Party during this week and I'm enclosing a copy for you. I've also sent copies of the Manifesto to Sir David Attenborough and to the organiser of the Extinction Rebellion group.

I've been approved to have WiFi installed on my computer, so, hopefully, I'll have internet access soon. I'm also expecting soon to spend a day in Dundee having my dental work done. Life still goes on, as I'm sure it does for you too. But we both know that we are in each other's thoughts the whole time.

Yours etcetera

Saturday 25th May 2019. My late mother's name is Mrs Dorothy Mabel Ayres. She is also known as "The Door" and "The Area" as those words have a tenuous similarity to her name. She is known to her friends and relations as "Dolly", but her true spiritual identity is that of the vainglorious Archangel Lucifer; Satan's accomplice and the enemy of God and therefore the enemy of the human race. She now spends her afterlife in a state of abject loneliness, misery, heartache and fear, isolation and despair, I am happy to say. The old witch has asked for everything she gets for the way she has treated me all my life.

Having mental sex with that woman is known colloquially as "Opening the door", and this has been the graduation ritual for entry into manhood for all men in the International Community for decades now. She pretends to care about the future of humanity and the world we all live in, but she is a wolf in sheep's clothing. All she really wants is to have an incestuous affair with her own son, me. To achieve this, she gave me over seventy-five years of Hell which I am now repaying her for. Read my books to learn the full story.

I am Almighty God, and I forgive all those who truly repent, but Lucifer still insists on having a sinful incestuous relationship with me. UNREPENTANT SINNERS GO TO HELL. And that is where Lucifer is now. The extent of my mercy to her is that I will allow her to come back to life in the body of a rat. She will be happier as a rat than she was as a human being. She has been a two-legged rat to me all my life because of her insane incestuous obsession, so she can spend the rest of eternity as a four-legged rat. She didn't love me as a mother should. She just wanted to make a sexual conquest of the Lord God Almighty to please her own vanity.

She wanted sex with her own son, and for her son to be a REAL MAN, but that is logically impossible because a real man is not a motherfucker, whatever the provocation, as I have proven.

Sunday 26th May 2019. This week I prepared the first draft of The Survival Party of Great Britain. Some of my ideas may be controversial, but I believe they are the right ideas, not only for the present, but also for the future of this country. Here is my draft Manifesto:

MANIFESTO
OF THE SURVIVAL PARTY OF GREAT BRITAIN

MAY 2019

Party Leader, Robert Brooks Strong FIAP

My name is Robert Brooks Strong, and the following are the policies that I wish to pursue:

Survival

Everything depends upon our ability to survive. The world may not be life-supporting for much beyond 2030 unless the whole human race cuts its carbon emissions drastically before then. This is because the climate may overheat by a rise of 1.5° C which is the critical point, beyond which it will be too late to save the planet from Global Warming caused by Climate Change. I am therefore aiming to get Great Britain to be carbon neutral by 2025 or as soon as possible thereafter by the following policies:

My government would ban the manufacture of internal combustion engines and the production of vehicles using such engines immediately. All vehicle manufacture must be for electric vehicles. We would ban the use of vehicles with internal combustion engines on British roads from 1st January 2022. The same would apply to all other devices using internal combustion engines, such as lawn mowers and cement mixers etcetera.

We would immediately embark upon a programme of installing power points on lamp posts in all British cities and towns and villages, so that people could charge their electric vehicles from these power points. A system could be introduced whereby all electric vehicles would have a fourth pin on their electric plug, upon which would be encrypted the registration number of the vehicle, so that the electricity company would know who to charge for their electricity.

We would immediately invest in research and development of bigger and better batteries, for vehicles and also for electricity storage and distribution. We would also immediately invest in schemes to produce more energy from solar power, and also power from wind farms.

We would make power stations using the burning of coal, oil and gas obsolete by the 1st January 2023. We aim to make Great Britain free from all usage of coal, oil and gas by 1st January 2024. The only exception to this rule would be the oil used to fly jet aircraft. People would be encouraged to fly only when necessary.

Plastic pollution is a big problem at the moment. The world's rivers and oceans are becoming clogged up with the stuff. The people of Great Britain must play their part in this drive to recycle all plastic products. My government would ensure that we have enough recycling facilities and of sufficient size to recycle all plastic products used in this country. Anyone caught disposing of plastic thoughtlessly would get a one hundred pound fine when my government is in power. We will not allow plastic products to be sent to landfill sites.

Paper, wood, cardboard and all metals must also be recycled, and schemes to facilitate this would be introduced and made compulsory, with fines for those caught disobeying this rule.

Morality

We feel strongly that the issue of public morals is one that this government should make a stand on. Ever since 1967 when same-sex sexual relationships were legalised, there has been a steady decline in public morality, and the social consequences of this are now becoming intolerable. The rise in knife crimes and murders can be attributed to this "don't care" attitude to morals and the feeling that "anything goes". I will deal with crime shortly, but I want to say at this point that sexual morals need to be corrected. It is self-evident that acts of sodomy and lesbian sex are filthy, unnatural and sordid. They are disgusting behaviour and ought to be discouraged. We say that the best way to discourage them is to penalise them, but not by making offenders spend years and years in prison. We would give twenty-eight days' solitary confinement for each act of indecency, multiplied by the cardinal number of the offence. In other words, four weeks solitary for a first offence, eight weeks for a second offence, twelve weeks for a third and so on. Additionally, offenders would have to take injections of antipsychotic drugs to suppress their libidos and help them to lead celibate lives in future. This does, of course, mean an end to the public obscenity of same-sex marriages.

Social Guidance

There are two main types of criminals who come before the courts in this country. The first is the career criminals who make a living out of criminal acts, and the second is the social delinquents. Career criminals have to accept the principle of crime and punishment, and by and large they do so. They know that if they get caught, they will have to do their time in prison, and that is an end to the matter.

Social delinquents fall into two categories: firstly, there are those who carry weapons for their own protection because they don't trust the law to protect them. This has got to stop. The law must protect all people and be seen to do so; secondly, there are those who fall foul of the law because they don't understand society and how it works.

They don't know what they are, nor what their lives are all about. They are mainly young guys in various stages of adolescence. They want to prove themselves but they don't know how, nor what this entails. Most of them are looking for a reason for living, and most of them, at present, end up in the care of consultant forensic psychiatrists, who seldom know what life is all about themselves.

We propose the founding of a Ministry for Social Guidance to replace the work done by the Royal College of Psychiatrists. The Ministry would be in charge of the Social Guidance Institute which would be run by an elected council who would oversee the work done by Social Guidance Counsellors. These would be people chosen for their maturity and wisdom and would not be qualified by educational qualifications, but be chosen in a way more like that of judges, by their fellow counsellors.

It would be the job of Social Guidance Counsellors to talk to miscreants on a regular basis and to lead them to a fuller understanding of life; to get them to prove themselves, and to *find* God and to *find themselves* so that they will become useful citizens.

With very few exceptions, the minimum age for a Social Guidance

Counsellor would be fifty years, and ideally, they would have been married for at least two years and have children of their own, for they would be acting *in loco parentis.*

These jobs would largely replace those of probation officers, and would be ideal for the many members of society who have lived life to the full and gained experience and wisdom which these jobs would give them the opportunity to pass on to the next generation. They would be well paid and carry a lot of respect. Such jobs are badly needed in society at the moment.

Mental hospitals would be replaced by Social Guidance Centres where people would be held in custody until they make it obvious that they don't need that kind of treatment. Then they could then be called upon to just make regular visits to the centre for consultation with their counsellor until the counsellor feels that even this is no longer necessary. Receiving counselling would not carry the stigma of mental illness, which many people will always equate with madness. Receiving counselling is more like getting good advice from a caring parent, which is what people growing up in good homes get anyway.

This system would replace the mental health system which is shambolic at best at the moment.

Punishment

The Bible says so, and so does the works of William Shakespeare, and now I am saying it as well, "Spare the rod and spoil the child". We have raised a generation of spoilt children in this country under the soft laws of the "Nanny State". This is what has given rise to the current spate of knife crimes. Young people have little or no respect for authority and the rule of law. My government would change that.

Parents know their children best, and children know it when they have misbehaved. We would give parents back the right to give their child a smack on the thigh if the child is naughty. The child then knows that he/she must behave themselves, and is given a respectful understanding of the nature of the relationship between adults and children. This will prove useful when the child becomes an adult him/herself. Having taken their punishment, the child then knows that the matter is forgotten and they can then continue with a loving relationship with their parent.

We would give schoolteachers the right to punish misbehaving children, the punishment to be decided at the discretion of the head teacher. Again, once the child has taken his/her punishment the matter is then forgotten.

We would punish young guys who carry knives much more severely. For carrying a knife, inflicting a wound with a knife or killing someone with a knife, the offender would receive a very long prison sentence, the first part of which would be spent in solitary confinement. In all cases the prison sentence would be followed by a period of counselling by a Social Guidance Counsellor, until the judge is convinced that the miscreant has mended his ways.

In the case of female knife offenders, we would leave the punishment up to the judge and the Social Guidance Counsellor to decide.

Hard Drugs

A distinction must be made between those who deal in hard drugs, and those who only use them. Users will be treated as needing Social Guidance and kept in custody until they have been clean for two years and are free from addiction.

Dealers cause great misery to their customers and to the families of their customers. They would serve a long prison sentence starting with a long sentence in solitary confinement, and would be followed by a period of Social Counselling, until the judge is convinced that the miscreant has reformed his behaviour.

Offenders would also have their financial assets confiscated.

Prisons

Prisons are not meant to be holiday camps. Those caught with drugs in prison would be placed in solitary confinement for a period of time at the discretion of the prison governor, and disallowed visits and social interaction with friends and family. Those caught bringing drugs into prison would be banned from visiting prisons again. They can be identified by facial recognition technology.

BREXIT

The Brexiteers want to take control of the UK borders, but they still want to keep open the border between Northern Ireland and the Irish republic. No amount of talking about the "back stop" can square this circle.

Make up your minds! Do you want control of the UK borders or don't you? We say remain in the EU. It is worth sacrificing a degree of freedom concerning our trading partners in return for a guaranteed market of the twenty-eight countries comprising the European Union. If we want to trade with another country, then as an EU member, we can get the EU to trade with that country on behalf of all the EU members. The advantages of frictionless trade with the EU for component parts of manufactured goods secures jobs which would otherwise go abroad and greatly reduce our manufacturing capability.

The standard of living in Great Britain has already fallen considerably because of Brexit and will fall much more if this country goes ahead with the Brexit proposals. The 2016 referendum was a phoney exercise.

The people were misled and lied to. The people deserve another say in this matter now that we have more idea of what is involved with leaving the EU.

NORTHERN IRELAND

This territory was taken from the Irish people by force of arms in the first place, and colonised by the British. In a civilised world, this is no justification for the UK to retain possession of someone else's territory. We say, "Give Northern Ireland back to the Irish nation". Historically and geographically, the territory belongs to Ireland, not Britain. If anybody there wants to consider themselves as British, not Irish, then let them come to Britain. The territory is more of a liability than an asset to Britain.

I wrote again to Lucy today. This letter is the culmination of years of waiting and fighting that Lucy and I have gone through.

Sunday 26th May 2019

Lucy Lawless,

Dear Soulmate,

THE WORLD IS UNDER NEW MANAGEMENT AS OF TWELVE NOON TODAY

Well done, Darling. It was you, making Dolly feel fear that was the last straw that broke her resolve to stay human. Shortly before twelve o'clock she agreed to come back as a rat without further delay. I then guided her soul all the way from the male rat's sperm cell to the female rat's ovum, which she then fertilised. It is too late now for her to become anything other than a rat, of which she is, at present, an embryo.

We have both waited years for this moment, and it has now arrived. Now it is full speed ahead with all our plans. We have broken the back of our opposition, with help from all our friends in the media and in politics, all over the world.

I'll keep you posted of further developments as they happen. I am now the AWL.

Yours etcetera

Cc Dr Twee Dampensquib

I also wrote to Dampensquib, as follows: - Sunday 26th May 2019

Dr Twee Dampensquib,
Medical Director,
Alcatraz Island Hospital.

Dear Dr Dampensquib,

I am enclosing a copy of the Manifesto of The Survival Party, which you are invited to join if you want to, as well as a copy of my latest letter to Lucy which I'm sure you'll find more than a little interesting. I suggest we have a one-to-one conversation very soon to discuss the present situation.

I think you know what I want from you now.

Yours sincerely,

Robert Strong.
Cc Lucy Lawless.

During the week I also sent copies of the Manifesto to Sir David

Attenborough and to the organiser of the Extinction Rebellion group.

I am now reviewing my situation in the light of today's event. I must get out of hospital as quickly as possible because my plans won't carry credence if they are seen to be the plans of a mental patient. I will therefore need money, so I must get Dampensquib to put pressure on the Royal College of Psychiatrists to get me my public apology and my compensation as quickly as possible.

Monday 27th May 2019. As you were. I wrote to Lucy again today as follows: -

Monday 27th May 2019
Lucy Lawless,

Dear Soulmate,

I spoke too soon, yet again. I felt the presence of the old witch this afternoon. Dolly, Lucifer, is still around and still trying to make me have sex with her. But I AM sure that she will be gone soon. Maybe she will go on June the 7th when Theresa May steps down as Conservative Party leader, or maybe she will hang on 'til the end of July when the Conservatives elect a new Party leader and Prime Minister. I don't think she will hang on beyond the end of July because the behind-the-scenes efforts to ratify her are already overwhelming. Everybody knows that there will be no sacrifice and no blessing until Lucifer has been ratified and I am taken off the libido-suppressing antipsychotic medication. The world of the future NEEDS my libido.

Sorry I spoke too soon and gave you false joy, but we still have plenty of hope.

Yours etcetera
Cc Dr Twee Dampensquib

I wrote to Theresa May again this evening as follows. I enclosed my first thoughts on The Survival Party and a copy of the Manifesto: -

Monday 27th May 2019
Theresa May,
Prime Minister,
10 Downing Street,
London SW1.

Dear Theresa,

I wasn't surprised that you went to church yesterday. I, too, know what it is like to be rejected by those you love when you have done your best for them. I did try to warn you, but you ignored my letters when I told you that I am indeed the Lord God Almighty. By insisting on your Brexit deal you were defying my will, which is like trying to bat your head against a brick wall. Your successor won't have any luck with Brexit either, for the same reason. When you ignored my letters, I warned you that I would put you out of office, and your Party, the Conservatives, out of power for at least one generation. I do not make idle threats, Theresa, as I am now proving.

My late mother is the Archangel Lucifer, and now, just as before, she has ousted me from my throne in the Kingdom of Heaven; and now, just as before, I am claiming it back by casting her down into the world of animals. The world has used your demise as Prime Minister as an allegory for Lucifer's demise as a human being. But I am aware that you are NOT Lucifer. There is hope for you, but not for that unrepentant sinner. She has always insisted upon having an incestuous sexual relationship with me, against my will. Lucifer's soul will be coming back to life in the body of a rat very soon. This is what is meant by ratification, as I think you are already aware.

I was driven to homicide and detained for forty-three years and tormented with libido-suppressing drugs for almost all that time, not because of my mental health, but because of WHO MY LATE MOTHER IS, and WHAT SHE WANTS.

Time is now of the essence. I am enclosing for your information, two documents on The Survival Party, which you are invited to join as a founder member if you want to. It won't take long before The Survival Party becomes the Party of government in Great Britain. But I need the freedom to operate before I can get the Party off the ground, as quickly as possible. So, I am asking you again to use your influence to get me out of hospital with an absolute and unconditional discharge as soon as possible.

I hope you are now aware of the folly of ignoring my letters; Jeremy Corbyn made the same mistake and now observe his misfortunes.

Kind regards,

Robert Strong, (God).

Wednesday 29th May 2019. I wrote to Lucy today as follows: -
Wednesday 29th May 2019
    Lucy Lawless,

Dear Soulmate,

    I am enclosing a copy of a letter which I wrote to the Prime Minister
on Monday. I thought you'd find it interesting. I'll let you know if I get a
reply.

    My shingles rash has nearly gone now, and so has the pain. I still take
lactulose daily for the constipation and it works. The workmen have
apparently given the flush in my toilet priority, but they still haven't fixed
it yet. I'm hoping that it will all be sorted by June 7th, including Lucifer's
demise.

    Your very name is an admonition of my late mother. Your very identity
is encapsulated by your hatred of her and therefore your love for me. You
won't regret it. Keep making the old witch feel the fear of you.

    My lamp still shines on your picture on my wall 24/7, just as it has
done for years now. I'm sure this knowledge protects your spirit.

    I felt us coming together at about one a.m. on Monday morning (UK
Time) which would have been about twelve noon on Monday 27th for you
in New Zealand. Thank you, Darling, for bobulucydating me. I often feel
your loving feelings and they always make me very happy.

    Yours etcetera

Sunday 2nd June 2019. I wrote to Lucy again today as follows: - Sunday 2nd
June 2019
    Lucy Lawless,

Dear Soulmate,

    We came together shortly before one thirty p.m. (UK Time) yesterday,
which would have been just before twelve thirty a.m. on Sunday 2nd June
for you in New Zealand. It was wonderful, Darling. We belong to each other
completely and I couldn't be happier. I'm still feeling bobulucydated and
enjoying the afterglow, as I'm sure you are too. It is now nine a.m. on
Sunday here.

By the way, our friend who wrote "The Owl and the Pussy Cat" was Edward Lear, not Lewis Carol as I originally thought. When this nightmare of our separate lives is over, I'm looking forward to spending a couple of months' holiday on a cruise ship with you, giving ourselves time to get to know each other. I think we both want to get to know each other as people, to see how we get on in real life, and to see if we are as compatible as we both hope that we will be.

I think my shingles will be all gone by Friday 7th June and there is every chance that my late mother, Lucifer, will be gone by then as well. She knows, now, that she will never get the only thing she wants as long as she remains in human form.

She wants an affair with her own son, myself, who is a real man, but as I have said so often, a real man is not a motherfucker, so what she wants is logically impossible. I think she still follows Sigmund Freud, the father of modern psychiatry, who said that every man wants to kill his father and have sex with his mother. Freud was a paranoid motherfucker and an idiot and all his followers are idiots in my opinion.

I think Lucifer now realises that the longer she prolongs the agony of her existence, the greater the peril that she puts the world in, and the sooner she clears off the more chance we have got of saving the planet. If she leaves it much longer there won't be a world left for any of us to come back to after we die. To be perfectly frank, I don't care if she goes "eek" or "quack" in her next life as long as she gets out of the human race and stays out.

Yours etcetera

Wednesday 5th June 2019. I wrote a letter to my brother, Bill, yesterday, as follows: - Tuesday 4th June 2019

Bill Brooks,

Dear Bill,

My third book will be published this month. I'll send you a complimentary copy. My fourth book has been approved for publication and is with the production department of the publishers at the moment. I am now writing my fifth book.

I thought you'd like to see my work on The Survival Party, so I'm enclosing a copy of documents for you. I anticipate leaving hospital soon and then embarking on a career in politics. I know the odds are stacked against me but stranger things have happened! If I can't save the planet then I don't know who can.

All the best,

Bob.

I enclosed, for Bill's benefit, copies of my documents, "First Thoughts on The Survival Party" and the Manifesto. The former comprises extracts from this journal dated 23rd April 2019, 25th April 2019, 22nd April 2019 and 2nd May 2019. I think the last two sentences of my letter to Bill are important for posterity.

Thursday 6th June 2019. I wrote to Lucy again today as follows: - Thursday Evening 6th June 2019

Lucy Lawless,

Dear Soulmate,

Lucifer hasn't gone yet, but I'm pretty sure that she will be gone by this time tomorrow. Theresa May will have stepped down by then as Prime Minister, and also the weather is due to break tomorrow. It has been quite pleasant here, in the south of England, today, and also in the north of France, where they have been celebrating the seventy-fifth anniversary of the D-day landings. The media are full of signs that Dolly, Lucifer, is due to depart tomorrow – some of them big and some of them small.

Donald Trump has been having a state visit to Great Britain this week, and one newspaper headline read, "DUCK, it's Donald!". I'm pretty sure Lucifer will turn herself into a duck tomorrow. The weather is due to turn stormy. There is a weather front coming up from France tonight bringing torrential rain, thunder, lightning and very strong winds. This front will spread all over the UK during the next three days starting tomorrow.

I think this bad weather will be caused by the rage of Dolly's remaining followers who are angry at me for getting rid of her. Those who survive will see things from my point of view before long, and those who don't will worship me or go to Hell. I've had a bellyful of the point of view of Dolly's followers on the television over the last few days, when there has been nothing else but the D-day landings on the news channel.

I won't be sure of Lucifer's departure until the weather presenters on the news channel stop using the word "Areas" and use the word "Regions" instead. Then I'll know that Dolly's demise is widely recognised and people are following MY will. I will write to you again when that happens.

My third book will be published this month, and my fourth book is with the production department of my publishers. This letter will be published in my fifth book.

Whatever happens, we must keep believing in ourselves.

Yours etcetera

Cc Dr Twee Dampensquib

Sunday 9th June 2019. This is today's letter to Lucy. It is very significant: -

Sunday 9th June 2019

Lucy Lawless,

Dear Soulmate,

Needless to say, my late mother, Dolly, hasn't gone yet, although there has been atrocious weather over England lately and it is set to get worse next week. Theresa May stepped down as Conservative Party leader on Friday, but she is staying on as Prime Minister until the Conservatives elect a new leader, which won't be until the week beginning 22nd July.

I still follow the allegory of Theresa May's demise as Prime Minister being synonymous with Lucifer's demise as a human being, and I'll tell you why. Back in 1975 I had a girlfriend called Theresa Brunton. Now, at the age of seventy-five it is obvious to me that Theresa Brunton was sent to me by Heaven to make me aware that the allegory of Theresa May carrying the brunt of our expectations is real.

That is why I think we must wait until the week beginning 22nd July before Lucifer finally departs. I think the signs are overwhelmingly strong that that is what will happen that week. So, we have just over six weeks to wait. We have waited all our lives for the moment when Lucifer finally departs, so we can wait another six weeks.

Few things are definite in this world, but I think we have got our best chance in the week beginning 22nd July. Lucifer tried to ruin our progeny, our creation, the human race with her decadent ways. Her accomplice, Satan, tried to destroy humanity by undermining the moral values of society, and she continued with His work; even though I got rid of Satan, she nearly enabled Him to succeed posthumously. I think WE have arrived

42

just about in time to save the world from Climate Change for all living things, including people.

If WE can't save the planet, then I don't know who can. And I don't think anyone else does either. Lucifer isn't just Satan's accomplice and partner-in-crime, she is the enemy of God, and therefore humanity. No wonder we both hate her.

Yours etcetera

Cc Dr Twee Dampensquib.

Chapter 3

The Handover of Power in the United Kingdom

Events and Thoughts from Sunday 9th June 2019

Sunday 9th June 2019. The staff here injected me with 100 mil paliperidone on Thursday, and I'm sure they'll do the same again on the 6th July, but I think that that will be my last injection for reasons I explained in my last letter to Lucy at the end of the last chapter. As soon as my late mother, Lucifer, becomes a duck, I shall be the man in charge, and my first order will be to take me off all antipsychotic medication immediately.

Friday 14th June 2019. I make no apology for publishing my letters to Lucy, because they tell my story most effectively. This is the letter I wrote to Lucy today: - Friday Evening 14th June 2019
    Lucy Lawless

Dear Soulmate,
    We have had several months' rainfall in England in the last ten days. Some places have had a month's rainfall in an hour. I'm sure that all this rain is caused by Lucifer crying as I have broken her heart. She can wallow in self-pity all she likes and I'm glad. This is paying her back for all the years of misery she gave me as a child, and then as an adolescent, and then as an adult, right up to the present time. I want her to hurt so badly that she takes herself out of the human race altogether, just to get away from US. And I think that that may happen fairly soon.
    Six weeks from now, the UK will have a new Prime Minister and Theresa May will be history. And I believe Lucifer will be history as well. The outstanding favourite to win the Conservative Party election for the new leader is Boris Johnson. Boris is so popular because his name is a combination of MY name, "Bob", and the maiden name of the woman I

killed, "Iris Johnson". I'm flattered in one way, but upset in another because Boris Johnson's political views couldn't be more different from mine.

I still think that my best plan is to pursue my own agenda, as I expressed in my Manifesto of The Survival Party. Firstly, I must fight for my freedom, then for my public apology and my compensation from the Royal College of Psychiatrists; then for exoneration and to clear my name. I want the verdict of my retrial to be "self-defence against extreme provocation and mental cruelty", because that is the truth. If there is no law allowing that, then I'll fight to have the law changed. I'll have to fight to change the law anyway in order to allow for a retrial after so many years since the original verdict.

A lot will depend upon Dr Dampensquib. If I can get him on my side then I'll stand a chance of getting freedom, apology and compensation as soon as Lucifer turns herself into a duck. The whole of the psychiatric profession will have to change their attitude to me, the moment the door is closed. I want them to admit that I have been misdiagnosed, misjudged and mistreated ever since July 1976.

Furthermore, I want the whole truth to come out – in a court of law if need be. I was driven to homicide, then detained and tortured for forty-three years because of WHO MY LATE MOTHER WAS and the fact that she had an insane obsession for an incestuous sexual relationship with me, which the whole of society conspired to make happen, against MY WILL.

I'm thinking of writing a new song called "Thank Heaven for my woman's love" because your love has made it all worthwhile now that we have each other's love.

Take care of yourself, my Love, I have much more to say to you, but it can wait until we talk, Bless you, my Queen,

Yours with Love, Affection and Friendship,

Bob XX
Cc Dr Twee Dampensquib

Sunday 16th June 2019. I am the living God because of the strength of my spirit. I have told, and I am still telling the story of my life in these books. I am no paragon of virtue. No one is. I have been a swindler, and I have been an adulterer; when pushed beyond the very limit of my endurance, I have even been a killer. I would not have been any of those things if I had been treated with the respect I deserve, which is how I try to treat other people. But I have atoned for my sins by protecting you, dear reader, when you were in danger! There are forces at work in life that would destroy the human race if they could. The reason they can't is because *I* am here to stop them, and the reason why I protect you, dear reader, is because I LOVE YOU.

At the dawn of humanity, I was Adam, and my soulmate, Lucy Lawless, was Eve. We were the first mating couple that started the ball rolling that created us all. We are all the progeny of Adam and Eve, and Lucy and I love the human race as OUR creation just as every parent and grandparent loves their progeny because they are their creation.

Every religion and philosophy on Earth recognises a higher power. Most belief systems call this power "the Great Spirit", by that or any other name, such as God, Allah, Jehovah or even Superman. I proved that that is WHO I AM by overpowering Edward Richard Pitchblack, who was Satan Himself. Every atheist, secularist, and unbeliever who has never experienced the power of Satan can thank their lucky stars for that. I didn't believe it either until the bastard took spiritual possession of the girl I loved. That was the start of a real-life nightmare for me, and I hope it never happens to you.

When I was fighting Pitchblack, I spent decades not knowing whether he would prove to be the stronger of the two of us, or whether I would be. This apprehension was terrible beyond words to say. I spent many years fearing that He would prove to be stronger than me, and knowing that if he was the stronger, that would be the end of humanity.

I thought of every student hoping for success in their exams, and every parent wishing for success for their children. I thought of every baby learning to talk and eat and every parent's joy at the success of their children. I thought of every young lover wondering if their sweetheart would turn out to be the right one for them, and every young woman's joy at knowing she was pregnant for the first time. I thought of every vicar's joy at knowing he had saved someone's soul and at every prisoner's joy at being released eventually.

Can you imagine the strain it put upon my nervous system, knowing that the responsibility fell to me to protect all the hopes and aspirations of all the people in the world?

And yet I had been found guilty of manslaughter by reason of diminished responsibility! Can you blame me for wanting to put the record straight?

Psychiatry recognises the higher power to be embodied by my late mother, Mrs Dorothy Ayres, whom they acknowledge with a dirty laugh as THE DOOR because she is the woman with whom almost all of them first proved their manhood, by OPENING THE DOOR. As I have said before, she is the Global Village bike.

But the men who follow Mrs Dorothy Ayres follow their pricks not their brains, for she is the Archangel Lucifer, and Satan's accomplice. Her only ambition is not to protect her people, it is to have forbidden sex with her own son, myself.

Men like Judge Richard Hone who insist on detaining me, and men like Dr Twee Dampensquib who insists on forcing me to take libido-suppressing drugs against my will; men like Sir Vince Cable who stated only last week that his door is always open; and men like Xi Jinping who stated recently that China would not be closing its doors but would be opening them even wider to trade with the West, are all examples of men who follow their pricks not their brains.

For she will stop at nothing to achieve her ambition to have sex with me, even though it means putting the whole world in peril of Global Warming caused by Climate Change. In another ten years it will be too late to save the world, for Climate Change is like a juggernaut. You have to apply the brakes early in order for it to stop in time.

Lucifer thought that she could do a better job than God of running the world, but look what a balls-up she has made of the job! Her decadent policy of condoning same-sex sexual relationships as socially acceptable has angered the Gods. The weather does not happen by accident. *Most of the "natural" disasters of recent years are the punishment of the Gods for defying MY WILL.*

Lucifer is so sinful that she denies the existence of sin, and she is totally unrepentant, which is why I am casting her down into the world of animals. That is my idea of Hell – to forfeit your very humanity. She forfeited her humanity by insisting on an incestuous sexual relationship with me. The taboo against incest is a universal human law, and incest is a sin in anybody's language. It is one sin that I will not commit. I am a man who would rather be a ladykiller than a motherfucker, and I have been made to prove both of those assertions.

Monday 17th June 2019. I sent Lucy a copy of the above extract from this journal, together with the following letter yesterday: - Sunday 16th June 2019

Lucy Lawless,

Dear Soulmate,

Dr Twee Dampensquib stated at my tribunal that I suffer from a delusional disorder and that I have grandiose delusions. I am hoping to correct this opinion of his by the enclosed extract from my latest journal, but I'm sure it won't really be corrected until I have turned Lucifer into a duckling. Seeing as Pitchblack is now a dog, the world will know why "The dog and duck" is such a popular name for a pub!

Twee is Indian, so I guess his religion is Hindu, although psychiatry is a pseudo-religious cult in its own right, worshipping THE DOOR, as they all call Lucifer. But I think his main religious belief is in the Indian cricket team! They are currently doing very well against Pakistan, or they were until play was stopped by the rain. Lucifer's tears are a nuisance for everybody in England. Except for me, because I'm glad the old witch is crying. I hope it gets worse for her until she clears off altogether.

I was right to think that Dolly is an even bigger menace to mankind than Satan. This is because she seemed so supportive of humanity, but as I've said before many times, she is a wolf in sheep's clothing; even though her disguise is so very good. What proves to me that she is such a menace is that she is proving to be so very hard to get rid of. This is because so many men are taken in by her disguise. The idiots follow their pricks, not their brains. They'd follow them all the way to oblivion if it wasn't for me.

Five weeks tomorrow marks the week that we see the back of Lucifer, if she hasn't gone by then already. I'll be very interested in the weather between now and then.

As soon as Lucifer is gone everybody will concentrate on liberating you, so WE can be together. All our plans are maturing nicely.

Yours etcetera

Cc Dr Twee Dampensquib

Thursday 20th June 2019. The following letter to Lucy, which I wrote today, is, as always, self-explanatory: - Thursday 20th June 2019

Lucy Lawless,

Dear Soulmate,

We came together shortly after nine thirty p.m. (UK Time) on Tuesday, which would have been just after eight thirty a.m. for you in New Zealand. It was, as always beautiful, Darling. I'm so proud of both of us that we can bring each other to orgasm in spite of the most difficult circumstances imaginable. Our enemies have put so many obstacles between us but our true love is conquering all of them.

My brother, Bill, lives in the south east of France where they have been having atrocious weather lately, which has spread to the south east of England. I had hoped that Lucifer would clear off when she got over her crying fit, but no such luck. So, I have been chiding her by calling her a coward. I've told her that she hasn't got the guts to do what every duck does, and that's to get together with a copulating drake and hen duck and come back to life as one of their offspring. She's had her day and she knows it. This is the end of her era that she chose for herself, so she's got no one but herself to blame for being expelled from the human race.

My shingles rash hasn't cleared up yet, and I've been told that it may take months. But, thankfully, there's no great pain with it any more. The maintenance workers fixed the flush in my toilet about a fortnight ago, thank Heaven.

Five weeks tomorrow we'll have a new Prime Minister. It is certain to be Boris Johnson, which is the people's way of telling me that they see me as the top man, by choosing someone with Boris's name. When I'm free I shall fight to become the top man for real. I think Lucifer will have duckified herself by five weeks tomorrow, and then I'm expecting everything to start going my way. I'm sure that when that happens, I'll soon get all the things I want by way of justice. AND SO WILL YOU. I'LL MAKE SURE OF IT.

When I get my compensation, I plan to buy a small house in Dundee, which is where I will be having my dental work done. I also plan to register The Survival Party of Great Britain as a political Party and to canvas support for the Party. That will be my life's work from now on. I would love you to support me and help me with it if you want to, and to be my wife if you want to be. I can only say I love you truly and hope you want to be my wife as soon as you are free from your present circumstances.

Yours etcetera

Cc Dr Twee Dampensquib

Sunday 23rd June 2019. I wrote the following letter to Lucy today: - Sunday 23rd June 2019

Lucy Lawless

Dear Soulmate,

The weather in Great Britain and France for the last month has been dominated by Lucifer's misery and we are expecting more storms today and tomorrow. After that we will be joining the rest of the northern hemisphere which has been experiencing the God Almighty heatwave that I threatened this summer. I do not make idle threats. This heatwave will have caused tens of thousands of deaths by the time it is over and these deaths will all be on the consciences of Dr Twee Dampensquib and Judge Richard Hone for not believing in me, and for following the late Mrs Dorothy Ayres. Let this be a warning to all Dolly's remaining followers – she is Lucifer Herself, but she cannot protect you from the wrath of the Lord God Almighty.

Maybe Donald Trump, Vladimir Putin, Xi Jinping and Muhammad bin Salman will get the message.

I did write to them and I told them what I would be doing this year.

My Journey Back – Part Two comes out next week. It is subtitled "The Arrival of God's Kingdom".

Needless to say, I'll send you a copy. Olympia Publishers are preparing another video for me to advertise my books. It will be shown on Facebook, YouTube and Twitter and will be included on my website. I still don't have WiFi installed on my computer, so I have written to the right people in this hospital asking permission for PC World to come and install it for me, seeing as the chap who does these things in this hospital is unreliable.

Last night, I lay on my recliner listening to the singer of the world competition on BBC3 when I felt your love so very strongly. It was wonderful, Darling, I really felt appreciated, understood and loved. I hope I make you feel that way too.

Yours etcetera

Cc Dr Twee Dampensquib

Wednesday 26th June 2019. I wrote the following letter to Lucy this morning: - Wednesday 26th June 2019

Lucy Lawless,

Dear Soulmate,

The two chaps remaining in the race for the Conservative Party leadership are Boris Johnson and Jeremy Hunt. I don't care which one wins because they are both Dolly's proteges. There was a man in the race called Michael Gove, who would have made a much better Prime Minister than Boris Johnson or Jeremy Hunt, but he got voted down by Dolly's followers because his name was wrong!

The above is an explanation of the joke that is British politics today.

Neither guy will get Brexit through the British Parliament because it is against MY WILL. They will have to call another General Election, and then the Conservatives will get voted out of power for good.

They will become an insignificant minority who will only exist as a reminder of our imperial past.

The Liberal Democrats are also having a leadership election at the end of July when Sir Vince Cable steps down. The two guys vying for my support will be having a televised debate at ten a.m. tomorrow; I shall watch that with interest.

The choreography for the handover of power in the UK is as follows: – The winner of the race for the Conservative Party leadership will be formally announced on Tuesday 23rd July. Then on the following Wednesday morning, Theresa May will attend the House of Commons for Prime Minister's question time, then she will go to Buckingham Palace to hand in her resignation to the Queen, who will accept it. Then the new Conservative Party leader will go to the Palace to ask the Queen if he can become the next Prime Minister and she will accept this. This will complete Theresa May's demise as Prime Minister, and I believe Lucifer's demise as a human being. I will then be the next Actual World Leader, at long last.

The record for a heatwave in Europe was in 2003 when the temperature in France reached 39° C; today it is set to reach 45° C, obliterating the record by six degrees. Record temperatures will tumble today, all over Europe. The heatwave in 2003 killed twenty thousand people in Europe. This year's death toll will be significantly higher, and Dr Twee Dampensquib will be to blame for all those deaths for injecting me with paliperidone against MY WILL. ***Be it known that you defy the will of God at your peril.***

We came together just before three p.m. (UK Time) yesterday and I felt us coming together in spirit as well as a wonderful sexual climax. The strength of our telepathic communication is growing, Darling, I am happy to say. I sometimes get the feel of what you are saying to the world when you are holding forth. I feel your wonderful personality and I know that the people of the world have a lot of sympathy for your plight. Continue to be patient, Darling. We will rescue you as soon as possible.

Yours etcetera

Cc Dr Twee Dampensquib

Wednesday 3rd July 2019. I wrote again to Lucy today, just to keep in touch. I received my copies of *My Journey Back – Part Two* on Monday and despatched a dozen of them to people on my mailing list, including Lucy: - Wednesday 3rd July 2019

Lucy Lawless,

Dear Soulmate,

We have come together twice since I last wrote to you a week ago. I can tell that I have made you happy, also because the weather here has been very pleasant. We are now having a lovely summer in England.

Three weeks from now we will have a new Prime Minister in the UK, and Theresa May will be history. I think that Lucifer will also be history, but we will have to wait and see. If she is still prolonging the agony in three weeks' time then it will be back to the drawing board for everyone in Europe. I have made all the leaders in Europe aware that if we don't get rid of Lucifer soon, then it may be too late to save the world for all of us. Every important person now understands the urgency, including Dolly herself, so I'm still hoping that she will do the decent thing and go! Her only alternative is to continue with an existence of the utmost misery and despair. She will be better off as a duck and I think she knows it. She won't be forgiven for her sins until she does come back as a duck, and then she will find acceptance as such a being, which she never will again as a person.

My shingles rash is still lingering, and the flush in my toilet has stopped working again. It works by a sensor which you just have to put your hand near and it flushes, but unfortunately it keeps on breaking. I don't like using the communal toilet in the shower room so I just flush my loo with jugs of water from the sink. It is time consuming but it works. It takes weeks to get my flush mended.

Your telepathic transmission of your feelings is getting stronger all the time and so is my love for you. I hope you can feel my love, Darling. As Bob Dylan wrote, "There is nothing that I wouldn't do, to make you feel my love".

Continue to be patient, Darling. With any luck, there'll be a major breakthrough in our fortunes three weeks from today. We'll know for sure that the old witch is gone when the weather presenters and the newscasters stop using the words "Area" and "Areas", and start using the words "Region" and "Regions" instead. I'll tell you when that happens.

Yours etcetera

Cc Dr Twee Dampensquib

Saturday 6th July 2019. I despatched another six copies of *My Journey Back – Part Two* to some more world leaders on my mailing list, and I finished reading the book myself today. Last week I purchased a WiFi adaptor called a dongle and connected it to my computer and ran the software that came with it. But I still couldn't get connected to the internet. I think the password I have been given is incorrect, but I'm hoping to get it sorted out on Monday. I wrote the following letter to Lucy this evening: - Saturday Evening 6th July 2019

Lucy Lawless,

Dear Soulmate,

I received another injection of paliperidone this evening. I'm sorry I can't satisfy you as often as you would like but it really is the fault of the drug. It inhibits my sex drive and that frustrates both of us. With any luck, today's will be my last injection if Lucifer departs on time, two weeks from next Wednesday.

The week before last, the England women's football team played Norway in the World Cup and Lucy Bronze scored a fantastic goal. I always felt that her name was a misnomer and that was confirmed by the media after the game. One newspaper headline read, "Bronze is pure gold!". Her manager said, and all the pundits agreed with him that, "Lucy Bronze is the best footballer in the world".

I saw that Rafa Nadal won the French Open tennis tournament last month and this week he had a grudge match against another player. One pundit said that it was more like a battle of wills than a tennis match but Nadal won I'm happy to say.

Your glory is reflected in the names of our heroes.

I watched the debate between the candidates vying for the leadership of the Liberal Democratic Party, and I wasn't impressed by either of them. There was a man and a woman but neither of them struck me as a real leader. They were both twee little people, politically correct, and afraid to make any strong arguments on the issues of the day, such as a second referendum on the UK leaving the European Union.

On that showing, I think that the Liberal Democrats are just as doomed as the Conservative and Labour Parties. So, I'm keeping my support for the Green Party until I can get my own Party, The Survival Party, up and running. That obviously won't be until I get my freedom and start to clear my name, which won't be until the old witch, Lucifer, disappears. Everything depends on that happening.

When she goes, my first priority is to get my freedom, and the second is my public apology and compensation from the Royal College of Psychiatrists. What I do with my time when I am free depends on how long it takes to get my compensation. I am demanding £x, which is a modest amount considering my loss of earnings during the last forty-three years. If it looks like it will take a long time to get my money, then I will have to do something to earn a living while I am waiting. I'm thinking of going as a freelance executive management consultant, specialising in man-management. Some people need encouragement, some need to be set a challenge, some need an unpleasant shock such as being made redundant, and some just need good advice from an older and wiser head than their own. I can provide all these things, and that will be my selling point.

If, on the other hand, I get my £x without delay or quibble, then I'll set about registering The Survival Party and canvassing support for the Party immediately. That is my REAL work and it is vital that I get on with it quickly, for everybody's sake.

Yours etcetera

Cc Dr Twee Dampensquib

Monday 8th July 2019. I wrote to Lucy again today as follows: - Monday 8th July 2019

Lucy Lawless

Dear Soulmate,

I finished writing my latest song "We Thank Heaven" this morning, so I'm enclosing a copy of the words and guitar chords for you. As you can see, it is a duet for a man and a woman. I hope we will sing it together before very long, but in the meantime, you can sing it with other musical partners until we get together.

I'm not sending Dampensquib a copy of it. That would be like casting pearls before swine.

My shingles rash is still lingering and my toilet flush is still not working. Also, the hot water does not work in my sink and in my shower, so I have to shower every morning in the communal shower room.

Apparently, there is a broken pipe underground, and it is taking weeks to fix it. These people couldn't run a booze-up in a brewery. The management here leaves a lot to be desired. They need to employ a management consultant. They would never get away with this inadequate management in a commercial enterprise. I could sort the idiots out if they employed me to do so.

Yours etcetera

I thought that you, dear reader, would like to see a copy of my latest song, so I'm enclosing here a copy of the words with the guitar chords.

We Thank Heaven by Robert Brooks Strong

MAN
A A⁷ D
She makes me know it when she wants to dance
E⁷ A
And I make her know it when I want romance.
A A⁷ D
We both know magic beneath the stars above
E⁷ A
And I thank Heaven for my woman's love.

WOMAN

I make him feel it when I want to dance
And he makes me feel it when he wants romance.
I know he gives me all the love he can
And I thank Heaven for the love of my man.

BOTH

We've found the real thing that everyone desires
And it's a meaning that just could not be higher.
For we are soulmates like a hand and glove
And we thank Heaven for each other's love.

Saturday 13th July 2019. I wrote the following letter to Lucy this evening: -
Saturday 13th July 2019
Lucy Lawless,

Dear Soulmate,

This letter won't go out in the post until Monday 15th so I don't think you will receive it until Tuesday 23rd which will be in the denouement of Theresa May's premiership, and hopefully, of Lucifer's existence as well. I think she may try to hang around after 24th July, to supervise my management of world affairs, which would defeat its own objective because I won't really be in charge until after she is gone. Theresa May stated that she wants Great Britain to be carbon neutral by 2050. My ambition is to make the whole world carbon neutral by 2030. This is imperative if we are to combat Global Warming and Climate Change.

I hope you received your copy of my latest book all right and that you enjoyed reading it. Much of it you will already be familiar with as I sent you copies of the text at the time. I hope you liked the cover illustration. That is my way of saying that I am the spiritual light of the world. I transmitted that picture telepathically in 1976 when I first felt that people were asking me who I thought I am. Millions of people all over the world received that vision. That is what is meant by the phrase, "I've seen the light".

My sex life has been non-existent for a couple of weeks now because of the drug. I won't forgive the psychiatric profession easily for doing this to me for all these years.

I bought a WiFi adaptor called a dongle. I plugged it in and ran the software that came with it but I still couldn't get my computer connected to the internet. I think the password that I was given was wrong so I have asked the IT department at this hospital for a correct password. It should be sorted out soon.

I'm still waiting to get my dental work done. I had to get Dampensquib's permission to spend my own money on my own dental work, then I had to wait until I completed a medical history form, which meant waiting 'til my ward manager came back from holiday. Perhaps she will book my dental appointment now. It means spending a whole day at Dundee having my remaining upper teeth extracted and four temporary implants inserted together with bridges. Six months' later, when my gums have hardened, I will go back for six permanent implants together with bridges to be fitted. The work is expensive but I am convinced it will be worthwhile as I envisage doing some public speaking in the future, and at the moment I have a speech impediment due to my missing upper teeth.

My shingles rash is not quite gone yet and my toilet flush still doesn't work. Thankfully the hot water supply to my sink and shower has now been restored after several weeks without hot water. This means I can shower in my own shower room in the mornings, which is a blessing.

Talking of blessings, I hope you liked the song I sent you called, "We thank Heaven". I was rather pleased with it. I don't know if you can read music, but I'm sure you know a musician who can play you the melody from the music sheet I sent you.

Yours etcetera

Cc Dr Twee Dampensquib

Friday 19th July 2019. I wrote the following letter to Lucy this morning: -

Friday 19th July 2019

Lucy Lawless,

Dear Soulmate,

The next three days are set to be the hottest July days ever in Great Britain and Europe. This is because all the leaders of the human race, including you and me, are working at stuffing Lucifer's soul into the sperm cell of a copulating drake and guiding it down the hen's fallopian tube until it fertilises the hen's ovum and Lucifer is conceived as the embryo of a duckling. I think our endeavours will prove successful on Thursday because the weather here is predicted to be quite pleasant on Friday.

The new leader of the Conservative Party will be announced this morning and Boris Johnson is the overwhelming favourite for reasons I have already told you. Boris will have to call a General Election before October 31st as that is the date the European Union have set for the conclusion of the Brexit negotiations. Boris won't get Brexit through the British Parliament and by the time the election comes I will be free and promoting The Survival Party. Unfortunately for the Conservatives, Boris is a bungling idiot and this is becoming apparent to everybody. I shall have the job of persuading the British people that I am not Boris Johnson and he is just an allegorical figure for me because of his name.

The new leader of the Conservatives will become the Prime Minister tomorrow afternoon, and I believe Lucifer will be gone on Thursday, which is set to be the hottest July day ever in this part of the world.

Magic has promised me that he will look at my computer again today. I hope he can sort out my internet connection.

Yours etcetera

Cc Dr Twee Dampensquib

Chapter 4

Boris's Victory

Events and Thoughts from Thursday 25th July 2019

Thursday 25th July 2019. I wrote to Lucy this evening as follows: - Thursday 25th July 2019

Lucy Lawless,

Dear Soulmate,

I am chronicling the story of recent events in these letters to you which I shall be publishing when my latest book, *My Journey Back – Part Four* gets printed. *My Journey Back – Part Three* is already with the production department of my publishers.

Boris Johnson was declared the winner of the election for the Conservative Party leadership at around mid-day on Tuesday. Theresa May has gone and Boris was declared Prime Minister yesterday. Today was his first full day in office and he is living in cloud cuckoo land as became obvious today when he started speaking in Parliament. Lots of Conservative MPs follow him in his delusional ideas. He thinks he can get a deal with the EU on Britain's withdrawal although they have already said that a new deal is out of the question, especially one that does not have arrangements for the border in Ireland, known as "the back stop". He plans to exit the EU without a deal if he fails to get a deal with the Europeans, but his own Party will block the attempts to leave without a deal, so he will have to call a General Election, which I'm sure he will lose because MY Party, The Survival Party, will be in contention at the next election. Time will tell how well I do, but I am optimistic about my chances since everybody knows that I am the main man.

I sensed Lucifer's presence this evening, and yours, and I am confident that she is now on the verge of her departure. Today has been the hottest

July day ever in Great Britain, France, Holland, Belgium and Germany. The forthcoming days are set to remain hot, and there will also be thunderstorms with heavy rain, lightning and hailstones the size of golf balls. This hot and stormy weather is caused by Lucifer's desperation. She is a bad loser, but WE know she has already lost, even though she is still trying to pretend that we don't know that. She is dragging out her own denouement, but the weather isn't going to change until she goes. I will, of course, let you know when that happens.

She thought that she had what every man wants from a woman, but I have proven her wrong and she can't take it. I have proven that I have got what every woman wants from a man. Her own incestuous desires are proof of it, which she can't deny, even to herself, so I have won, and so have you, Darling.

I'm not bothering to write to Dampensquib again until Lucifer has gone. Then I shall write to him again, informing him that I am now the Boss Man and he must do as I say.

Take care of yourself, my Love,

I have much more to say to you, but it can wait until we talk,

Bless you, my Queen,

Yours with Love, Affection and Friendship,

Bob XX

Saturday 27th July 2019. I wrote the following letter to Lucy this morning:
- Saturday Morning 27th July 2019

Lucy Lawless,

Dear Soulmate,

Dolly, Lucifer, is still dragging out her denouement and the world is in her hands. The Arctic ice cap has already melted and wild forest fires are now raging in the Arctic Circle. Alaska, Greenland and Siberia are now ablaze. The Antarctic ice cap is melting and sea levels are expected to rise by several metres in the near future. The only way to halt irreversible Global Warming is for the whole world to get carbon admissions down to zero by the year 2031.

If Lucifer has the sense to turn herself into a duck NOW then I stand a CHANCE OF GETTING THE WORLD TO REDUCE ITS CARBON

EMISSIONS TO ZERO BY THE YEAR 2031. (That was the Gods again, playing with my caps lock button). If the human race doesn't ratify her NOW then they won't survive and they won't deserve to. The only way the human race can survive is to put ME in power as soon as possible with my Survival Party, the updated Manifesto of which I am enclosing for you.

The new leader of the British Liberal Democratic Party is a woman called Jo Swinson and she recently said, "My door is always open". If people listen to idiots like her then they are doomed. The only way to survive is to close the door immediately.

I am getting close to the point where I stop trying to save people from themselves. Unless they see sense very soon then they won't survive and they won't deserve to.

Yours etcetera

Cc Dr Twee Dampensquib.

Sunday 28th July 2019. I wrote to Dr Dampensquib this morning as follows: - Sunday 28th July 2019

Dr Twee Dampensquib,
Medical Director,
Alcatraz Island Hospital.

Dear Dr Dampensquib,

I have a message to all the REAL leaders of the human race (and they know who they are) as follows: -

Either you close the door on the bygone era in the history of the world or you become extinct through Global Warming in the foreseeable future.

If you choose to survive you MUST close the door immediately and make ME the Actual World Leader (the AWL) and also the Official World Leader (the OWL) and collaborate with my plan to make the whole world carbon neutral by the year 2031.

As soon as the door is closed, I will expect you to do as I say because I will then be your boss. My first command is that you take me off all neuroleptic drugs immediately.

Your sincerely,

Robert Strong

Monday 29th July 2019. I wrote to Lucy again this evening as follows: -
Monday Evening 29th July 2019

Lucy Lawless,

Dear Soulmate,

In twelve years' time Global Warming will be irreversible, so the human race has got eleven years, until 2031, to reduce its carbon emissions to zero across the whole world. I AM THE MAN WITH THE PLAN TO ACHIEVE THIS, so it is vital that I get into power as quickly as possible. This is the case whether Dolly, Lucifer, decides to go or whether she continues to prolong the agony of her existence. I should be in 10 Downing Street, not Alcatraz Island Hospital.

The politicians in the House of Parliament spend all their time talking about Brexit and the European Union. They are like a group of silly children playing a game of tiddlywinks in the living room while the house is burning down all around them. The only topics worthy of consideration are Climate Change and Global Warming. Everything else is irrelevant as the world is doomed unless I get into power very soon.

In order to get into power, I need my freedom and some money to promote my Party, The Survival Party, and I will also need the credibility that a full public apology from the Royal College of Psychiatrists would give me. So, I am sticking to my demand for £x in compensation from the Royal College as well as my public apology.

I am relying on cooperation from Dr Dampensquib to get these things.

We came together at ten a.m. (UK Time) yesterday and I felt your pleasure in doing so. I also felt your gratitude to me for making you come so beautifully. It makes me happy to make you happy, Darling.

That's because I love you so very much. Thanks again for bobulucydating me.

I felt that Dolly, Lucifer, has decided to turn herself into a duck because she knows that she will never be the alpha female as long as she remains in human form. She has accepted that that's who YOU are because of my love for you. She is now looking forward to the challenge of her next adventure in the world of ducks. She will try to progress from the bottom to the top of the pecking order in the world of ducks seeing as we have knocked her off her perch in the world of human beings.

Yours etcetera

Tuesday 30th July 2019. I wrote to my shrink, Dr Twee Dampensquib, this morning, as follows: - Tuesday Morning 30th July 2019

Dr Twee Dampensquib,
Medical Director,
Alcatraz Island Hospital.

Dear Dr Dampensquib,

The establishment of the International Community, especially the psychiatric profession, have deified a woman who is unable to accept reality, namely my late mother, Mrs Dorothy Ayres. She is the one with the delusional disorder, not me. The FACTS that she is unable to accept are as follows:-

1, She is my mother not my wife. She should stop trying to seduce me or rape me and accept the fact that I have a partner of my own who I am happy with.

2. She has been dead for thirteen years. She should Rest in Peace and let me fight for my own position in the world in my own way, not keep me detained in a mental hospital and treated like a madman. If she can't Rest in Peace, then she should come back to life, whatever she chooses to come back as.

3. In my opinion, she is NOT the world's alpha female. Lucy Lawless is, and it is my opinion that matters most in my own love life.

4. If the people of the world want a communal sexual identity, then they can find one by dancing with me and Lucy, otherwise known as "opening the book" not by "opening the door". That is a thing of the past, now.

5. She is NOT God, whatever anyone believes. She is just an easy lay because she has always been a woman of easy virtue and low morals.

The world is being put in jeopardy by men like Judge Richard Hone who insist on keeping me in hospital because that is the will of my late mother, which men like him obey because of their own sexual inadequacy.

It is beginning to look as if the world is going to be destroyed by Global Warming because the men of the world are unable to move with the times.

It is utter folly for people to keep their door always open like so many idiots insist on doing. Their precious DOOR insists on keeping me locked up and drugged with libido suppressing drugs when I am the man with a plan to save the world.

Yours sincerely,

Robert Strong
Cc Lucy Lawless

Wednesday 31st July 2019. I wrote the following letter to Lucy today: -
Wednesday 31st July 20129
Lucy Lawless,

Dear Soulmate,

I don't know what is going on in your life, but I got the impression today that you are troubled. I want you to know that I can sense it when you are feeling that way and I am comforting you in my mind. I hope you can feel me comforting you. In my mind I have got my arm round your shoulders; I am kissing your forehead and offering you my shoulder to cry on. And I am telling you, truthfully, that everything is going to be all right.

My shingles rash has almost gone and the maintenance man, Tony, fixed the flush in my toilet yesterday. All that was wrong with it was that it needed a new battery for the control mechanism. At least I know what to ask for, next time it stops working.

I have been getting encouraging signs from the people on TV that Lucifer will be gone soon. I think she just decided to hang around for another week to see what sort of a job I would make of running the world, but I think she has had enough now and will go soon.

Nothing worth having ever came easily! You don't knock the alpha woman off her perch without having everything you are tested to the limit, but you are passing all your tests with flying colours, Darling.

You really are proving that you are the Queen of Heaven.

Yours etcetera
Cc Dr Twee Dampensquib.

Friday 2nd August 2019. I wrote the following letter to Lucy this morning. Note that I am including a copy to Dr Marionette Madre; this is because I know that she is a medium for my late mother and that she, Lucifer, will know what Dr Madre is reading.

Friday 2nd August 2019

Lucy Lawless,

Dear Soulmate,

If the human race continues trying to force me to have sex with my late mother, then I shall let them destroy themselves with Global Warming, which is what they are doing at the moment.

I am the only man with the leadership qualities needed to unite the human race in the battle against Climate Change, but I cannot do that whilst I am treated this way. I am kept a prisoner in a secure hospital and I am having my libido suppressed by these filthy drugs by people who won't listen to reason, and I am kept relatively impecunious. I need a lot of money to promote my Party, The Survival Party, and I need the freedom to do things my own way.

The only way out of this impasse is for my late mother to duckify herself immediately, or it will be too late, even for me, to save the world.

You and I have waited too long already. If she doesn't go NOW then it will be too late.

Yours etcetera

Cc Dr Twee Dampensquib,
Dr Marionette Madre.

I have the following to say to the human race: - If you don't accept my leadership, then we are all doomed to die along with all other living things from Global Warming in the foreseeable future. If you do accept my leadership then start treating me like a leader, not like a madman as of NOW and stop following my late mother, Mrs Dorothy Ayres, as of NOW. I want you to do the following things urgently:-

1. Tell the late Mrs Dorothy Ayres to come back to life in the body of a duck immediately.

2. Tell Dr Twee Dampensquib to take me off all neuroleptic drugs immediately.

3. Tell Paul Rees, the Chief Executive of the Royal College of Psychiatrists, to agree to my terms for a settlement with the psychiatric

profession, and to write to me and tell me so immediately. I want £x in compensation for forty-three years loss of earnings plus a full public apology. I wouldn't ask for £x if I didn't think they could raise that amount.

4. I expect the cooperation of British society in my plans to make The Survival Party the Party of government in Great Britain, THIS YEAR, with myself installed as Prime Minister in No 10 Downing Street. I can then organise an international conference at which I will inspire all other national leaders to follow the lead of Great Britain by rolling out my plans for the elimination of the burning of all fossil fuels, as per the details in my Manifesto of The Survival Party, in their own countries.

5. I want all my mother's followers to know that if they persist in keeping their door always open then they are destined to follow her into the world of ducks when they die.

I sent a copy of the above journal entry to Lucy.

Saturday 3rd August 2019. I wrote to my shrink this morning as follows: -
Saturday Morning 3rd August 2019
   Dr Twee Dampensquib,
   Medical Director,
   Alcatraz Island Hospital.

Dear Dr Dampensquib,
   The longest chapter in the Book of Revelations in the Bible is called "The End of All Things". That is what is going to happen if my late mother continues to prolong the agony of her existence. The world is going to come to an end and she will be to blame for clinging onto power instead of handing it over to me, and YOU will also be to blame for forcing me to take drugs which suppress my libido; a libido which, if not suppressed, would give mankind an alternative to "opening the door" and give people psycho-sexual fulfilment.

   Making ME take antipsychotic drugs is the most stupid thing in the world that anyone can do and you psychiatrists have been doing it to me for too long already. Stop it now, before it is too late.

   I have proven that I have the courage, the wisdom, the intelligence, the maturity, the understanding and the love for people to be a great leader, which is what the world needs at the moment. Treating me like a madman is utter folly. Stop it now before it is too late.

Yours sincerely,

Robert Strong
Cc Lucy Lawless

Sunday 4th August 2019. I wrote the following letter to Lucy this morning:
- Sunday Morning 4th August 2019
    Lucy Lawless,

Dear Soulmate,

When my late mother, Lucifer, realises that by prolonging the agony of her existence and clinging onto power instead of handing it over to me, she is the one who is bringing about the end of the world through Global Warming, then I am sure she will duckify herself. Even *she* is not so stupid as to deliberately destroy the world for all living things.

She has got no choice. We have got her over a barrel, Darling. It is game, set and match to US! I am one hundred per cent sure of it. It is just a question of waiting now, for the reality of the situation to dawn on her.

The sooner it dawns on her, the more chance I have got of saving the world with my plan for The Survival Party. No one else has a plan anywhere near as credible as mine, and no one else is as credible a leader as myself.

I now have a date of the 2nd September to go to Dundee for my dental work. Magic comes back from leave tomorrow and I have been told that he will sort out my internet connection. My shingles rash has almost completely gone now, and is not painful at all.

We came together most beautifully at 9.25 a.m. (UK Time) on Friday. Thank you, Darling for being so wonderful and bobulucydating me. You are the best; the world's alpha woman.

Your etcetera

Cc Dr Twee Dampensquib,
Dr Marionette Madre.

Monday 5th August 2019. I wrote to my shrink this evening as follows: -
    Monday 5th August 2019
    Dr Twee Dampensquib,
    Medical Director,

Alcatraz Island Hospital.

Dear Dr Dampensquib,

The followers of my late mother, Mrs Dorothy Ayres, include all the members of the establishment of the UK as well as many sections of the international community, especially those in the so-called "free world", as well as a majority of the ordinary men and women of those communities. This includes the British legal profession and the psychiatric profession.

All these people have persecuted me all my life for refusing to have sex with my mother. This includes all the Tribunal judges that I have been before over the last forty-three years and all the psychiatrists who have forced me to take neuroleptic drugs when there has never been anything wrong with my mental health.

All these people will be to blame for the end of the world through Global Warming which will happen in the foreseeable future unless they stop trying to make a motherfucker out of me. I am the best man with the best plan to save the world from Global Warming by getting the whole world to reduce its carbon emissions to zero by the year 2031. This is necessary for the survival of all life on Earth because Climate Change will be irreversible in twelve years' time. And the world will then be doomed.

As a matter of interest, my late mother wouldn't be so determined to have sex with me if I wasn't who I claim to be! She really is the paranoid Archangel Lucifer, and look what a mess she has made of running the world. She must go before it is too late.

She has been doing Satan's dirty work for him by peddling decadence in the name of diversity. So many people have bought her immoral ideas because that is the easy road that she has led them down. I am the new broom that will sweep clean.

Yours sincerely,

Robert Strong.
Cc Lucy Lawless,
Dr Marionette Madre.

Tuesday 6th August 2019. I wrote the following letter to Lucy this evening:
- Tuesday 6th August 2019
    Lucy Lawless,

Dear Soulmate,

The chances of getting the whole world to cut its carbon emissions to zero by the year 2031 are slim and getting slimmer with every passing day that my late mother, Lucifer, prolongs the agony of her existence. It may already be too late but all we can do is try.

I am not afraid of much. I like to think that a man must have the courage to overcome all his fears, but I have one fear that may be too much for me and that is the scenario written about in the Book of Revelations called "The End of All Things". I don't want all my hopes for the future of humanity to be dashed, but it looks as though Lucifer is dashing them by prolonging the agony of her existence and clinging onto power instead of trusting me with it. She should trust me. I am the one who has guided and guarded the human race for the last three hundred thousand years, ever since I was Adam in the Garden of Eden.

Dr Twee Dampensquib is also to blame for not recommending my discharge to the Tribunal or to the Ministry of Justice. The stupid bastard had me injected with paliperidone again today. And after all that I've told him in my letters he still does what Lucifer wants him to do. He is a psychiatrist before he is a man, I am ashamed to say of him.

I repeat that all I can do is to go on trying to protect humanity, but it is hard to protect them from themselves.

We came together at 4.50 a.m. (UK Time) today. It was, as always, wonderful, Darling. Thank you for being you, and thank you for bobulucydating me.

Maciej (pronounced Magic) and another person called David tried to get my computer connected to the internet today, but the problem defeated both of them. I think I shall have to buy a new laptop as my desktop PC doesn't seem to want to connect to the internet, and I have to rely on the hospital IT dept. for my broadband connection and the router. There is no one else I can turn to, to solve the problem, and I want internet access, so I shall make enquiries about a new laptop to get internet access.

Yours etcetera

Cc Dr Twee Dampensquib
Dr Marionette Madre.

Friday 9th August 2019. I wrote the following letter to Lucy today: - Friday afternoon 9th August 2019

Lucy Lawless,

Dear Soulmate,

I thought you would like to see the details of my plan for the future, as follows:-

Stage 1 To get an absolute and unconditional discharge from hospital, either by Dr Dampensquib recommending me to the Ministry of Justice or by supporting me at a Tribunal.

Stage 2 To persuade the Royal College of Psychiatrists to accept my demand for a public apology and for £x in compensation.

Stage 3 To fight for a change in the law in the UK in two respects:-

Firstly, to allow a retrial after all these years on the grounds that a miscarriage of justice has occurred, and Secondly, to accept a plea of "self-defence against undue social pressure" as a legal defence in a murder trial.

Stage 4 To undergo a retrial and fight for my plea of self-defence to be accepted because that is the truth.

Stage 5 Having thus exonerated myself, I will fight for the balance of my compensation in the amount of £y from the British government.

Stage 6 To canvass support for my Party, The Survival Party, and to get myself elected as Prime Minister.

Stages 1-6 will obviously take time, but should be possible once I am the Actual World Leader.

Stage 7 To start implementing my plan for the abolition of the burning of fossil fuels and all the other policies detailed in my Manifesto.

Stage 8 To summon all the heads of state, or their representatives, to an international conference to be held in London, at which I will inspire them to roll out my plans for the abolition of the burning of all fossil fuels, as per my Manifesto, in their own countries. All the social pressure in the world will be brought to bear on any recalcitrant countries not willing to sign up to the agreement.

These plans will get the world's carbon emissions down to zero, hopefully by the year 2031. If it takes any longer than that then Climate Change will become irreversible and the world will be doomed.

These plans will mean the almost complete closure of the oil industry and the coal and gas industries, but will create opportunities in the renewable energy industry. Under good leadership, there is nothing to stop the human race from covering the world's deserts with solar panels and creating an international electricity grid to power the whole world with electricity.

Everything depends on my late mother, Lucifer, coming back to life, presumably as a duck, in the immediate future. If she doesn't do that then the world is doomed.

I will say again what people said when I was fighting Satan: the world has got two hopes – Bob Hope and No Hope.

We came together again yesterday morning (UK Time) and it was wonderful, as always. We'll be able to dance properly and more often when these stupid people take me off their evil drugs. They must know by now that they are never going to get me to have sex with my mother, which is what they have spent decades trying to do. It is time now to call this cruel joke to an end, and for my late mother to depart. Even *she* must know that. The world will be doomed if she doesn't.

Yours etcetera

Cc Dr Twee Dampensquib
Dr Marionette Madre.

Saturday 11th August 2019. I wrote the following letter to Paula, my grandson, Troy's, mother today: - Saturday 11th August 2019
Paula Evans,

Hiya Paula,

I hope you are back from your holiday in Spain and that you and your dogs had a good time there. Whereabouts in Spain did you go to? Did you stay in a hotel or were you camping? Did your dogs realise that you were taking a break?

I hope you received my latest book, which I sent you a copy of. Do you have any news of Troy for me? And have you heard from Chris at all? Please write and let me know.

If I die today, I will die happy knowing that I have made men out of both my surviving sons. I will also die knowing that I have felt the love of the woman that I love, Lucy Lawless.

I don't blame my sons for not wanting to know me. I wasn't there for them when they needed me, when they were growing up. Chris told me that he thinks I am evil because of what I did in July 1976, but I hope that one day he will understand that what I did was self-defence against undue social pressure. I had no choice. Society made me do what I did, but I don't expect many people to understand that.

Growing up without me has meant that both my boys have had to find from within themselves what it takes to survive in a world which can be hard and cruel at times, but in doing so they have both become men and I am proud of both of them.

Please ask Troy if he minds me having his address so I can write to him, and if he doesn't mind then please let me know his address. I can give him good advice which will help him as he matures. I love Troy, as well as Chris and Tony, and I love you too, Paula, as a very dear friend.

Take care of yourself, my dear,

Lots of love,

Bob XX

Wednesday 14th August 2019. I wrote the following letter to Lucy, this morning: - Wednesday Morning 14th August 2019

Lucy Lawless,

Dear Soulmate,

I'm enclosing a copy of Sunday's journal entry for you. Paula is Christopher's ex-girlfriend and Troy's mother, so it is a good idea to maintain my friendship with her, quite apart from the fact that I like her.

We came together on Sunday morning (UK Time) and it was, as always, beautiful, Darling. Thank you for bobulucydating me.

I can feel your love as I write this, and it is wonderful and most precious to me. I would never do anything to jeopardise these loving feelings I get from you. They make my life worthwhile. I wonder if Dampensquib values the love of the people that he loves. He wouldn't be so quick to call me deluded if he does!

I don't know how much longer Lucifer is going to prolong the agony for. I can't think what she is now waiting for. She should have gone by now. She is just wasting our precious time, and everybody else's, including her own. There won't be a world for ducks to come back into if she doesn't go immediately.

Maciej is liaising with the IT department of the hospital to try and fix my internet connection. I've been told to wait until those people come up with something, before I buy a new laptop computer. I'll give them another week or so, and then I'll buy a new laptop anyway. I really do want internet access.

My shingles rash has almost completely gone now. Perhaps it is waiting for Lucifer to go before it goes as well.

Yours etcetera

Cc Dr Twee Dampensquib
Dr Marionette Madre

Sunday 18th August 2019. I wrote the following letter to Lucy this evening. It is followed by my statement to the CPA meeting on 1st October 2019.

Sunday Evening 18th August 2019
Lucy Lawless,

Dear Soulmate,

By making the enclosed statement, I am going over the head of my late mother by making an appeal directly to the establishment to let me lead them. They have no choice but to accept my offer of leadership and they know it. In so doing, I have disconnected my late mother from her power base. Whatever she does now, and whatever attitude she takes are inconsequential. She is yesterday's woman.

It has taken the Global emergency of Climate Change to achieve it, but I am now the Actual World Leader. You can guess what the human race will do to her now that they realise she has been leading them down the road to extinction, and that I am here to save them. Be prepared to see my fortunes sky rocket now.

In case you fear a change in the protection that you have been getting from me, don't despair. I had an accident and broke my lamp, so it doesn't shine on your picture at the moment. I will buy a new lamp as soon as possible, and connect it so that it shines on your picture.

My sex drive is dormant at the moment because of the drugs. Hopefully that will change very soon.

Yours etcetera

Cc Dr Twee Dampensquib
Dr Marionette Madre.

Statement by Robert Brooks Strong 18th August 2019

All the Climate Change scientists agree that Climate Change will be irreversible in twelve years' time, in the year 2031., unless the world cuts its carbon emissions to zero by that date. I have a plan to achieve just that and I am the man to see it through. The world is desperate for a strong leader who can unite the human race in the battle against Global Warming and Climate Change. That is WHO I AM.

My plan involves the phasing out of the burning of all fossil fuels over a five-year period, and although my Party, The Survival Party, is British, I can inspire and persuade all other national leaders to emulate my plan in their own countries. I allow for a five-year time span to get my Party into power, then I can commence my five-year plan for the abolition of the burning of all fossil fuels.

I intend to put the whole human race on a war footing in the battle against Global Warming and Climate Change in the name of the survival of all life on Earth. This will be necessary because the plan will involve huge disruption in everybody's way of life.

I will obviously depend upon the cooperation and the collaboration of the establishment to make this plan work. This means the legal profession, the psychiatric profession, the political establishment and the national and international media.

This scenario is more important than anything else in the world: more important than the sex life of Mrs Dorothy Ayres or that of anybody else. Unless my plan works, we are all doomed along with all life on Earth.

Those who wish to know more about me can learn the whole story from my autobiographies. They can be accessed from my website. The address is http://www.robert-brooks-strong.olympiapublishers.com/

Chapter 5

The Fight Back in Earnest

Events and Thoughts from Wednesday 21ˢᵗ August 2019

Wednesday 21ˢᵗ August 2019. I wrote the following letter to Lucy this morning: - Wednesday Morning 21ˢᵗ August 2019
    Lucy Lawless,

Dear Soulmate,
    I have taken over the leadership of my late mother's army by making it obvious that I offer them their best chance of survival against certain extinction if they continue to follow the late Mrs Dorothy Ayres. Now that I have well and truly knocked her off her perch, the establishment of the international community are MY army. I think the weather presenters on the TV will continue to use the words "Area" and its plural "Areas" until the door is finally closed, so there is a bit of mopping up to do. I'm sure my army will make short work of duckifying her.
    Dampensquib is on holiday until next week, but I'm sure he will be only too happy to do things by the book from now on. This will mean that he takes me off the drugs immediately and recommends to the Royal College of Psychiatrists that they give me my public apology and compensation without further delay or argument. As soon as I have got my compensation money, all £x, I shall leave hospital without further delay.
    It occurred to me that when I bought my computer from PC World, six years ago, I asked them to take out the internet feature as I wasn't allowed internet access at the time. They may have taken out more than just the WiFi adaptor so this may be the root of my problems with my computer, in which case I shall get them to send an engineer round to my room to put back whatever they took out. This should solve the problem of my internet connection.

Take care of yourself, my Love, I have much more to say to you, but it can wait until we talk, Bless you, my Queen, Yours with Love, Affection and Friendship,

Bob XX
Cc Dr Twee Dampensquib

Friday 30th August 2019. I wrote the following letter to Dr Dampensquib this afternoon: -

Friday 30th August 2019
Dr Twee Dampensquib,
Medical Director,
Alcatraz Island Hospital.

Dear Dr Dampensquib,

Further to our conversation this morning, I wish to refer you to my letter of the 9th August, in which I outlined my plans for the future. I am enclosing another copy of the letter for you. My plans are substantially the same except for the decision to wait until I receive my compensation money and my public apology before I leave hospital. There is also a change in that I am not waiting for my late mother to come back to life before getting on with my political ambitions. I don't need to wait for her to do that. I have already taken over the leadership of the establishment of the international community.

As far as my covert profile is concerned, I am still a private citizen and will remain so until I get recognition for my political views. I therefore will need a public apology along the lines that I suggested in my letter to Paul Rees of the 14th February 2017 (a copy of which I am enclosing for you). I made a mistake in February 2017 in thinking that my late mother had already come back as a duck, but the substance of my demand is the same. I also wish the public apology to state that a series of mistakes have been made insofar as I have been misdiagnosed, misjudged and mistreated ever since July 1976. I think that's the best way to put it, as long as it is clearly stated that I am not mentally ill and that there has never been anything wrong with my mental health.

Yours sincerely,

Robert Strong.
Cc Lucy Lawless

Sunday 1st September 2019. I wrote the following letter to Lucy today: -
Sunday 1st September 2019
Lucy Lawless,

Dear Soulmate,

I'm enjoying the mopping up operation. There are still some idiots living in the past. Most of them are monkeys like the weather presenters on TV who say what they are told to say. The fun lies in identifying the organ grinders and knowing that having done so, my followers will enjoy ripping the bastards to shreds, financially, professionally, socially and sexually. The main organ grinder is the Director General of the BBC who is, like Lucifer herself, jealous of me and spiteful with it. I don't even need to know the bastard's name. My influence vastly exceeds his and my followers vastly outnumber him and his cronies.

I had thought of having my enemies assassinated, but it is much easier, safer and quicker to simply identify the bastards and then to tell my army that they know what to do. I'm sure that the Director General of the BBC is an aggressive homosexual, and I don't like people like that. His influence needs to be curtailed for that reason alone.

I am still waiting to hear from Dr Dampensquib that he has taken me off the antipsychotic medication.

I am tempted by other women who I find attractive and who do talk to me and make it obvious that they fancy me. You are in danger of losing me if you don't do the same,

Yours etcetera
Cc Dr Dampensquib

Monday 2nd September 2019. I wrote the following letter to Lucy today: -
Monday Morning 2nd September 2019
Lucy Lawless,

Dear Soulmate,

There are still some people on the TV who are living in the past and upset me by using the words "Air", Area" and "Areas". It's not what they say but the way that they say it. They emphasise those words knowing that that upsets me and they think that they can get away with doing that, but they are wrong. I have a long memory and I won't forget the attitude of those people. The day will come when they offer me their heartfelt apologies and beg me for mercy but I'll make them earn it before I have mercy on them. The worst offenders will be going to Hell. Until then I enjoy the knowledge that I have knocked the jealous, spiteful, vindictive incestuous old witch that those spiteful, ungrateful little people have for a heroine off her perch and she won't be getting back on it ever again, whether they like it or not. I saved their lives by overpowering Satan. They would all be dead by now if it wasn't for me. They owe me their very lives and I won't let them forget it – the ungrateful scum. They can worship the memory of Lucifer, Satan's accomplice and partner-in-crime, all they like. Her soul will soon inhabit the body of an animal and they can join her when they die if they want to, which it looks like they do at the moment.

Mrs Ayres has led the world to the brink of extinction yet those idiots still follow her. Perhaps they want the world to end. They are behaving like it.

I'm off to Dundee this morning to have my teeth seen to. I'll finish this letter this evening.

It is now Monday evening and I've had my tooth implants and a bridge fitted. It looks very good, I'm pleased to say, but my speech still needs some improvement. The doctor said that will happen when the anaesthetic wears off.

I'm due for an injection of paliperidone on Friday unless Twee Dampensquib takes me off it by then. I'll keep you posted. My sex drive is still dormant because of the vile muck. I'm sorry I said you were in danger of losing me. Of course you aren't, but I do miss female intimacy, and I want the pleasure of your company.

I look like being free and being worth £x before long and having the reputation of my sanity restored by a public apology. Maybe then you will want to know me, which you don't seem to at the moment any more than you have done for the last twenty years. Please start looking forward to spending a couple of months on a cruise ship with me, at my expense in the near future.

Yours etcetera

I also wrote the following letter to Dr Twee Dampensquib this evening: -
Monday 2nd September 2019

Dr Twee Dampensquib,
Medical Director,
Alcatraz Island Hospital

Dear Dr Dampensquib,

I limited my compensation demand to £x because I thought that would be all the Royal College of Psychiatrists could afford, but the offer you made me on Friday reveals that they can lay their hands on more money if they want to. When I get out, I will have legal fees to pay in order to get a verdict of "self-defence" accepted after a retrial. I will also need money to buy a flat in London, which isn't cheap, and I will also have the expenses incurred in establishing a new political Party and canvassing support for it.

I am therefore revising my compensation demand to £y as well as a full public apology. This is what I really want to make me happy and it is not an exorbitant amount for forty three years of suffering.

Yours sincerely,

Robert Strong.
Cc Lucy Lawless

Tuesday 3rd September 2019. I wrote the following letter to Dr Twee Dampensquib today: - Tuesday 3rd September 2019

Dr Twee Dampensquib,
Medical Director,
Alcatraz Island Hospital.

Dear Dr Dampensquib,

If you were a reasonable man, you would accept the fact that I am now your leader and you would do as I ask. I note that you have not yet taken me off the antipsychotic medication so I am repeating my request that you do so. You should know that there is nothing wrong with my mental health and never has been.

What psychiatrists call my "mental illness" amounts to no more than a difference of opinion concerning my identity.

If you do not accept my proof of who I am, then I assume that you either follow someone else as your leader, or you wish to have a battle of wills with me to establish who is the boss out of the two of us.

To those who still follow the late Mrs Dorothy Ayres I have this to say, "Mrs Ayres has led the world to the brink of extinction. Perhaps those who still follow her want the world to come to an end, because that is how they are behaving".

If you wish to compete for the leadership with me, then I will simply point out that my influence greatly exceeds yours and my followers are far greater in number than your friends and supporters. So, you would be very unwise to persist with this challenge. I like you, Twee, but I really do think that if one of us is mentally ill then it is you not me.

Yours sincerely,

Robert Strong.
Cc Lucy Lawless.

Sunday 8ᵗʰ September 2019. The staff here injected me with paliperidone again on Friday, so I wrote the following letter to my shrink this morning: - Sunday 8ᵗʰ September 2019

Dr Twee Dampensquib,
Medical Director,
Alcatraz Island Hospital.

Dear Dr Dampensquib,

I AM the Lord God Almighty and I don't like being doubted. I have got to come off the libido suppressing drugs for the sake of humanity as well as for myself and my partner, Lucy Lawless. My reasoning doesn't influence your attitude but a demonstration of my power will. So that is what will happen even though it hurts me to hurt you. When every door you try to open becomes closed to you and the smallest of dreams won't come true. When your life and that of all your loved ones becomes a living nightmare, when you feel as though you are in Hell already, then you will know that it is MY influence that is behind it all. That is when you will regret your attitude and agree to obey my will in future. You are a good chap, Twee, but I will make a God-fearing man out of you.

Yours sincerely,

Robert Strong.
Cc Lucy Lawless

I wrote the following letter to Lucy this evening: - Sunday Evening 8th September 2019

Lucy Lawless,

Dear Soulmate,

I was mistaken in thinking that I had replaced my late mother as the leader of the establishment of the international community. This is evidenced by the fact that Dampensquib had me injected again and there is nothing I can do about it and also by the fact that the monkeys on TV keep using the words, "Area" and "Areas" in spite of my protestations. Dolly, Lucifer, will be in power as long as she exists. I don't think that will be for much longer for the following reason: -

I reckon it will take me five years to get free, clear my name and get my Party, the Survival Party, into power; then one year to persuade all the other national leaders to emulate my plan, then another five years to cut the World's carbon emissions down to zero. I think I can just about do it all in eleven years, by the year 2031, after which time it will be too late to stop Climate Change from being irreversible.

I was right in thinking that I have a contract with society to have Lucifer brought back as an animal and for me to come off the drugs.

I don't like making idle threats. I threatened Theresa May with the sack when she refused to discharge me from hospital and I made good that threat. I also threatened to kick the Conservative Party out of power for at least a generation and I am making good that threat as well. I also threatened to have Jeremy Corbyn and his Labour Party kicked out and I am making good that threat as well. Corbyn would make a terrible Prime Minister. He would borrow vast sums of money that would take a generation of austerity measures to repay. And with Boris Johnson, it is now obvious that the Conservatives have put in a boy to do a man's job, and he is making a right cock-up of it. He promised to deliver Brexit by October 31st but his own Party have thwarted his plans. He is trying to get a "NO DEAL BREXIT" through by that date, but his MPs have stopped that from happening. They insist we have a deal. They are forcing him to go back to Europe to get an extension to the 31ˢᵗ January 2020 for Brexit.

That is my reason for thinking that Lucifer will be gone by that date. That is the final date for the REAL deal for the REAL Brexit. I don't think Britain will ever leave the European Union because it is not economically viable to do so and this is now apparent. It is also against MY WILL because I want to be President of Europe before too long, not just the Prime Minister of Great Britain.

We came together again yesterday and I am still enjoying the afterglow. It was wonderful, Darling.

Thank you for bobulucydating me.

Yours etcetera

Cc Dr Twee Dampensquib

Monday 9ᵗʰ September 2019. I wrote the following letter to Lucy today: -
Monday 9ᵗʰ September 2019

Lucy Lawless,

Dear Soulmate,

Further to yesterday's letter, it is apparent that I am still the Crown Prince and you are still the Warrior Princess. Lucifer still rules at the moment and I reckon it will take us about another four months to get rid of her. I suggest that the best way to achieve this is for us to lay claim to our thrones in the Kingdom of Heaven right away. We both know that it is only a pretence at the moment but if we and all our friends pretend hard enough for long enough then it will become reality. That is how a self-fulfilling prophesy works. It takes time and effort and belief, but it works. We both know that the thrones of the King and Queen of Heaven are ours by right and would be ours already if it wasn't for that usurper, Lucifer, who took advantage of my youth and inexperience to steal my throne.

She gave the game away by running around squawking when I claimed to have knocked her off her perch, so I am sticking to my claim even though everybody knows it is only a pretence at the moment, it will be reality before the 31ˢᵗ January 2020. That is how to undermine the authority of a monarch and get rid of her. I predict that she will duckify herself within about four months from now if we both keep up the pretence, MY QUEEN. The Kingdom of Heaven is NOT a democracy; if it was, it would be ours already. WE both enjoy enormous popular support, but by being pretenders to the thrones we can reclaim them by undermining her authority until she has had enough and duckifies herself.

I am copying this letter to Twee Dampensquib to give him the chance to become one of our friends.

What he does is up to him, but he can join our circle of friends if he wants to. I will reward those who stand by us when I am King.

Yours etcetera

Cc Dr Twee Dampensquib

Wednesday 11th September 2019. I wrote to my shrink again today, as follows: - Wednesday 11th September 2019

Dr Twee Dampensquib,
Medical Director,
Alcatraz Island Hospital.

Dear Dr Dampensquib,

The human race still follows my late mother, Mrs Dorothy Ayres. This is evident from the people on the TV who use the words "Air", "Area" and "Areas" because these words sound a bit like my late mother's surname and people think it makes them look big or clever to use those words. People are mistaken to continue following Mrs Ayres and I fear that they may only realise this when it is too late for me, or anyone else to save them. She has led the world to the brink of extinction and if they continue to follow her then they will follow her to their doom. We only have just over eleven years before Climate Change becomes irreversible, and when that happens, the World will rapidly become uninhabitable, and there will be nothing that anyone can do to stop this from happening.

I have a plan to bring the world's carbon emissions down to zero by 2031 but I cannot put it into operation whilst I am treated this way. It is essential that the human race follows my plan because that is the only way to stop Climate Change from becoming irreversible.

The world will continue to follow Mrs Ayres as long as she is the main sexual outlet for people. As you know, they all love "opening the door", in other words having mental sex with Mrs Dorothy Ayres. It is
Mrs Ayres who insists on treating me this way, with detention and libido-suppressing drugs, because that is her way of ensuring that if I don't have mental sex with her, then I can't have it with anyone else either.

By insisting that I take antipsychotic medication, you are following the wishes of Mrs Dorothy Ayres, and thereby playing a significant part in the destruction of the World. If you took me off the drugs, then people would have an alternative to opening the door by having mental sex with me and Lucy, otherwise known as "opening the book".

This would be the start of a worldwide change in people's behaviour which would save the World from Global Warming as I would then be free to carry out my plan. One small match can ignite a worldwide conflagration, Twee, and YOU are the match that can do this IF YOU HAVE THE COURAGE AND THE WISDOM TO DO SO.

Mrs Ayres no longer cares for people. All she really cares about is what turns her on, sexually, which is to have forbidden sex with her own son, myself. People think she cares about them but they are wrong.

She is a wolf in sheep's clothing.

So, I ask you once again to have the courage and the wisdom to defy Mrs Ayres and take me off the paliperidone before next month.

Yours sincerely,

Robert Strong.
Cc Lucy Lawless

Thursday 12th September 2019. I took my computer into PC World today, but they said they couldn't fix it for me, not even at their workshop as the parts needed weren't bookable for a computer as old as mine. So, I bought a brand-new laptop computer instead. I am not fully conversant with working a laptop nor with Windows 10, so I've got quite a lot to familiarise myself with, but I'm looking forward to doing just that.

Yours etcetera

Saturday 21st September 2019. I wrote the following letter to Lucy today:-
Saturday 21st September 2019
Lucy Lawless, the rightful Queen of Heaven,

Dear Soulmate,

My late mother's attitudes to sexuality are not only sacrilegious, immoral, perverse and stupid, they are also immature. They are borne of the imagination of a rebellious girl, who resents the authority of God the father,

84

not those of a mature woman who appreciates the love and protection that I give humanity.

When confronting an enemy, it is best to understand that person; what makes them tick. Much of human behaviour is that of attitudes acquired in childhood, which some people never grow out of. These are the people who never grow up, and the late Mrs Dorothy Ayres is one of them.

The weather presenters on the TV still use the words "Area" and its plural "Areas" but they are in a minority. Since I wrote what I did about the Director General of the BBC he has been hauled over the coals and sacked. So much for the organ grinder but the monkeys still annoy me.

I felt very happy yesterday because people all over the world are becoming aware of the dangers of Global Warming and Climate Change. Yesterday's events saw a protest of many millions of people in over one hundred and fifty countries, protesting about the inaction of governments all over the world, with respect to Climate Change and Global Warming. I don't need to tell you about the forest fires in Indonesia, Malaysia, the Amazon rainforest and the Arctic Circle, the rainforests of Alaska, Greenland, Northern Scandinavia and Siberia. I'm sure you watch the news on TV in Auckland and see the same tragedies that I see on the news in the UK. The world is catching up with where I was six months' ago.

Yesterday there was a Cambridge professor on TV who said what I've been saying for months, viz:

The British government has set a target date of 2050 to get Britain carbon neutral. This will be too late and too parochial. WE NEED TO GET THE WHOLE WORLD CARBON NEUTRAL BEFORE THE YEAR 2031 OR IT WILL BE TOO LATE TO SAVE THE WORLD FROM EXTINCTION. This is now becoming apparent to the public.

The likes of Donald Trump cannot hide it any longer. I am the only man that I know of who has a credible plan to achieve this, and I am the best leader of men and women to carry this plan through.

The Climate Change emergency has put the world into my hands. I have got the world by the short and curlies, and everyone who matters is aware of it. I reckon it will take me about eleven years to get the worldwide carbon emissions down to zero, just about in time to save the world, PROVIDED THAT THE WORLD STARTS TREATING ME DECENTLY and not like a madman, AS OF NOW. (That was not deliberate to put those words into capital letters but I guess it was meant to be so I left them in). I have a saying that greatness is often mistaken for madness within a man's own lifetime. Many people being interviewed on TV use the keyword "Strong" a lot.

I couldn't get my desktop to access the internet so I have bought a brand new laptop computer. I can now access the internet on my laptop, but I haven't yet installed Microsoft Office. I shall get help to do that next week.

We have come together three times since I last wrote to you, and every time is as fresh as new. It is so obvious that we belong together, Darling. Not too much longer now before we can get together and all our dreams will come true. Even Dampensquib must now concede that I have put up a STRONG case for coming off his evil drugs, and for getting a public apology and £x compensation in the very near future.

Keep looking forward to our cruise. Try looking up cruises in the brochures and decide which cruise you would like to go on.

Yours etcetera

Cc Dr Twee Dampensquib

Sunday 22nd September 2019. I wrote the following letter to Lucy this morning: - Sunday Morning 22nd September 2019

Lucy Lawless, the rightful Queen of Heaven,

Dear Soulmate,

Further to yesterday's letter, I have the following to say: the most devoted of the followers of the late Mrs Dorothy Ayres will follow her until the end of the world, which WILL happen before long if the bastards continue to challenge my authority and thwart my plans. The weather presenters on the TV work for the Meteorological Office so I am going for the organ grinders at the Meteorological Office starting with the Chief Executive and working my way down the line management chain until I get to the organ grinder who tells the weather presenters what to say. My army have got instructions to rip the bastards to shreds until the monkeys say what I tell them to. I want them to use the words "Region" and "Regions" instead of "Area" and "Areas" when making the weather forecast on TV.

The same goes for the psychiatric fraternity, starting with Paul Rees, the Chief Executive of the Royal College of Psychiatrists, then work their way down the line management chain until they get to the organ grinder who tells monkeys like Twee Dampensquib what to do. I will *make* the bastards stop their nonsense with their evil drugs.

I will not have my authority challenged by these cheeky little people. I've brought down the Prime Minister, Theresa May, and the Director General of the BBC so I'm not anticipating much trouble bringing down the other organ grinders who challenge my authority.

I promised not to bully YOU, and I will keep my promise. I just want to make you happy, which you will be when you are seen to be the woman by my side. I will reward you for giving me your love, Darling, by making you the happiest woman in the world. Doing that is what makes ME happy. I am NOT your father, Lucy, but I couldn't love you any more if I was. You fought my late mother for me, and for that I will be eternally grateful and I will love you for ever. When one of us dies, and it will probably be me that dies first, we will go on being lovers until we are both back in the Kingdom of Heaven where we will reign for thousands of years. We will then have plenty of time together to organise our next lives. This life is beginning to go according to plan now.

Yours etcetera

Cc Dr Twee Dampensquib

Monday 23rd September 2019. I wrote the following letter to Lucy this evening: - Monday Evening 23rd September 2019

Lucy Lawless, the rightful Queen of Heaven,

Dear Soulmate,

Further to yesterday's letter, I saw on the news on TV, Greta Thunberg gave a speech to the United Nations today. She said exactly what I have wanted to say for years. I have been thinking that the world has just over eleven years to go before it is too late, but according to Greta (and I believe her) Global Warming has been accelerating, caused by all the recent forest fires, so that we now have only EIGHT YEARS to get worldwide carbon emissions down to zero before it is too late to save the planet.

My plan to cut carbon emissions will take FIVE YEARS, so that means I have got just THREE YEARS from now to get my Party, The Survival Party, into power. That means I will have to fight for power at the same time as fighting to clear my name. I'm up to the challenge but it does mean that time is of the essence and there is no time to lose. So, I'm hoping that Twee Dampensquib doesn't waste any more of my time fart-arsing about in this hospital.

I've got to know that he will back my claim for an absolute discharge at my next Tribunal, and that he will back my claim for £x compensation as well as a full public apology from the Royal College of Psychiatrists in the immediate future. I don't think it would do any good for Twee to recommend my discharge to the Ministry of Justice as they recently turned down my application for unescorted leave.

Going by what people are saying on the TV, I am winning the fight against Mrs Dorothy Ayres. I just hope I win in time. I make the weather presenters on the TV nervous by telling them that I will make them eat their words every time they use the words "Area" or "Areas" on the TV. I think their organ grinder is already starting to feel the heat, but I won't stop until I have roasted the bastard. We'll see what the monkeys do then. The same goes for the shrinks including Dr Twee Dampensquib. He can't deny that my time is coming. I just hope that it comes in time for me to stop Global Warming and Climate Change.

Yours etcetera

Cc Dr Twee Dampensquib

Wednesday 25th September 2019. I wrote the following letter to Lucy this evening: - Wednesday Evening 25th September 2019

Lucy Lawless, The rightful Queen of Heaven,

Dear Soulmate,

I think the hour of my late mother's departure is imminent. She knows that she is to blame for the fact that the world has only got another eight years before it will be too late for me to save the world from Global Warming and Climate Change. It is because of her selfish concern for her own sex life and her futile attempts to get me to have sex with her that this current state of affairs has come about, and she knows it. I keep rubbing her nose in these facts and telling her to GET OUT, NOW. She knows that she is living on stolen time. She has already left it too late for any semblance of comfort. She is leaving me with a desperate situation and she knows it. I don't think she is so stupid as to leave me with no hope at all. Because that would mean there is no hope for her either, nor any other living thing.

This does mean that when she goes, her most devoted followers, those who have surrendered their very souls to her, will be buried alive. Their bodies will still be functioning but they will have no spirit. Their souls will have gone with Lucifer, and I will laugh at their predicament. They will be getting what they deserve for the way they have treated me and you all our lives.

I recall a little ditty which comes to mind. It goes like this:

Be kind to your web-footed friend,

For a duck may be somebody's mother,

Be kind to the denizens of the swamp,

For it's dismal dark and damp.

You may think that this is the end,

WELL IT IS.

I am going to start advertising The Survival Party on Facebook in the next few days. There is no time to lose. Note the fact that I now have an email address on my letterhead. I installed Microsoft Office on my laptop yesterday.

Yours etcetera

Cc Dr Twee Dampensquib

Chapter 6

The Waiting Game

Events and Thoughts from Friday, 27th September 2019

Friday 27th September 2019. I wrote the following letter to Lucy yesterday:
- Thursday 26th September 2019
    Lucy Lawless, The Queen of Heaven,

Dear Soulmate,
    On Tuesday morning the eleven judges of the supreme court of the United Kingdom ruled that it was unlawful for Boris Johnson to suspend Parliament as he had got the Queen's authority to do. They ruled that his advice misled Her Majesty. They made that ruling because I told them to telepathically, and they decided to follow ME. Yesterday's headline in the Daily Mail read, "BORIS BLASTS, 'WHO RULES BRITAIN'?". The joke is that I do, now. I have now got the better of two Prime Ministers, the Queen, the Director General of the BBC and most importantly, the late Mrs Dorothy Ayres! Today's weather tells me that she is still running around the floor of the chicken coup squawking because I have knocked her off her perch and she knows it. (Even though the weather presenters and Dr Twee Dampensquib don't seem to! They all will before long).
    I have now got eight years to use my power to save the world from Global Warming and Climate Change. My only power comes from the people. I do not have the powers of a dictator, so the only countries I rule are the democracies. I must therefore play the game of politics in order to have my way. I do not have the force of arms to rule by decree.
    I am typing this on my new laptop computer. I'm still getting the hang of the Windows 10 operating system and the latest version of Microsoft Word.

Take care of yourself, my Love, I have much more to say to you, but it can wait until we talk. Bless you my Queen,

Yours with Love, Affection and Friendship,

The King of Heaven,
Bob XX
Cc Dr Twee Dampensquib.

Monday 30th September 2019. I wrote the following letter to Lucy this evening: - Monday Evening 30th September 2019

Lucy Lawless, The Queen of Heaven,

Dear Soulmate,

I repeat that I think the hour of my late mother's departure is imminent, and I'll tell you why. She wants me to have sex with her. I want her to become conceived as an animal, presumably a duck. Unless one of us gives in, the world will rush headlong into the abyss of irreversible Climate Change. We have only eight years left before that happens, and it will take all of that time to get worldwide carbon emissions down to zero, which has to happen to avoid disaster.

Out of my late mother and me, one of us has to blink first and it has to be her. She made me realise that I am a man forty-five years ago. She cannot expect me to behave like a boy after that. It has fallen to me to show the world what a real man is, by stating that I will see the end of the world before I behave like a mother's boy *and I am actually proving it.*

She has always been jealous of my glory (The glory of God) and she thought she could outshine my glory with her own. But her claim to glory was based on easy sex, immorality and hedonism. My claim is based on love and protection, decency and self-control. I am sure that my claim will win.

There is no time lose. She has to go, and go NOW, before it is too late.

All that remains is for us to say to her, "Goodbye duck".

Yours etcetera

Cc Dr Twee Dampensquib.

Wednesday 2nd October 2019. I wrote the following letter to Dr Twee

Dampensquib this evening: - Wednesday Evening 2nd October 2019
    Dr Twee Dampensquib,
    Medical Director,
    Alcatraz Island Hospital.

Dear Twee,

    I cannot, realistically, pursue my plans to progress The Survival Party whilst I am a patient in a Mental Hospital. I am therefore writing to ask you to support me if I apply for an absolute discharge to a Mental Health Review Tribunal in the immediate future. If the question of risk bothers you, I can assure you that I will be a much bigger danger to society if you keep me in than if you let me out.

    In the former case, I will have to allow the human race to follow the late Mrs Dorothy Ayres all the way into the abyss of irreversible Climate Change. In the latter case I will have the opportunity to implement my policies which stand a chance of preventing irreversible Climate Change by reducing worldwide carbon emissions down to zero in time to prevent disaster.

    Time is of the essence in my plans.
    Yours sincerely,

    Robert Strong.
    Cc Lucy Lawless

Sunday 6th October 2019. I wrote the following letter to Lucy this morning:
- Sunday Morning, 6th October 2019
    Lucy Lawless, The Queen of Heaven,

Dear Soulmate,

    I thought you would like me to tell you that WE are now clearly winning the war against the late Mrs Dorothy Ayres. SHE is now the pretender. On Friday evening, the news on TV reported THE START OF A NEW ERA in swimming with the formation of the International Swimming League (the ISL). This is more encouraging than the remarks previously of the END OF AN ERA in various fields. WE turned the tide of public opinion recently when I broadcast, telepathically, the information that humanity has the stark choice of closing the door or becoming extinct through Global Warming in the foreseeable future, along with all other life on Earth. The human race has no other choice.

Dolly's followers are still behaving as though she were still in charge, but they don't fool me. When the weather presenters use the words "Area" and the plural "Areas" I just say to them "Shut up, you fool. You are backing a loser and you will soon be buried alive". The same goes for Dr Twee Dampensquib and his fellow psychiatrists. They have all staked their very souls upon backing a loser, the fools.

The weather here in the UK tells me that Dolly is now very desperate. September was one of the wettest on record and it looks like October will also be very wet and windy. One storm after another keeps hitting the UK from the Atlantic Ocean and traversing the country from west to east bringing heavy rainfall onto ground which is already saturated, thus causing floods. It is impossible to differentiate between hitting Dolly's followers and our people with the weather. Our people also suffer, but that is the price of victory and they know it. Victory will soon be ours when Dolly comes back as a duck. I just hope that happens in time for me to save the world from Global Warming and Climate Change.

Dampensquib will get his staff to inject me with paliperidone again today. The monkeys don't realise the harm that they are doing. Their attitude is that they are just doing their job.

We came together again most beautifully on Friday. Thank you, Darling, for bobulucydating me. I'll be able to dance with you properly when Dolly has gone and I come off the drugs. I don't think that will be very long now.

Yours etcetera

Cc Dr Twee Dampensquib

Monday 7th October 2019. I wrote the following letter to Lucy this evening:
- Monday Evening 7th October 2019

Lucy Lawless, The Queen of Heaven,

Dear Soulmate,

It is Dolly, Lucifer, herself that is the organ grinder who tells the monkeys who present the weather on the TV what to say, and she is also the organ grinder who tells the monkeys in the psychiatric profession to insist upon injecting me with their evil libido-suppressing drugs. So it is *her* influence that I must get rid of rather than have her followers punished. These people have no minds of their own. They cannot listen to reason because their only mind is Dolly's, Lucifer's, mind. They have surrendered their very souls to Lucifer, and their minds go with their souls.

I am happy that Lucifer will very soon be duckified, because I have made the overwhelming majority of the men and women of the world aware of the need to get rid of her before it is too late. Lucifer has left me with a monumental task, to get the world's carbon emissions down to zero before the year 2028, as that is the year when Climate Change becomes irreversible unless we get the world's carbon emissions down to zero by then. If that happens then the world will rapidly become uninhabitable and there will be nothing that anyone can do to stop it.

Dolly, Lucifer, knows that the longer she hangs about, the harder my task will be, so there is no excuse for her to hang about any longer: not for another year, another month, week, day or hour but NOW is when she has to go. It is now the height of the mating season for ducks, so I am sure she can find herself a copulating drake and GET ON WITH IT.

She can forget her desire to commit the sin of incest with me because it is not going to happen. She must accept that the punishment of the Lord God for being an unrepentant sinner and also for challenging God's authority is expulsion from the human race and GO. I forgive all those who truly repent, but that does not include Lucifer. She has made slaves to her vanity out of a large section of the human race. She and they must now pay the price.

Yours etcetera

Cc Dr Twee Dampensquib

Wednesday 9th October 2019. I wrote the following letter to Lucy this morning: - Wednesday Morning 9th October 2019

Lucy Lawless, The Queen of Heaven,

Dear Soulmate,

I said I'd let you know how I get on with my latest attempt to get my freedom. It seems that I still have some hoops to jump through to satisfy the "authorities" that I am ready for discharge. I have to have some psychology sessions first, to convince the Prison and Probation Service that I am not a dangerous lunatic, then I have to be tested with some unescorted leave for a few occasions before the Tribunal Judge will accept that I am ready for discharge. Twee Dampensquib will support me when I have jumped through these hoops, but it will take a few months of my precious time. I have written to Twee, asking him to arrange the psychology sessions. I'll let you know of course how I get on.

When anyone says to me, "Well Bob, what d'you know?" I reply, "I know my woman loves me and that's the most important thing a man can know." That's how you make me feel, even though you don't write to me. We came together again last night and it was, as always, absolutely wonderful, Darling. Thank you for bobulucydating me.

I don't think Dolly, Lucifer, has gone yet, but I don't think it will be long now. We are well into the endgame in this scenario and I really want her gone as quickly as possible because I won't be coming off the drugs until she disappears.

Yours etcetera

Cc Dr Twee Dampensquib

Saturday 12th October 2019. I wrote the following letter to Lucy this morning: - Saturday Morning 12th October 2019

Lucy Lawless, The Queen of Heaven,

Dear Soulmate,

I make no apology for telling the story of our love in these letters of mine to you, and publishing them in the form of my autobiographies. In years to come, men and women will marvel at our strength of purpose and will know that only the King and Queen of Heaven could sustain a love so fraught with difficulties for decades: you being trapped as you are, and me being a patient locked up in a mental hospital and having my libido suppressed with filthy drugs. When my books become well read and the story of our love becomes well known, every man and woman will delight in having ourselves in the world as living people at this time in the history of the world and will be very happy to dance with us to celebrate our love for each other and for our people.

I had a terrible dream on Thursday night. I dreamt that I was in bed with my stepmother, Iris. Several bizarre and surreal things happened – luckily sex was not one of them, but I awoke feeling disgusted with myself and with Iris for hijacking my unconscious mind whilst I was sleeping.

There was a woman called Rebecca in the dream who clearly looked upon Iris as her boss; she did whatever Iris told her to do. Neither my mother nor my stepmother have any right to assume they can have a sex life with me, because I have not given any other woman than yourself that right. They were my father's wives not mine. For continuing to pester me for sex, I have decreed that my mercy for both of those women has now become exhausted and they can both go to Hell. The purpose of love is to make someone happy, but I do not wish happiness on either of those women. They have both made my life a thorough misery and I wish them both to suffer abject misery until they come back to life as animals in their next lives. They are not fit to call themselves human beings in my book.

I cannot foresee any way that the "authorities" will let me out of hospital until my late mother has come back to life as a duck. My popularity will then be so great that it will be difficult for them to argue with me.

Yours etcetera

Cc Dr Twee Dampensquib

Wednesday 16th October 2019. I wrote the following letter to Lucy this morning: - Wednesday Morning 16th October 2019

Lucy Lawless, The Queen of Heaven,

Dear Soulmate,

I'm feeling very ebullient this morning, and I'll tell you why. Here in the UK, we are having the wettest start to October on record. We are having torrential downpours of rain as one storm after another comes in from the Atlantic Ocean. This is the consequence of Dolly and Iris both crying because not even the Lord God loves them any more. They are both experiencing the full horror of being driven out of the human race and I have no sympathy for either of them. They are getting what they deserve for setting themselves up as being above God, the fools. I think they will both be gone within days from now: Dolly as a duck and Iris as a rat.

For decades now, the definition of mental illness followed by the psychiatric and the legal professions in the UK has been "Disagreeing with Mrs Dorothy Ayres". The instant she becomes the embryo of a duckling, that definition changes to "Disagreeing with Mr Robert Brooks Strong".

When that happens the world really will be under new management, and then woe betide little creeps like the Minister of Justice, who thinks I lack understanding of my mental illness! I really will be in a position to have the bastard's guts for garters. The same goes for Paul Rees, the Chief Executive of the Royal College of Psychiatrists; he'd better give me my £x and my public apology straight away. And Twee Dampensquib can write again to the Minister of Justice recommending my absolute and unconditional discharge immediately. I expect all these creeps to say to me, "Yes Sir, No Sir, Three Bags Full Sir!" I've got 76 years of having to put up with their shit to make up for.

I shall immediately take steps to get a retrial and to have a verdict of "Self defence against undue social pressure" brought in, because that is the truth. I shall have my public apology from the Royal College of Psychiatrists say that I have been misdiagnosed, misjudged and mistreated ever since July 1976. As soon as Dolly disappears, I will have REAL POWER to make of this world what I will, and I shall have fun doing just that. There will be some big changes taking place very soon now. I shall, of course, see to it that you very soon get everything that your heart desires, including your absolute freedom to do as you please and to love as you please.

Yours etcetera

Cc Dr Twee Dampensquib

Thursday 17th October 2019. I wrote the following letter to my shrink today:
- Thursday 17th October 2019

Dr Twee Dampensquib,
Medical Director,
Alcatraz Island Hospital.

Dear Twee,

I wish to make the enclosed entry on Facebook as soon as I have got my email facility sorted out on my computer. I am inviting members of the public to email me with their names and postal addresses so that I can then send them copies of the Manifesto of The Survival Party. There is no time to lose, so I am starting the Party whilst I am still a patient in Alcatraz Island. I intend to have copies of my Manifesto printed professionally, ready to despatch to people who respond to my Facebook entry. I shall include a letter in which I shall invite applications for the job of Party Treasurer and Administrator, so that this person can handle the clerical side of running the

Party for me.

I am giving you this information now so that you can let me know your thoughts on Tuesday 22nd at my MDT meeting.

Yours sincerely,

Robert Strong.

This is the entry I wish to make on Facebook: -

Facebook Entry 01

The Government want to get carbon emissions down to zero in Britain by the year 2050. I say this is far too late and too parochial.

So, I am starting a new political party called THE SURVIVAL PARTY of Great Britain. I have policies to reduce carbon emissions down to zero before the year 2028 in Great Britain and to persuade all other countries to emulate my policies in the name of the survival of all life on Earth, because unless we get worldwide carbon emissions down to zero before 2028, it will be too late to prevent irreversible climate change. This would mean that the world would rapidly become uninhabitable and there would be nothing that anyone could do to stop it.

If you email me with your name, email address and postal address, I will send you a copy of my manifesto and you can then make up your own mind if you want to support THE SURVIVAL PARTY. Robert Brooks Strong, email:

Friday 18th October 2019. I wrote the following letter to Lucy this morning:
- Friday Morning 18th October 2019

Lucy Lawless, The Queen of Heaven,

Dear Soulmate,

Yesterday a deal was agreed with Boris Johnson's team and the European Union on Brexit. I have now realised that this is an allegory for the contract that I have with society and so I am advocating that the deal be ratified by Parliament on Saturday. I have now also realised that Boris Johnson was sent from Heaven to be an allegorical figure for myself and I thank Heaven for him. The leaders of the Labour Party and the Liberal

Democrats and the Scottish National Party and the Irish DUP are all Dolly's people and the Brexiteers of the Conservative Party are, albeit unwittingly, my people. The battle between me and Dolly will be fought in Parliament tomorrow. The ratification of the Brexit deal will mean the duckification of Mrs Ayres straight away as well as the ratification of Mrs Iris Brooks.

I have enclosed, for your information, a copy of yesterday's entry in my journal, it is self-explanatory.

I'm sorry but my libido has been suppressed for over a week now. I'm looking forward to getting it back when Dolly is a duck.

Yours etcetera

Cc Dr Twee Dampensquib

Sunday 20th October 2019. I wrote the following happy letter to Lucy today:
- Sunday 20th October 2019

Lucy Lawless, The Queen of Heaven,

Dear Soulmate,

I was hoping for a showdown between Dolly's people and OUR people in Parliament yesterday, but a man called Oliver Letwin tabled an amendment to the Brexit bill and that amendment was passed, meaning that the Brexit bill did not get debated or voted on yesterday. This delaying tactic means that the bill will not be debated and voted on until tomorrow evening. Boris hopes to get the whole Brexit deal ratified by October 31st. I anticipate that when that happens both Dolly and Iris will exit the human race.

Once Dolly has gone, I anticipate that it will only be a few days before I get my freedom, my public apology and the first £x of my compensation. You should be free by this time as well, and then we can be together in person, at long last after being together in spirit for so long, and all our wishes will come true. We can then spend a couple of months planning the future aboard a cruise ship.

I hope this prospect appeals to you. I suggest you plan for a cruise in the southern hemisphere as winter is drawing on in the north. We came together again on Friday (UK Time) and it was, as always, beautiful, Darling. Thanks again for bobulucydating me. I'm looking forward to seeing your beautiful face and feeling your beautiful body when we make love, before very long.

I expect you will receive this letter on Monday 28th October so I'm anticipating happy vibes from you one week from tomorrow.

Yours etcetera

Cc Dr Twee Dampensquib

Thursday 24th October 2019. I wrote the following letter to Lucy this morning: - Thursday Morning 24th October 2019

Lucy Lawless, The Queen of Heaven,

Dear Soulmate,

Sorry I haven't written since Sunday. I've been waiting for progress on Boris Johnson's Brexit bill in the House of Commons. The bill was passed on Tuesday evening, but not the timetable for the final ratification. This is yet another delaying tactic by Dolly's people. She is turning the shenanigans in Parliament over the Brexit bill into a game, but, having realised that, I'm not playing it any more. Global Warming isn't playing games and Climate Change is not giving in to delaying tactics. We've got just EIGHT years to get carbon emissions down to zero across the whole world and there is no time to lose, so I've been telling Dolly to GO and GO NOW before it is too late, whatever the state of play in Parliament over Boris's Brexit bill.

People have prayed to Heaven to save them from Climate Change and Global Warming, and Heaven has answered their prayers by sending ME into the world. But I can't save them whilst I am being treated like a criminal lunatic. This is all Dolly's fault for selfishly putting her incestuous sexual desires above the good of humanity. If humanity had any sense, it would make her GO and GO NOW.

I was told on Tuesday at my MDT meeting that this hospital no longer allows patients to make entries on Facebook, so that is yet more delay in my plans to combat Global Warming. People love playing games – it's what they do, even though it may bring about the end of the world, they can't resist being infantile.

We came together most beautifully on Sunday (UK Time). I really felt we were closer together than ever before and I've never been so happy before. Thank you for being you, and thank you again for bobulucydating me. Dolly tried to spoil things for us on Sunday but we didn't let her succeed. You proved that your sexuality is stronger than hers, I'm happy to say.

100

Yours etcetera
Cc Dr Twee Dampensquib

Tuesday 29ᵗʰ October 2019. I wrote the following letter to Lucy today: -
Tuesday 29ᵗʰ October 2019
    Lucy Lawless, The Queen of Heaven,

Dear Soulmate,
    At the end of 1967, I was given the sack from my job as an analyst/programmer with Tate and Lyle, the sugar refiners. That evening I wrote the following song lyric: -

"I sat alone and sank my weary body into oceans of despair.
    I missed the boat that all the others ride on 'cos no one wants me there.
    "Too late," I cried, to the moon, I cried.
    "Too late," I cried to the moon."

I have now realised that the immense sadness which I felt at that time was because this was a premonition, not just of my own demise, but of the demise of the world. I fear that Dolly has already left it too late for me to save the world from Global Warming and Climate Change. It always was a tall order to cut the world's carbon emissions down to zero in just eight years, but Dolly's intransigent refusal to give up power has meant that it is too late, even if she duckifies herself now, which she shows no sign of doing.
    I had hoped that that premonition was just a warning. I try to be optimistic, but even my optimism now seems unrealistic. We must all face reality. Dolly's insane obsession with incestuous sex with me is bringing about the end of the world from Global Warming and there is nothing I can do about it. I AM THE KING. I will not be a sex slave to that woman, even if it means the end of the world. We will all go down together.
    The people of California are among the first who are already becoming refugees from Global Warming as their land becomes uninhabitable. This will now happen to the rest of the land area of the world.
    Yours etcetera
Cc Dr Twee Dampensquib

Thursday 31st October 2019. I wrote the following letter to Lucy today: -
Thursday 31st October 2019

Lucy Lawless, The Queen of Heaven,

Dear Soulmate,

I'm sorry if Tuesday's letter was too pessimistic. Maybe there is still a chance that things will turn out all right. After several abortive attempts, Boris Johnson finally got approval for a General Election, to be held on 12th December 2019. This was necessary because Boris does not have an overall majority in Parliament and so stands no chance of getting his Brexit bill ratified the way things are at the moment. Maybe Dolly is waiting for the ratification of Boris's Brexit bill before she clears off. Maybe that is the rules of the game she is playing; in which case we must hope and pray that Boris wins the Election in December. The European Union have given the UK an extension to the end of January 2020 to get the Brexit bill ratified by the British Parliament, although they will ratify the bill as soon as we do.

I think that Boris will win the Election in December and be returned with an overall majority, as he is well clear of all his rivals in the opinion polls. This is because he is an allegorical figure for myself, and I am by far the most popular man in the country. I am sure to get my way once Dolly clears off, and then my party, The Survival Party, will get into power and really do something about Climate Change and Global Warming.

The way I see it, that is the only hope that the world has got. All we can do is to hope and pray that Boris gets elected; the Brexit bill gets passed; Dolly duckifies herself; and I then get discharged from hospital; clear my name and get my Party elected at the next election and that there is then time to bring down carbon emissions to zero across the whole world by the year 2028.

It is a tall order but it might be possible with help from Heaven. Pray for this with me.

We came together on Sunday and again this morning (UK Time). I'm so glad we are still together in spirit and still both fighting for the same cause. We don't even know each other socially yet, but I really do love you, and we both know that true love is a spiritual thing that we have got together.

Yours etcetera
Cc Dr Twee Dampensquib

Saturday 2nd November 2019. I wrote the following letter to Lucy today: -
Saturday Evening 2nd November 2019

Lucy Lawless, The Queen of Heaven,

Dear Soulmate,

The pharmaceutical company that Alcatraz Island use is called "Ashton's". Alcatraz Island have run out of my TOSTRAN GEL, and so have Ashton's. They say they can't get any more until the end of this month. This stuff is my testosterone supplementation, so I won't be able to achieve orgasm for another month or so.

It has occurred to me that Twee Dampensquib is being cruel in order to be kind to me by making me take paliperidone. And I also think that Ashton's apparently bad management in running out of Tostran Gel has happened accidentally-on-purpose. The people managing me, including Twee Dampensquib, know damn well that I am a special person, that is why they are treating me this way. It is a conspiracy to deprive me of a sex life, because that is how to open my third eye which they regard as essential for a real leader.

Maybe that is what Dolly is waiting for as well, although I doubt it. I think her lower chakra is her sex organs and they have always been too active for true spiritual development. Her love for me never was platonic.

My stepmother, Iris, had a third eye which she used to spy on me with. She used to tell me things which she couldn't possibly have known without spying on me when I was in the privacy of my own house. Thousands of other people spied on me as well, and then used their secret knowledge of me to take the piss out of me on television. They have more respect for me these days although I still get some more gentle fun made of me by people with third eyes spying on me.

I concluded three years ago that the way of the third eye was not for me. Iris's third eye was no match for my right arm and the hammer I was holding, so I figured that the third eye wasn't worth the bother. But now I have been forced to think otherwise, so forgive me if I don't come together with you for another month or so. I am now trying hard to focus my supernatural senses on you as you are the only one I really want to look at. I'll let you know about it if I have any success.

I'm enclosing a book for you called *The Opening of the Third Eye*. It is very technical and I'm sure that most people who have third eyes wouldn't understand a word of it. The main key to the opening of the third eye is, I am sure, sexual abstinence – celibacy, so that is the path I am now going down. I'll let you know how I get on. It is no coincidence that many spiritual disciplines teach the way of celibacy, even though it is unfashionable in today's hedonistic society.

Yours etcetera

Cc Dr Twee Dampensquib

Tuesday 5ᵗʰ November 2019. I wrote the following letter to Lucy this morning: - Tuesday Morning 5ᵗʰ November 2019

Lucy Lawless, The Queen of Heaven,

Dear Soulmate,

Today is my birthday. I am now seventy-six years old. I am guessing that you too feel that you are a victim of a conspiracy to deprive you of a sex life. I suggest that we work together AT OPENING OUR THIRD EYES. (That was the Gods again, playing with my caps lock button. Those capital letters weren't deliberate). We must continue to work at strengthening our spiritual bond whilst abstaining from sex. Our feelings of togetherness have been getting stronger in recent weeks anyway so I am sure this is the right path for us both to be going down. Enjoy getting closer to me whilst feeling unusual sensations in the middle of your forehead. As these sensations get stronger you will know that this is the opening of your third eye. That is the stage I am at, at the moment. I feel that my third eye will open soon. When we both have our third eyes open, we can dance again, but next time we will be able to *see* each other when we make love with our minds. I am sure that this experience will be worth sacrificing our sex lives for, for a while. We can then have fun depriving others of their sex lives, knowing that we are apparently being cruel, only to be kind.

This is the meaning of mental good health, and is the reason why the doctors have accused me of mental illness for so long, when I had felt that there was nothing wrong with me. I feel so relieved knowing that I am on the right lines at long last!

Yours etcetera

Cc Dr Twee Dampensquib

Chapter 7

The Third Eyes

Events and Thoughts from Thursday 7th November 2019

Thursday 7th November 2019, I wrote the following letter to Lucy this morning: - Thursday Morning 7th November 2019

Lucy Lawless, The Queen of Heaven,

Dear Soulmate,

This morning I was given another brand of testosterone gel, as Ashton's still have no Tostran. I will be having this new brand every day until they get some fresh supplies of Tostran. In a few days' time I expect I will be able to achieve orgasm again but I do not intend to do so because I AM SERIOUS ABOUT BEING CELIBATE, AT LEAST UNTIL MY THIRD EYE IS OPEN. (The Gods are determined to put some of my words into capital letters!). I am sure that celibacy is the key to opening the third eye, and that is the key to getting off antipsychotic medication and discharged from hospital with a clean bill of health.

I am sure that you appreciate this wisdom and are happy to go down the path of celibacy with me until we both open our third eyes, together. We can still enjoy the feeling of togetherness and strengthening our spiritual bond. I love you so very much and I can tell that you feel the same way about me because I can sense your feelings. It's so good to have someone who is on the same wavelength as yourself.

I don't know for how long we will have to be celibate, before our third eyes open; maybe a few weeks, or possibly only a few days; or maybe a few months, or even years, but however long it takes I remain convinced it is the right road for us to be on.

I do know that Iris had a third eye and she still wanted sex with me, so I'm sure it is not a permanent end to our sex lives. Iris was only forty-three years old when I killed her. Paranoia is a dangerous thing. Iris thought (and probably still does think) that she is the REAL Queen. She certainly convinced a great many people of that. If she had convinced me of that I would not have killed her, I would have married her. I killed her because I did not accept her as my Queen, and I have to live in the same society as all those people who thought, wrongly, that way about Iris. Killing her was the only way I could convince them that I am the REAL leader, not Iris. That was what she challenged me to prove.

YOU have proven yourself to me with love, kindness and understanding, not by bullying like Iris used to do, that was why so many people wanted me to kill her. And you have proven yourself to the people in Heaven, who guided me to you, so I have no doubts about you being my REAL Queen!

Take care of yourself, my Love, I have much more to say to you, but it can wait until we talk, Bless you, my Queen,

Yours with, Love, Affection and Friendship, The King of Heaven,

Bob XX
Cc Dr Twee Dampensquib

Sunday 10th November 2019. I wrote the following letter to Lucy this morning: - Sunday 10th November 2019

Lucy Lawless, The Queen of Heaven,

Dear Soulmate,

My late mother, Mrs Dorothy Ayres (AKA "the door") has been visiting me recently. She appears in a very distressed state and is looking for sympathy, but she doesn't get any from me: all she gets is a reminder that she has led the world to the brink of extinction and if she doesn't GO, NOW, she will push it over the edge. She thought she knew better than me, God, what was good for the human race, but events have proven her wrong and she can't understand it. She is confused and bewildered and as miserable as sin, which is appropriate because she thought she could sin and get away with it. I have proven her wrong on that count as well. She is an unrepentant sinner who does not accept ME as God and there is therefore no place in Heaven for her: she has been sentenced to the Hell of forfeiting her very humanity.

Be it known that I AM THE JUDGE and that is MY LAW. I AM the God of mercy, and I forgive all those who truly repent. That does not include Lucifer. She is the Devil's accomplice and partner-in-crime and the human race has followed her for decades, which is why they are now facing extinction. They should have heeded my warnings written in the Holy Bible, "I am the Lord, thy God, and thou shalt have no other Gods before me". It is also written in the Bible, "Man shall not go with man". They thought they could defy God in 1967 when they passed the law allowing same-sex sexual relationships. I was too young at the time to do anything about it, but I have now proven them all wrong. They are now facing extinction and it is their own fault for defying ME, the Lord God Almighty.

Same-sex sexual relationships offend me and consequently the Gods in Heaven, who control the climate. That is the REAL reason why the human race is facing a Climate Change emergency. Mankind must address the moral reasons for Global Warming as well as the practical reasons or they will not fix the problem!

I am making progress with my attempts to open my third eye. I am beginning to see things but I am learning to control the visions and to focus the eye. I won't say it is truly open yet. I was going to send a copy of this letter to Justin Welby, but I thought better of it. He doesn't deserve to know my thoughts.

Yours etcetera

Cc Dr Twee Dampensquib.

Monday 11th November 2019. I wrote the following letter to Lucy this evening: - Monday Evening 11th November 2019

Lucy Lawless, The Queen of Heaven,

Dear Soulmate,

I had my case conference this afternoon here at Alcatraz Island. They call it a "Care Plan Approach (CPA)" meeting here. They restated their opinion that I suffer from a "delusional system of beliefs" when I told them that I am God. I can understand their doubting me; it is a difficult thing to believe such an enormous assertion; it is much easier to believe that I am deluded. They want me to have some psychology sessions to convince the "authorities" that I no longer suffer from delusions and then to have some unescorted leave before my next tribunal. Twee Dampensquib was kind to me and said that he will try to get it all sorted as soon as possible.

However, I do not intend to lie about the events leading up to my "index offence", nor about my identity. I shall make everyone believe what I say, by making them afraid to do otherwise. I shall do that by turning the soul of *she-who-must-be-obeyed* into the body of a duck. Everyone who matters will then be afraid for their very soul in case I do not have mercy on it. Their way to win my mercy will be to believe and to obey what I say. Turning HER late father into an animal was how she made everybody afraid of HER. Now I am doing the same thing to her that she did to her father and for the same reason! I have no fears because the buck stops with me. I really am *God-the-Father,* unlike her.

Twee says he will not take me off paliperidone, even if I prove it is unnecessary by opening my third eye. This confirms my suspicion that he is afraid of *she-who-must-be-obeyed,* and that is why he will not listen to reason. I'm sure he will change his tune when she is a duck.

I am sure that the Gods in Heaven are on our side and that they do not need telling what to do. I predict that Boris Johnson will win the General Election, one month from tomorrow, with an overall majority and that the Brexit bill will be ratified by the end of January 2020; Dolly will take that as her cue to duckify herself, and that I will soon be free after that. I have some dental appointments in February and March and it suits me to stay here for them. It will take a little time to organise another tribunal, and it may be a good idea to jump through some of the silly hoops that the "authorities" want me to do, just for appearances sake, and to give Twee more of a leg to stand on at my tribunal.

I think, therefore, that I may well be free by the end of April. Your son, Judah, has his eighteenth birthday on the 7th May and will then, legally, be a man. I expect that he will be wanting to assert his independence by that time, so I reckon that we'll be all right to book a cruise in the northern hemisphere for June and July of next year. I'm sure that our patience will be rewarded.

Twee still wants me to drop my claim for a public apology. I'm not so sure about that. I'd like to know what you think. Maybe I'll drop the claim in return for a total compensation from the Royal College of Psychiatrists of £x.

My third eye is starting to open already. I've been getting some clear visions. I don't think it will be long before it is open properly. I won't be happy until I can *see* you with it.

The weather in the UK, especially in England, has been atrocious lately, with strong winds, torrential rain and floods. This is the doing of Dolly and Iris, and I'm sure it will continue and get worse because I'm fully confident that I can maintain the pressure on both of them until they both get out of my Kingdom: Dolly as a duck and Iris as a rat.

Well done to you for giving me your support. Your love makes everything worthwhile.

Yours etcetera

Cc Dr Twee Dampensquib.

Wednesday 13th November 2019. I wrote the following letter to Lucy today, and sent it to her together with a photo of myself: - Wednesday 13th November 2019

Lucy Lawless, The Queen of Heaven,

Dear Soulmate,

The more I think about Twee Dampensquib's attitude, the angrier I get. I had credited him with the altruistic motive of helping me to open my third eye. But there is nothing altruistic in his attitude to neuroleptic drugs. He is a psychiatrist before he is a man. He is therefore a member of a fraternity who are conspiring to bully me into being a motherfucker. They can all go to Hell.

When I have duckified their precious Mrs Dorothy (Dolly) Ayres, I will be in charge, and then when I say, "JUMP", they will say, "How high, Sir?" Otherwise I will make them dance barefoot on hot coals. The mood I'm in at the moment, that won't be just metaphorically speaking.

I have decided; I WILL have my public apology, which will totally exonerate me, and a total of £x compensation immediately from the Royal College of Psychiatrists I will get the other £y that I demand from the British Government when I am cleared of manslaughter and diminished responsibility with a verdict of self-defence, in court.

I am having my photo taken this afternoon, and I'll send you a photo with this letter. I did promise you a photo of myself with my new teeth. I hope you like them. I always do my utmost to keep my promises, and I don't make a promise unless I am confident I can keep it. I'm sorry it has taken so long, but I had some difficulty in getting permission to have my photo taken. I thought you'd like a recent picture of the man who is waiting for you. Sorry it's not a very good pose.

As soon as Dolly has gone you can book a two month cruise. I'm pretty sure we can go on our cruise in June and July of next year, but as I say, wait until Dolly has gone before you book the cruise. I think she'll GO in January when the BREXIT deal is ratified. I will of course let you know when she has gone, but I think you'll know it anyway. Then you'll be free to behave like a woman who loves me, as I'm sure that is what you really are, despite appearances to the contrary at the moment. I know that things are not what they seem to be. I know the truth about people.

I can remember, when I was a boy, I heard my mother saying about *her* father, "Well, he had a good innings didn't he?" and, "He was only prolonging the agony". Now it is my turn to say the same things about *her*. She also said, about US, "You have to let them win in the end".

WE are winning whether she lets us or not. Global Warming isn't hanging about. This is the end!

Yours etcetera

Cc Dr Twee Dampensquib.

Paul Rees, Chief Executive, the Royal College of Psychiatrists.

Saturday 16th November 2019. Here at Alcatraz Island Hospital, I write a piece on the news in the monthly newsletter. Today I wrote a plug for The Survival Party to be published at the beginning of next month, as follows:-

CLIMATE CHANGE

I'm Robert Strong from Castlegate Ward and I have started a new political party called "The Survival Party" with policies to cut carbon emissions down to zero within the next eight years in Great Britain and throughout the world. This is necessary because unless we, the human race, do this by the year 2028 then the world will overheat by the critical figure of 1.5° C and then climate change will be irreversible. Don't take my word for it: according to the BBC news there are eleven thousand scientists all saying the same thing. If Climate Change becomes irreversible then it will not take long before the whole world becomes uninhabitable.

I am looking for supporters for The Survival Party. If you contact me, I will send you a copy of my Manifesto and you can then make up your own mind if you want to join the Party. This offer is open to patients, staff and everyone else. I am particularly looking for someone on the outside with IT skills to handle the administrative side of running the Party for me. I have a financier who is supporting the Party.

We hope to field candidates for election as Members of Parliament, not this year, but at the next General Election.

Yesterday my late mother paid me a visit and said that she wanted to see what I had written in my journal about her. So, this morning I re-read my last six letters to Lucy, hoping the old dead woman would know what I had written. I then said the following things to her, hoping that she could hear me:-

Dear Mother,

There are tears in my eyes as I write this letter.

I know that I am the man that you love best, but I think you know by now that you want something that can never be. I am asking you to let go of that which you love most in the name of the survival of all life on Earth. I know you love the human race, but you must let my people go, and trust me to look after the people and all other living creatures. You are leaving me with an almost insurmountable problem: to cut carbon emissions to zero across the whole world before 2028, but with help from above it might be possible.

The sooner you turn yourself into a duck, the greater the chance I have of being able to save the world. Global Warming isn't wasting time.

I will see to it that you are remembered for ever as the woman who sacrificed everything she held most dear, including her own very humanity, in order to save the world. The human race will never forget you, Mother. Now find yourself a copulating drake and hen duck and GET ON WITH IT.

Goodbye duck,

Bob XX

Monday 18th November 2019. I didn't sleep at all last night. I spent the night talking to my late mother, and in the small hours of this morning I think I succeeded in talking her into turning herself into a duck. That's what she is now: the embryo of a duckling. She will hatch into a duckling in about a month's time. I hesitated to make this claim as I have thought this, wrongly, so many times over the last few years, but this time I think it is for real. She proved, in the end, that she did really love me – enough to let me go. And she proved that she really loved the human race – enough to save us by leaving us. She proved, in the end, that she was a real heroine, by turning herself into a duck. Goodbye Mother, and thanks for everything.

My job now is, first, to confirm Dolly's departure, then to organise my public apology, my compensation and my freedom. Then I must buy myself a flat in London and move in, and then start canvassing support for The Survival Party. At the same time, I must find a way to liberate you from whatever is restricting you from doing what you want, but this is difficult if you still don't communicate with me.

I've just heard some guy on the television use the word "Areas", so I doubt that Dolly has actually departed yet although I don't think it will take long now. She is still playing games, but I am winning them. She knows that she MUST actually GO for real in order to give me the power I will need in order to save the world from Global Warming and Climate Change. Boris Johnson is still talking about making Britain carbon neutral by 2050. There won't be a 2050 unless Dolly goes right away and lets ME take over. I need the power to make people afraid that I will not have mercy on their souls, so I have to prove that I can ratify people including duckifying my late mother. She can't say that she doesn't deserve it.

Tuesday 19th November 2019. I wrote the following letter to Lucy this evening: - Tuesday Evening 19th November 2019
    Lucy Lawless, The Queen of Heaven,

Dear Soulmate,

Have you seen the news on telly? What is happening in New South Wales with the bush fires and the drought, and the wild fires in California and the floods in Venice, all indicate that THIS IS THE BEGINNING OF THE END OF THE WORLD, caused by Climate Change. (That really wasn't deliberate to put those words into capital letters. It really was the doing of the Gods). You only have to look at the desperation on the faces of the people of Sydney to know that the human race is fighting for its survival. We are all fighting for our lives and, under the leadership of the late Mrs Dorothy Ayres, WE ARE LOSING. (I put those words into capital letters myself). But the people on my telly all say that they are keeping their door always open, and they all insist on mentioning the word "AREAS" at every opportunity, as if that somehow protects them; the idiots.

The only person who can do anything about this is the late Mrs Ayres herself, but she doesn't seem to have the decency to clear off and let me take over. So, we must pray that she finds what it takes to prove me wrong, because that is the only hope that the world has got. Let us pray, therefore, that Mrs Ayres finds the courage and the decency to exit the human race before it is too late. There isn't any time to lose.

If this planet does become uninhabitable, as seems likely at the moment, then we will all have to venture into space in spirit form, to find another inhabitable planet somewhere in the Universe and try to come back to life as members of whatever animal species live there. But whatever happens, Darling, we will always be lovers because of who we are: Time and Nature, and we rule, not just this planet but the whole Universe. It will just be our sadness if the human race does not survive to conquer the Universe as a lot of us hoped we would. It seems a shame to end the adventure of humanity when there is still so much yet to discover. But Mrs Dorothy Ayres will be to blame.

Whatever happens, Lucy Darling, I will always love you and I have absolutely no doubts that you will always love me. We will love each other for ever, whatever happens, because of who we are: Father Time and Mother Nature.

Yours etcetera

Cc Dr Twee Dampensquib.

Thursday 21st November 2019. I wrote the following letter to Lucy this morning: - Thursday Morning 21st November 2019
Lucy Lawless, The Queen of Heaven,

Dear Soulmate,
Following on from Tuesday evening's letter, it is obvious that the only

way that we, the human race, can survive is by A CHANGE OF LEADERSHJIP. We, the human race, must kick out the late Mrs Dorothy Ayres and put me, God, in power before it is too late. It is now obvious that she is not going to go willingly, so we must adopt a "stick and carrot" approach. We must make her life as a human being intolerable and exemplify the virtues of being a duck. To do this we must ostracise her and make sure that she is friendless. Anyone who gives her sympathy is *persona non grata* and will also be ostracised.

I have created a political party, The Survival Party, with policies to cut carbon emissions across the whole world to zero before the year 2028. This is necessary for our survival, and although it will be very hard, it should be possible if we act NOW. My Party will also correct the moral reasons for Climate Change as well as the practical reasons: same-sex sexual relationships are an anathema to the Gods in Heaven, who control the climate. So, to appease the Gods, we must declare same-sex sexual relationships as immoral and penalise them. My Party will do this.

I repeat that what is happening in New South Wales and California is the beginning of the end of the world, and our only hope is to change the leadership and take drastic action to cut carbon emissions, as well as to appease the Gods, who don't like current moral attitudes. I wish I was wrong, but Climate Change keeps proving me right.

You and I must hope and pray that our fellow human beings see the sense of my argument and do as I have suggested in this letter. Whatever happens, we will love each other for ever, my Darling, and thank you for the love that I can feel.

Yours etcetera

Cc Dr Twee Dampensquib.

Friday 22nd November 2019. I wrote the following letter to Lucy today: - Friday 22nd November 2019

Lucy Lawless, The Queen of Heaven,

Dear Soulmate,

I learned today that the Alcatraz Island "authorities" will not let me put my plug for The Survival Party in the monthly newsletter. I am sure that this is Dolly's influence at work, thwarting my plans as usual, even my plans to enable mankind to survive. Just like they would not let me advertise the Party on Facebook. All the people who can help me, and all the people I see on my television, are obsequious, sycophantic toadies to the sick mind of the late Mrs Dorothy Ayres. Yet they are the hypocrites who talk so vociferously about "mental illness" – the sick idiots. They think it is big and clever of them to talk about "opening the door" and to take the piss out of me by using the words "Area" and "Areas" as if those words help anyone or anything. They will regret their attitude when Global Warming and Climate Change start killing people in this country like they are already doing in Australia, but by then it will be too late for me to save them!

In future I will use the word "Toadies" to refer to the followers of the late Mrs Dorothy Ayres.

Twee Dampensquib and all the other shrinks who have insisted I take their filthy libido-suppressing neuroleptic drugs are Toadies. They haven't got minds of their own, or if they have, they haven't got the balls to use them.

I liberated millions (not just thousands as I originally thought) of people from sexual slavery to Iris when I killed her, at enormous personal cost to myself, and in doing so I earned their love, respect and gratitude. But that achievement was not so great as my efforts in overcoming and then dogifying Edward Richard Pitchblack, aka the Devil himself, who would have destroyed mankind if it hadn't been for me. I repeat that for that achievement, EVERY MAN, WOMAN AND CHILD IN THE WORLD OWES ME THEIR LIFE. I would have thought that those in my debt would repay me by helping me in my hour of need, which is NOW. I need all my real friends to help me turn the soul of the late Mrs Dorothy Ayres into the body of a duck.

That is the only way out of this impasse, short of waiting for the world to end caused by Climate Change, which will otherwise happen in the foreseeable future.

I suggest that the best way to persuade Dolly to duckify herself is to turn her into a complete and utter pariah. Ostracise the old witch before it is too late!

Yours etcetera

Cc Dr Twee Dampensquib.

115

Sunday 24th November 2019. I wrote the following letter to Lucy this morning: - Sunday 24th November 2019

Lucy Lawless, The Queen of Heaven,

Dear Soulmate,

The psychiatric profession have certified me as being mentally ill for over forty-three years but it is my late mother, Mrs Dorothy Ayres, who is the one with the sick mind, not me. They have followed her, believing her claim to be God for decades, but she is not God, I am. She is Lucifer, the Devil's accomplice and partner-in-crime and they have followed her because she is sexy, not because she is wise, which she isn't. She condones immoral same-sex sexual relationships, which antagonises the Gods, who influence the climate, and that is why the world is now facing a Climate Change Emergency. People should have learned from the Bible story of Sodom and Gomorrah; the same thing is happening again but on a Global scale this time. If the human race hasn't got the sense to kick her out NOW, before it is too late, we will all regret it for all eternity.

It was the Devil who ruined my happiness with the girl I loved, by taking spiritual possession of her mind. But it was his partner, Dorothy, who put him up to it because she was jealous of my girlfriend and wanted sex with me herself. I realised all that at the age of thirty, but I didn't realise at the time how influential she was. I have been fighting to escape her influence ever since then, and I will succeed when we have turned her into an animal, which she deserves to be. She will be lucky to become a duckling and not a maggot, so that is the extent of my mercy on her.

When she has been duckified, I will have the record put straight concerning my mental health, with a full public apology from the Royal College of Psychiatrists.

Yours etcetera

Cc Dr Twee Dampensquib.

Further to that letter, I wrote another one today: - Sunday 24th November 2019

Lucy Lawless, The Queen of Heaven,

Dear Soulmate,

Further to my last letter, I have the following piece of evidence to convince the world that my late mother has always had a sick mind. I accuse her of stirring up gender hatred by accusing men of misogynism. It is her who, because she resented the authority of her father and because she resented the authority of the Almighty, myself, is guilty of androgynism. She stirs up the "battle of the sexes" when the relationship between the sexes shouldn't be a battle, it should be a dance. Decent guys are turned into wife-beaters by jealous mothers, as happened with me and my partner. Girls and boys should be taught this simple piece of wisdom that "If you are close to someone who is more powerful than yourself, it makes sense not to antagonise them, but to keep them sweet". This applies to emotional power as well as physical power. Battered wives and jilted lovers should do well to bear this piece of wisdom in mind.

The social pressures put upon the male sex in our society mean that the vast majority of suicides are committed by male people, and the vast majority of people locked up in mental institutions and prisons are males. Women would do well to think about that before they moan about how hard done by they are, and don't let the shit-stirrers like Mrs Dorothy Ayres put you off loving your fellow human beings. The so-called feminists are often actually androgynists.

I have always found that women respect a man who behaves like a gentleman in their company. Women like a man who steps aside and says, "Ladies first" if there is any doubt when two people are both trying to go to the same place. Women like to have a man who pays the bill when a couple eat out at a restaurant; a man who buys the tickets when taking a woman to the theatre or a concert or the cinema. Women appreciate these niceties, and understand why they are often paid a bit less for doing the same job as a man. They can see an employer's point of view when he invests in training a female for a job, only to have that money wasted when the woman leaves to have a baby with no guarantee that she will later return to the same job.

Men and women ARE equal, but different. We have different roles in society. It is a woman's privilege to bear children and to look after them especially when they are little. And a woman's psychology means that she is happy to have a man who earns enough to look after her and put food on the table, especially when there are young children who obviously benefit from having a loving mother to look after them instead of being farmed out to a child minder. Although I know from first-hand experience that that is seldom possible in today's society. Both parents need to work to make enough money to live on.

I feel it is incumbent upon me to speak up for my sex. Don't forget, ladies, when a man tries to make a pass at you, that women also make life uncomfortable for an attractive man. I have lost over forty-three years of my life because of the unwanted sexual desires of a dominant woman – my own mother. So, ladies, don't be an androgynist, a man hater, like Mrs Dorothy Ayres, because that really is a sign of mental illness.

Be grateful that men protect you and look after you and don't fight your menfolk. All we want is your love.

Yours etcetera

Cc Dr Twee Dampensquib.

Monday 25th November 2019. I wrote to Lucy this evening as follows: -
Monday 25th November 2019

Lucy Lawless, The Queen of Heaven,

Dear Soulmate,

It was on Friday the 22nd instant that I could sense that my thoughts were turning you on sexually and when I felt that, I couldn't resist the desire to satisfy you, so my attempt at celibacy flew out of the window and we came together again most beautifully. Thank you, Darling. I can't help loving you.

I see visions with my mind's eye, I'll tell you all about them when we talk. Some of them seem a bit surreal, but I can tell illusions from reality. I get the impression that you sometimes curl up in your armchair with your feet lifted up onto the chair when you think of me. When we talk you can tell me if that's just my imagination, or if it's real.

I can sense telepathically that I have made my point about the need for the human race to kick my late mother out. People sense what I write and they have read my recent letters and they agree with me. The world is now on OUR side and I am now the one who is leading the human race.

The weather presenters on the TV still use the word "Areas", but they are sick idiots who will regret their attitude when their precious Mrs Ayres is turned into a duck. That won't take long now, I feel sure. They are all

Toadies, just like the psychiatric profession. They will all follow their sick, incestuous, androgynous leader to the end, even though I have made it clear that she is an unworthy leader who must be replaced in the interest of the survival of all living things, not just the human race. They are all led by their libidos not their brains, and I will make them all spend a very long time in Purgatory when they die. That will make them regret their attitude.

I think we are still on course for our cruise in June and July of next year. Start looking forward to it, I am. I'm really looking forward to getting to know you personally, as I'm sure you are with me.

Yours etcetera

Cc Dr Twee Dampensquib.

Wednesday 27th November 2019. I wrote the following letter to Lucy this evening: - Wednesday Evening 27th November 2019

Lucy Lawless, The Queen of Heaven,

Dear Soulmate,

I felt a wave of nausea this morning coming from my late mother. It was her that was making me feel sick as she duckified herself. Late this afternoon I was visited by the spirit of my late stepfather, Mr Maurice Ayres. I could tell by his mood that he had lost forever the woman that he loved, but he actually lost her a long time ago when she first set her sights on an affair with me. That was when he started calling her "Duck". I am ninety-nine per cent sure that that is what she is now.

The slight element of doubt comes from the weather presenter on TV who used the word "Area" this evening. I'm pretty sure it is just that idiot living in the past already, unless he was referring to MISTER Ayres. I won't be happy until the monkeys who present the weather use the words "Region" and "Regions" instead of "Area and "Areas". It is not in their interest to annoy me. I've had enough of their bullshit and now they haven't got their precious Mrs Ayres to protect them from my wrath; the idiots.

The newscaster on the TV just used the word "Area" and spoke of someone's difficulty in stepping in. Maurice always said to me that I should "step in". So, I think that confirms my suspicion that this nonsense is caused by Maurice and the dilemma he is in now Dolly has gone. He doesn't know whether or not to follow her into the world of ducks, poor man.

I'm confident that Dolly has actually gone for real, now. You know my priorities now. I have already mentioned them in a letter to you a few days' ago. I don't think I will have to take neuroleptic drugs any more from now on. It's more than Twee's career is worth to inject me again. I suggest he arranges for a one-to-one conversation with me about the present situation. Upsetting ME is now a definition of "mental illness". Twee might ignore my letters but he'll be hard put to ignore my followers who don't like their leader having his libido suppressed. He hasn't got his precious Mrs Ayres now to protect him from my wrath either.

We came together again this morning and all day I've felt your love and also the love of all my people. Thank you, my Darling, for bobulucydating me. I've felt great all day. None of the politicians in this country are very popular. The country is waiting for MY ARRIVAL IN POLITICS. (That was the Gods again, playing with my caps lock button). However, I intend to clear my name first, with a public apology and a retrial with a self-defence verdict.

You can study the brochures from the cruise liner companies now, with a view to our holiday, at my expense, next June and July.

Yours etcetera

Cc Dr Twee Dampensquib.

Chapter 8

Almost the Road to Freedom

Events and Thoughts from Thursday 28th November 2019

Thursday 28th November 2019. I wrote the following letter to Lucy this afternoon: - Thursday 28th November 2019

Lucy Lawless, The Queen of Heaven,

Dear Soulmate,

There are still a lot of people on the TV using the words "Area" and Areas" and one guy this morning used the phrase "Open the door". But they don't fool me. I know people. They are just piling on the pressure to test my confidence. That just confirms what I know – that the old witch has finally duckified herself. The door has now closed on her era in the history of the world and MY ERA, the era of the Kingdom of God, has now begun. I am now fulfilling the words of the Lord's prayer "Thy Kingdom come, thy WILL be done on Earth as it is in Heaven". I want my father, Frank, and my stepfather, Maurice, to bury their differences and forgive each other their trespasses as we forgive them that trespass against us. The cause of their quarrel, Dorothy, doesn't exist any more. They are both good men, and as long as they both continue to love ME, then they are both welcome in the Kingdom of Heaven. They both deserved better treatment than they got from Dorothy, but she has now paid for her sins by forfeiting her very humanity. The Kingdom is now mine, and the Power, and the Glory for ever and ever, AMEN.

I want Dr. Twee Dampensquib to consider the question "What constitutes a psychosis?". In theory, it is a mental condition, but in practise it is a political expediency. In Dolly's era SHE decided what constituted a psychosis. Now it is up to ME. I have decided that from now on, homosexual and lesbian tendencies will be considered as psychoses and will be treated with injections of antipsychotic medication. This does of course mean that now Dolly has gone I do not suffer from a psychosis, and therefore do not need antipsychotic medication.

Now that I have proven that I am indeed God, by turning the soul of Mrs Dorothy (Dolly) Ayres into the body of a duck, I suggest that the psychiatric profession gives me my freedom, my public apology and my £x compensation, in the immediate future or there will be Hell to pay. I want the public apology to state that I am not and never have been mentally ill, that I have been misdiagnosed, misjudged and mistreated ever since July 1976 and that the Royal College of Psychiatrists apologises to me for over forty-three years of unjust detention and for being cruel to me by injecting me with antipsychotic drugs when there has never been anything wrong with me for over forty-two of those years, for destroying my family life by keeping me apart from my sons for all those years, for ruining my career which was that of a promising career in business, for losing my income for all those years and for losing my house and for subjecting me to the humiliating status of a mental patient for all that time. I want the public apology to be broadcast on the BBC news and the ITV news and to be published in all the UK national newspapers where it will be of sufficient size so that no one could miss it. I want advance notice of when the apology is to be made public, and I want my name mentioned in full.

Take care of yourself, my Love, I have much more to say to you, but it can wait until we talk, Bless you, my Queen,

Yours with, Love, Affection and Friendship,

The King of Heaven,
Bob XX
Cc Dr Twee Dampensquib.

Paul Rees, Chief Executive, The Royal College of Psychiatrists.

Saturday 30th November 2019. I wrote the following letter to Lucy this morning: - Saturday 30th November 2019

Lucy Lawless, The Queen of Heaven,

Dear Soulmate,

There was a terrorist incident in London yesterday, and I could tell from the way people who were interviewed on TV used the word "AREA", that Dolly still exists and that millions of people are terrified at the thought of losing her. This is presumably because they know that they will be buried alive when she disappears and they are delaying that inevitable day for all they are worth. But I want Dolly to know that it is better for millions of people to be buried alive than that the whole world comes to an end from Global Warming and Climate Change which will otherwise happen in the foreseeable future unless she GOES and GOES NOW.

I hope and trust that Dolly knows what I am writing. I was sent into this world from Heaven in order to save the world from Global Warming and Climate Change (amongst other things) and the longer Dolly hangs about, the smaller the chance I have got of being able to do what I came here to do. She must turn herself into a duck, and GET ON WITH IT before it is too late. The people who will be buried alive have only got themselves to blame for investing their souls in an unworthy God and for trying to make a motherfucker out of me, the REAL God.

I sense that Dolly herself knows that she must GO and GO NOW before it is too late. We have only got until 2028 to get carbon emissions down to zero across the whole world, and she knows it. It might be possible with the cooperation of all sensible people, and the goodwill of the Gods in Heaven, so I think that for Dolly and all her most ardent followers, THIS IS THE END.

This really is the end of her era. She should be thankful that she is coming back as a duckling and not as a maggot which is what she deserves to be for what she has done to me. On top of my plans for myself and you, Dear, I will also ensure that my stepmother, Iris, gets ratified. There is no place for *her* either in my Kingdom.

Yours etcetera

Cc Dr Twee Dampensquib.

Paul Rees, Chief Executive, The Royal College of Psychiatrists.

Sunday 1st December 2019. I wrote the following letter to Lucy this afternoon: - Sunday Afternoon 1st December 2019
Lucy Lawless, The Queen of Heaven,

Dear Soulmate,

I saved the world from sexual slavery to that paranoid, bullying tyrant that I have for a stepmother, Iris, and I saved the world from the Devil Himself, Edward Richard Pitchblack, who would have destroyed mankind if it wasn't for me overpowering him. Now I am here to save the world from the human folly of Global Warming and Climate Change, but first I have to save the world from my late mother, Mrs Dorothy Ayres, who is Lucifer, the Devil's accomplice and partner-in-crime. SHE has brought about the Climate Change Emergency by condoning immoral sexual relationships which antagonise the Gods who influence the climate. My war with her has gone on for far too long already. If she has not duckified herself by this time tomorrow, I WILL have her turned into a maggot which is what she deserves to be for treating ME this way for this length of time.

I am due for another injection of paliperidone on Friday. If that injection takes place, then I will have NO MERCY on the soul of Twee Dampensquib when HE dies. I have had enough. How dare people treat ME this way?

I am going to close this letter now by thanking you, once again, for your love. We came together again most beautifully yesterday. Now I am going to study on Google the reproductive system of flies, as there are still some people who don't realise my power. They all will before long.

Yours etcetera

Cc Dr Twee Dampensquib.

Paul Rees, Chief Executive, The Royal College of Psychiatrists.

Tuesday 3rd December 2019. I wrote the following letter to Lucy this evening: - Tuesday Evening 3rd December 2019

Lucy Lawless, The Queen of Heaven,

Dear Soulmate,

I can't guarantee that my Party, The Survival Party, with its policies to cut carbon emissions will save the world from the impending catastrophe of Climate Change, but I can guarantee that this is the best chance that we, the human race, have got. However, I cannot put my policies into operation until I am a free man, and that won't happen until the soul of the late Mrs

Dorothy Ayres is brought back to life as an animal. I am doing all I can to turn her into a fly's egg which will hatch into a maggot. If she would rather be a duckling then she had better GET ON WITH IT herself.

The sick idiots on television who use the words "Area" and "Areas" at every opportunity aren't just merely stupid, they are positively dangerous. Levels of carbon dioxide in the atmosphere aren't just dangerously high, they are still rising, like they have been doing for decades. Decades in which Mrs Dorothy Ayres has been in power as the Actual World Leader. THE CLIMATE CHANGE CRISIS IS HER FAULT. We must have a change of leader as soon as possible, which means we MUST expel her from the human race and put myself in power. She won't go willingly so we have to evict her, which means we have to make her life as a human being intolerable by turning her into a pariah. Using the words "Area" and "Areas" only encourages her to stick around which is the last thing that we, the human race, should be doing if we want to survive the impending Climate Change catastrophe. I repeat that Climate Change becomes irreversible in 2028 unless we cut carbon emissions to zero across the whole world by then.

The Toadies on television do not even have an argument. My logic is faultless. I know about faultless logic. I was a computer programmer for many years.

I felt your love and appreciation of me most strongly this afternoon and I have never felt so loved and appreciated in my life before. I have never been so happy before. Thank you, Darling, for making me so happy. I really feel that you and I belong to each other. I hope I can make you feel appreciated too, because you really are the most wonderful woman in the world.

Yours etcetera

Cc Dr Twee Dampensquib.

Paul Rees, Chief Executive, The Royal College of Psychiatrists.

Thursday 5th December 2019. I wrote the following letter to Lucy this evening: - Thursday Evening 5th December 2019
Lucy Lawless, The Queen of Heaven,

Dear Soulmate,

I'm sending copies of this letter and copies of the latest version of my Manifesto to all the sensible people that I know. Perhaps you, in New Zealand, and Rachel in Italy and Shaun in America and Bill in France can all start up versions of the Survival Party in your own countries if you like my plans to cut carbon emissions.

I repeat that Climate Change becomes irreversible in 2028 unless we, the human race, cut carbon emissions to zero throughout the world by then. Don't take my word for it: according to the BBC news there are eleven thousand scientists all saying the same thing, as well as the Secretary General of the United Nations. If Climate Change becomes irreversible there will be nothing that anyone can do to stop this world from becoming uninhabitable.

But there is hope. If all sensible people cooperate then there may be still enough time to do the necessary cutting of carbon emissions, and with the goodwill of the Gods in Heaven we stand a chance of doing this. My Manifesto addresses the moral cause of Climate Change as well as the practical causes. The Gods in Heaven influence the climate and they don't like the decadent attitude to same-sex relationships prevalent in Western society ever since 1967. Our satanic leaders have been peddling decadence in the name of diversity ever since then. With any luck, the last of those satanic leaders will be dead AND gone very soon now.

Yours etcetera

Cc Dr Twee Dampensquib.

Paul Rees, Chief Executive, The Royal College of Psychiatrists.
Paula Evans
Rachel Brooks
Bill and Christine Brooks
Shaun Van Steyn

Saturday 7th December 2019. I wrote the following letter to Lucy today: -
Saturday Afternoon 7th December 2019
    Lucy Lawless, The Queen of Heaven,

Dear Soulmate,

The monkeys injected me with paliperidone again yesterday. I don't blame the monkeys. They are having their strings pulled by Twee Dampensquib and he is having his strings pulled by the late Mrs Dorothy Ayres herself. SHE is the arch-demon behind all our misfortunes, Darling, and when we have turned her into a duck, then we will be free and the world will be ours. When things look bad, keep believing in that, be patient and be strong. We will get there in the end.

DAMPENSQUIB ISN'T JUST BEING A CRUEL BASTARD TO ME, BUT ALSO TO YOU, Darling, and I won't forgive him for that. (That really was the Gods again playing with my Caps Lock button. Those capital letters weren't deliberate). Perhaps he thinks that being cruel is what makes him a man, but if he really was a man then he would have the wisdom to know that you don't step on the toes of a giant unless you want your arse to be painfully kicked. He has got that fate to anticipate. I can bide my time. As it says in the Bible, "'Vengeance is mine' sayeth the Lord".

I'm sorry I haven't been able to dance with you lately, but it really is the fault of the drugs, for suppressing my sex drive. This isn't like the real me at all.

Our best hope, and the best hope of the world, is that Dolly isn't so stupid as to destroy her own home, because at the moment she is pushing her own home, along with everybody else's home, into the abyss of the Climate Change catastrophe. My plans to avert this catastrophe, as outlined in my Manifesto of The Survival Party, are the best plans, and I am the best person to carry them through. We must pray that Dolly realises this and comes back to life as an animal in the near future. It still seems as though a duck is our best bet for her; flies aren't doing much breeding until the warmer weather in a few months' time.

The human race is still fighting for its life against Climate Change and IT IS STILL LOSING. It is no coincidence that the late Mrs Dorothy Ayres is still the Actual World Leader. The human race doesn't seem to have the sense to kick her out by making her a social outcast. The dangerous idiots still keep using the words "Area" and "Areas", which only encourages her to hang about, wasting precious time.

Yours etcetera

Cc Dr Twee Dampensquib.

Paul Rees, Chief Executive, The Royal College of Psychiatrists.

Monday 9th December 2019: - I wrote the following letter to Lucy overnight: - Sunday Night 8th December 2019

Lucy Lawless, The Queen of Heaven,

Dear Soulmate,

Carbon dioxide levels in the atmosphere are still too high and they are still rising and the late Mrs Dorothy Ayres is still the Actual World Leader. The world must put two and two together and make four. Dorothy cannot deny that she is to blame for the impending Climate Change catastrophe. I repeat that Climate Change becomes irreversible in 2028 unless we get worldwide carbon emissions down to zero by the end of 2027, which gives us almost exactly EIGHT YEARS to avert disaster. The longer Dorothy hangs about, the smaller our chances of success. If she leaves it so long that she hands me the captaincy of a sinking ship then she, too, will drown when the ship goes down. That will be when the end of the world happens. One only has to look at the news to see what is happening in Australia to know that it is already beginning. The only person who can stop it happening is the late Mrs Dorothy Ayres, and she can do that by coming back to life as a duck, NOW, and letting ME take charge of the situation. MY plans to avert disaster are the best hope that the human race has got, but I can't do anything about the situation whilst I am still considered a criminal lunatic, by the people in power.

I am not scaremongering; I am facing reality, something which none of the British politicians have the courage to do. I can inspire Britain and the world to have the necessary courage to face reality and overcome adversity.

We came together most beautifully earlier on today, Darling, in spite of the drugs. It was wonderful for me and I could tell that it was wonderful for you, too. Thank you again for bobulucydating me. I'm still enjoying the afterglow and it is now Monday morning.

Let us pray that Dorothy does the necessary and does not drag us all into the end of the world.

Yours etcetera

Cc Dr Twee Dampensquib.

Paul Rees, Chief Executive, The Royal College of Psychiatrists.

Friday 13th December 2019. I wrote the following letter to Lucy this evening: - Friday Evening 13th December 2019

Lucy Lawless, The Queen of Heaven,

Dear Soulmate,

I have been proven right, yet again. I predicted that Boris Johnson would win the General Election here with an overall majority, and it was confirmed today that he now has a majority of eighty seats in Parliament over all the other parties put together. This means that his Brexit deal will be ratified by the end of next month, both here in the UK and also in Europe. As I've said before this is an allegory for MY contract with society, viz: the human race sacrifices the soul of the late Mrs Dorothy Ayres by bringing her back to life as an animal in return for the sacrifice that the human race wants from me. That is the REAL Brexit deal, and it is now going to go ahead and happen. It won't be long now before the old dead woman gets the point and clears off, leaving us free to live our own lives our own way. All our people are happy for us, because they know the score as well.

When the old witch clears off, the first thing I will do is to come off antipsychotic drugs, which put a dampener on my sex drive, as well as having several other unpleasant effects. I haven't been able to dance with you since Sunday although I've wanted to and I know that you want me to. I feel really bad about letting you down, Darling. It is frustrating for both of us. When the old witch has gone, I'll let you decide the punishment that we hand out to Twee Dampensquib for drugging me against my will.

I have been told that I have another CPA meeting in May of next year, but I don't think I'll be here for that meeting. I still think that we are still on course for our cruise in June and July of next year, but don't book the cruise until the old witch has actually disappeared. I'll get my freedom, my public apology and my £x compensation straight away when that happens, or else the Royal College of Psychiatrists will wish they had seen things my way, and so will Twee Dampensquib.

Yours etcetera

Cc Dr Twee Dampensquib.

Paul Rees, Chief Executive, The Royal College of Psychiatrists.

Saturday 14th December 2019. I wrote the following letter to Lucy this afternoon: - Saturday 14th December 2019

Lucy Lawless, The Queen of Heaven,

Dear Soulmate,

Further to yesterday's letter, I thought you'd like to know my analysis of the situation as follows: -

Dolly's star is falling, and both your star and mine are still rising. I wish to point out the following allegorical instances of once-popular women whose support has now dwindled to a handful of pathetic idiots.

One such woman is Aung Sang Su Xi, of Myanmar (formerly Burma). Su Xi was once a Nobel Peace prize winner for her work in the field of human rights, but she now stands accused of state sponsored genocide of the Rohingya Muslim people in the Court of Human Rights in The Hague, the Netherlands. She has lost in the court of public opinion as her guilt is obvious although she claims that there is no case to answer. The vast crowds that once loved her changed their hearts and minds, and she now has only a few pathetic fools for support.

Another, less salubrious, such woman is Jo Swinson. She was recently elected as the leader of the Liberal Democratic Party of the UK. She said as recently as this September that, "My door is always open". Her support dwindled to the point where her party only got eleven seats in Parliament at the election this week, when she had been expecting a landslide victory. She was hoping to become Prime Minister, but she actually lost her own seat in Parliament to an SNP candidate! She ended up with nothing except ignominy.

I cite the circumstances of both these women because THEY ARE BOTH ALLEGORICAL EXAMPLES OF THE LATE Mrs Dorothy Ayres, whose support has now dwindled to a few members of the avian species! (I keep saying this because it is the truth. Those capital letters were not intentional, but I figured they were meant to be, so I left them in!). Not even the ducks want her because OF THE DANGER THAT SHE HAS PUT THE WORLD IN. (Ditto for the capitals). If she was a soap powder, she would be DAZ – she was once the "A" person in the whole world but now she is the "Z" person. It says in the Bible, "The first shall be the last". My recent letters are doing the trick. My warnings ARE being heeded.

Contrarily, Boris Johnson is an allegorical figure for myself, and is now a very popular Prime Minister with a huge mandate to run this country. My star is still rising.

The Meteorological Office and the psychiatric profession and the legal profession are among the poor fools who still follow the late Mrs Dorothy Ayres. I think they will follow her until she becomes a duck, then they will all be buried alive. I predict that that will be within the next couple of months.

You, too, are doing well in the REAL world. Rafael Nadal is still the world number one tennis player, and many young women with your name, Lucy, are rising to prominence in all walks of life; such as Lucy Bronze, the English footballer, whose name is universally recognised as being a misnomer. I mentioned before, the news item which said, "Bronze is pure gold!".

We will have to talk about what public profile we want to keep. I want to be Prime Minister, not because of the status of the social position, but because there is no one else I trust to do the job of cutting worldwide carbon emissions down to zero before 2028. I think that if I succeed in doing that, it will be impossible to retire into anonymity. I may then get the chance to form a World Government and abolish all weapons of mass destruction. That would be a good achievement to end my life's work on.

Whatever happens, you will always be the Great woman behind the Great man that I am. Your love will ALWAYS MAKE MY LIFE WORTHWHILE. (The Gods again with my Caps Lock button).

Yours etcetera

Cc Dr Twee Dampensquib.

Paul Rees, Chief Executive, The Royal College of Psychiatrists.

Tuesday 17th December 2019. I had an MDT Meeting today, and I wrote Dr Twee Dampensquib the following letter this evening: - Tuesday 17th December 2019

Dr Twee Dampensquib,
Medical Director,
Alcatraz Island Hospital.

Dear Twee,

Further to our discussion today at the MDT Meeting, I would like you to reassure Sophia that I have no intention of doing anything so crude as to resort to physical violence in order to get revenge, and I am not so stupid as to threaten anything so crass. I am not making any threats, but I will make you a promise. I promise you that you will regret your attitude to antipsychotic medication in my case.

You said you have a duty to force me to take antipsychotic medication. A duty to whom? Or to what? May I ask? You are a doctor. Your duty is to obey your Hippocratic oath – to do good and not to do harm. What good does it do anybody to suppress my libido? I put it to you that the only person to benefit from doing that to me is my late mother, Mrs Dorothy Ayres. It suits her to dampen my sex drive because she is jealous of my ladyfriend, Lucy Lawless, and wants to have perverted incestuous sex with me herself.

This is the person that the psychiatric profession feels they have a duty to! An inadequate, dirty old woman who can't keep her mind above her waist, not even with her own son. She is so spiteful that she has ruined my whole life because of her insane obsession with incest.

I have no secrets from you. You have read my letters. I WILL be turning her soul into the body of a duck very soon, now, and when that happens, that is when you will regret your attitude. Because you will then feel about two inches small when you realise the harm that you have done to Lucy and me by keeping me on drugs for all these years, contrary to your own Hippocratic oath.

You will also realise that I have been right ever since July 1976, and that there is nothing wrong with my mental health and never has been, so I hope you will be man enough to make the public apology that I want from the Royal College of Psychiatrists.

Yours sincerely,

Robert Strong.
Cc Lucy Lawless

Paul Rees, Chief Executive, The Royal College of Psychiatrists

I also wrote the following letter to Lucy this evening: - Tuesday 17th

December 2019
Lucy Lawless, The Queen of Heaven,

Dear Soulmate,

My late mother has visited me again over the last couple of days, and I got the impression that she can hear my thoughts so I said the following to her: - "Well then, mother, what's it to be? Are you coming back as a duck in the immediate future? Or are you going to bring about the end of the world from Climate Change? Those are your only two choices."

We will discover which one she chooses in the immediate future.

Yours etcetera

Cc Dr Twee Dampensquib.

Paul Rees, Chief Executive, The Royal College of Psychiatrists.

Saturday 21st December 2019. I wrote the following letter to Lucy this morning: - Saturday 21st December 2019
Lucy Lawless, The Queen of Heaven,

Dear Soulmate,

Carbon dioxide levels are still dangerously high and still rising and the late Mrs Dorothy Ayres is still the only person who can do anything about this. All the world's glaciers are melting and so are the polar ice caps, sea levels are rising and small island nations ARE ALREADY BECOMING EXTINCT. Before long, all the world's sea ports will be submerged. Australia and California are already on fire, and it won't be long before the rest of North America and all of Europe go the same way. THEN the world will realise THE NEED FOR The Survival Party, but by then it will already be too late – Climate Change will be irreversible.

I repeat that I AM NOT SCAREMONGERING, I AM BEING REALISTIC. I am the only man I know of with political ambitions who has the courage to face reality and a plan to avert disaster. Unless the world gets the change of leadership that I am advocating THIS MONTH then we will have less than eight years to get carbon emissions down to zero across the whole world before Climate Change becomes irreversible.

The late Mrs Dorothy Ayres must GO and GO NOW or it will be too late. I am ready, willing and able to take over. If she leaves it too late, then she, too, will face extinction. I hope that she is not that stupid. Time is of the essence.

The UK, especially the south of England, is having atrocious weather at the moment, torrential rain, strong winds and floods. This is caused by Dorothy threshing about looking for a flaw in my argument and a fault in my logic, but she isn't finding any such things because my reasoning is sound, my argument is solid and my logic is faultless. She must pluck up the courage and GO, NOW, or it will be too late. Unless she goes NOW then disaster will SOON happen.

All that remains is for the world to say to her, "Goodbye duck".

Yours etcetera

Cc Dr Twee Dampensquib.

Paul Rees, Chief Executive, The Royal College of Psychiatrists.

Thursday 26th December 2019. I wrote the following letter to Lucy this morning: - Thursday Morning 26th December 2019

Lucy Lawless, The Queen of Heaven,

Dear Soulmate,

Antonio Guterres, the Secretary General of the United Nations, said recently that the world is lacking in the political will to come up with policies to combat Climate Change. Well, I've got news for Antonio; the political will is what I am here to provide. For Antonio's benefit, I will repeat that I am the only man I know of with political ambitions who has the courage to accept the reality of the situation and a plan to avert disaster. I am sending Antonio a copy of my Manifesto, and I am hoping that he can use his influence to get me out of hospital. I will restate here, for Antonio's benefit, that my late mother is Mrs Dorothy Ayres (aka "the door" and "the area"). In 1976, she got her followers to bully me into committing homicide, and ever since then, she has used her influence to keep me in mental hospitals where I have my libido suppressed with neuroleptic drugs. She has treated me, her own son, this way for all these years because I refuse to have sex with her, which I still refuse to do and always will. There is nothing wrong with my mental health and never has been.

I now have two associates to help me with my plans for The Survival Party. There is a man called Flyboy, who is one of my fellow patients. He is an eccentric billionaire and he wants to fund the Party and to put £ millions my way. The other is a man called Joshua (aka Josh) who is not a patient. He is outside of this hospital, and he wants to help me as a career move on his own part. He will handle the administrative side of organising the Party for me (i.e. handle the registration of the Party with the electoral commission of the UK; setting up a bank account for the Party; advertising the Party on Facebook; keeping a name and address list of Party members; organise the printing and distribution of the Manifesto; the printing and the issuing of Party membership cards; and the control of the accounts etc.). Joshua's name will appear on the Party's official documents as the Party treasurer.

I'm sorry I haven't been able to dance with you lately, Darling. It really is the fault of the paliperidone, suppressing my sex drive. It is frustrating for both of us.

Yours etcetera

Cc Dr Twee Dampensquib.
Paul Rees, Chief Executive, The Royal College of Psychiatrists.
Joshua, Flyboy,
Antonio Guterres, Secretary General of the United Nations.

Saturday 28th December 2019. I wrote the following letter to Lucy today: -
Saturday Afternoon 28th December 2019
Lucy Lawless, The Queen of Heaven,

Dear Soulmate,

I felt your desire to dance with me in the small hours of yesterday morning (UK Time), and I rose to the occasion for you in spite of the paliperidone. We came together most beautifully, Darling, and ever since then I have felt loved, understood, appreciated and accepted by everybody in the world. It is the best feeling I've ever had in this life, and I owe it all to you, my Love. You really are the Queen of the world! You lead the world in loving me!

Twee Dampensquib's attitude to antipsychotic drugs amazes me. For an intelligent man his attitude is amazingly daft. He should have the sense to stop treading on the toes of a giant unless he wants his arse to be kicked when I come to power, which I obviously will very soon now. Perhaps he is a masochist, or perhaps he just lacks the courage to join the rats who are deserting the sinking ship that is the late Mrs Dorothy Ayres. He has read my letters. He will do what he will do, and I will do what I will do. His fate is in his own hands.

I had a good Christmas. I bought eight radio-controlled talking watches, and gave them out as Christmas presents to some of my friends here in Alcatraz Island. I played guitar at the Christmas party, and I received a few, very nice presents from my friends. I feel sure that next year will be a good one for US, my Darling. I think my late mother will disappear by the end of January into the AVIAN WORLD. (That was the Gods again playing with my Caps Lock button). Leaving US, FREE, to make of our lives what WE want to. I think we are still on course for our cruise in June and July.

Yours etcetera

Cc Dr Twee Dampensquib.

Paul Rees, Chief Executive, The Royal College of Psychiatrists.

Chapter 9

The Religion of Time and Nature

Events and Thoughts from Wednesday 1st January 2020.

Wednesday 1st January 2020. I wrote the following letter to Lucy today. Note the inclusion of Justin Welby, the Archbishop of Canterbury, and of Pope Francis in the Cc list: - Wednesday 1st January 2020

Lucy Lawless, The Queen of Heaven,

Dear Soulmate,

The late Mrs Dorothy Ayres has been accused of presiding over the extinction of all life on earth. But she isn't just presiding over it, she has been causing it by peddling decadence disguised as diversity. The day after the Australians passed a law allowing same-sex marriage was the day the drought hit New South Wales, but nobody has had the sense to put two and two together and make four. It should be obvious that same-sex sexual relationships anger the Gods who influence the climate, but in this secular society no one, not even the religious leaders, has the courage to speak about the influence of the Gods.

In 1967 the law was passed in the UK allowing for same-sex sexual relationships to be legal. This wasn't just done in defiance of the will of God, but because it was against my will. This was my mother's challenge to me. It was her way of saying, "What can you do about it, God?" THE ANSWER IS CLIMATE CHANGE AND GLOBAL WARMING. Isn't it obvious that the more people advocate LGBT rights, the worse Climate Change gets? But still the idiots can't put two and two together and make four.

My late mother has been visiting me a lot recently, and I have made her aware that unless she comes back to life as an animal immediately then she faces extinction along with all other life on earth. She isn't completely stupid. I'm sure she will disappear very soon now.

Australia is now on fire. You only have to look at the news to see that this is the beginning of the end of the world. Yet still the world's religious leaders lack the balls to tell it like it is. It won't be very long before the rest of the world goes the same way as Australia. The human race really should have learned from the Bible story of the cities of Sodom and Gomorrah. The same thing is happening again but on a global scale this time.

I repeat that those fighting Climate Change should address the moral cause of Global Warming and Climate Change as well as the practical causes. To fail to do so is like trying to dry yourself with a fresh towel whilst still standing under the running shower!

I am making progress with my plans to promote THE SURVIVAL PARTY. The Party will be registered with the Electoral Commission before the end of next week, and then Josh will open the bank account. I plan to start this with a cheque for £x to cover the cost of advertising on Facebook, the printing of the Manifesto, stationery and postage. It is good to have a man outside of the hospital to handle the administrative side of running the Party, and Josh is the ideal man for me. He has a degree in accountancy and he is very reliable. He follows my lead and is not at all egotistical although he is very intelligent. We will use his home address as the Party HQ, and we will also use his email address on our advertisements. As soon as the Manifestos have been professionally printed, we will run the following ad. on Facebook: -

Facebook Entry 02

The human race is fighting for its life against Climate Change, and until now WE HAVE BEEN LOSING. The difference now is that I am here to provide the leadership that the people of Great Britain and the rest of the world need in the fight against Global Warming and Climate Change. I am Robert Brooks Strong and I am the founder and leader of THE SURVIVAL PARTY of Great Britain. I am a real man and a natural leader of men and women. Together with my right-hand man, Joshua, who is the Party Treasurer, we have formed THE SURVIVAL PARTY with policies to take practical steps to cut carbon emissions down to zero in Great Britain and the rest of the world by 2028. This is necessary because unless we, the human race, do this then that will be the year when Climate Change becomes irreversible with catastrophic consequences for all life on earth. Don't just take my word for this, there are eleven thousand scientists all saying the same thing. I am NOT scaremongering; I am facing reality; something that no other British politician has the courage to do. We are the only political party with the courage to face reality and a plan to avert disaster.

The present government of the UK has a majority in Parliament, but that does not necessarily mean that they will be in power for another five years. Many things can happen in politics. We hope to force a general election in 2022 at which THE SURVIVAL PARTY will win a landslide victory, because by then, the NEED for THE SURVIVAL PARTY will be overwhelmingly apparent to the British electorate.

If you email Joshua with your name, email address and postal address, we will send you a free copy of my Manifesto, and you can then make up your own mind if you wish to join THE SURVIVAL PARTY. It will cost you £12 a year for membership, and with that money we will field candidates at every constituency in the UK at the next General Election. Join us and do your bit to save the world! Robert Brooks Strong FIAP, Party leader. January 2020.

Joshua Good CFA, Treasurer. email address:

I'll let you know, of course, how we get on with the progress of the Party.

You responded to me yesterday evening when I felt sexy in spite of the paliperidone, and we came together most wonderfully as always. Thank you, Darling, for bobulucydating me.

Take care of yourself, my Love, I have much more to say to you, but it can wait until we talk, Bless you, my Queen,

Yours with, Love, Affection and Friendship,

The King of Heaven,
Bob XX
Cc Dr Twee Dampensquib.

Paul Rees, Chief Executive, The Royal College of Psychiatrists.
Justin Welby, Archbishop of Canterbury.
Pope Francis.

Thursday 2nd January 2020. I wrote the following letter to Lucy this morning. Justin Welby and Pope Francis are still included: - Thursday 2nd January 2020

Lucy Lawless, The Queen of Heaven,

Dear Soulmate,

Further to yesterday's letter, I repeat that I am the Lord God Almighty and my late mother, Mrs Dorothy Ayres (aka "The Door" and "The Areas") is Lucifer, the Devil's accomplice and partner-in-crime. ALL MY LIFE I HAVE BEEN PERSECUTED BY MY MOTHER'S FOLLOWERS BECAUSE I REFUSE TO HAVE MENTAL SEX WITH HER LIKE THEY ALL DID. The more they persecute me and try to make a motherfucker out of me, the worse Global Warming and Climate Change become. I first noticed this in the summer of 1976 when my mother's followers were bullying me into committing homicide. That was the longest, hottest summer on record in Great Britain and northern Europe at the time. The high pressure that caused the heatwave was caused by the pressure that society was putting on ME to commit homicide.

The more her followers use the words "Area" and the plural "Areas" the more it encourages her to hang about, wasting precious time, so this makes me angry and this makes Global Warming and Climate Change worse. Nine people have already died this year from Climate Change in Australia and over two hundred homes have been destroyed. This is just the start. What is happening in AUSTRALIA IS THE THIN END OF THE WEDGE.

They know that same-sex sexual relationships offend me. That is why they are allowed to happen. This is my late mother's defiance of me, God. Until she comes back to life as an animal then Global Warming and Climate Change will get worse and worse. There is no other way this situation can develop, save waiting for the end of the world, which will happen in the foreseeable future unless she comes back as an animal immediately. It has been ordained that she comes back as a duck. All that remains is for her to GET ON WITH IT, even if that means that all her followers will be buried alive.

Yours etcetera

Cc Dr Twee Dampensquib.
Paul Rees, Chief Executive, The Royal College of Psychiatrists.
Justin Welby, Archbishop of Canterbury.
Pope Francis.

Saturday 4th January 2020. I wrote the following letter to Lucy today: -
Saturday 4th January 2020
Lucy Lawless, The Queen of Heaven,

Dear Soulmate,

I am due for another injection of paliperidone on Monday. Consultant forensic psychiatrists don't qualify as such until they allow themselves to be indoctrinated with the belief that it is necessary for anyone other than my late mother, Mrs Dorothy Ayres, claiming to be God, has to be injected with antipsychotic medication. Mrs Ayres is excused this because she has mental sex with all the members of the establishment, which no one else can do because the medication suppresses their libido. It is Dorothy's idea and it really is quite clever. It means that all the shrinks are members of a fanatical quasi-religious cult of members who have been brainwashed into believing that Mrs Ayres is God and anyone else making that claim has to have injections of antipsychotic medication; a belief shared by all the establishment.

But it is not a true religion, and it is not a good religion because it relies on the inhuman torture of good men and women with neuroleptic drugs.

Our religion, which I am proposing here, is a new religion based on truth. It is centred around our love story: a story of Great Love, a truly spiritual love, Great suffering, Great courage, Great patience, Great fortitude, Great tenacity, Great determination and Great sacrifice. The story is told in these books of mine, which lately involve mainly the publication of my letters to you, and the involvement of Dr Twee Dampensquib. I call this religion "Time and Nature" because that is WHO WE ARE. It is the story of a real man and a real woman, kept apart by the machinations of a jealous, possessive, spiteful, paranoid and vainglorious mother-in-law who has an insane obsession with having an incestuous sexual relationship with her own son against his will. The story won't be told until the late mother-in-law is brought back to life as an animal and made to forfeit her very humanity as punishment for her own inhumanity. Such is the fate of the unrepentant sinner, for she is still trying to commit the sin of incest with me even though she has been dead for fourteen years. This story will touch the heart and mind of everyone who considers themself to be a real human being.

Yours etcetera

Cc Dr Twee Dampensquib.
Paul Rees, Chief Executive, The Royal College of Psychiatrists.
Justin Welby, The Archbishop of Canterbury.
Pope Francis.

Sunday 5th January 2020. I wrote the following letter to Lucy today: -
Sunday 5th January 2020

Lucy Lawless, The Queen of Heaven,

Dear Soulmate,

Twee Dampensquib is going to have me injected with paliperidone again tomorrow in spite of all that I have told him in my letters, which he reads. There is no reasoning with the man. When it comes to antipsychotic medication, he is, like all consultant forensic psychiatrists, a fanatical religious zealot who has closed his narrow mind to reasoning. The brainwashing technique used on these creeps is amazingly strong. I have promised him that he will regret his attitude and I will keep my promise. He will stop doing this to me once Dolly has disappeared, but until and unless she duckifies herself I can foresee no hope for myself nor for the world.

Whenever I feel despondent, I think of the word "Maybe". Maybe Dolly will duckify herself soon and maybe there will then be enough time for me to save the world from the impending Climate Change catastrophe, but at the moment neither of these things seems likely.

The human race will get what they deserve. Too few people realise the need to change the leader and how to do it, in spite of my writings. They should have heeded the words I wrote in the Bible in my last life, "I am the Lord thy God and thou shalt have no other Gods before me". Too many people still worship the false God, Mrs Dorothy (Dolly) Ayres. They will follow their leader to the end, even though she has proven to be an unworthy leader. Perhaps they think that they are fireproof! It is written in the Bible story of the great flood and Noah's Ark, "God said a fire not a flood next time". It is already happening in Australia, but people in the UK are behaving as if it couldn't possibly happen here. If that is what they think, then they have got another think coming!

Some people still find it amusing to annoy me by using the words "Area" and "Areas" and talk about "opening the door". The fools are only encouraging Dolly to hang about, wasting precious time. They will laugh on the other side of their faces when England goes the same way as Australia! But by then it will be too late for me or anyone else to save the world.

Yours etcetera

Cc Dr Twee Dampensquib.
Paul Rees, Chief Executive, The Royal College of Psychiatrists.
Justin Welby, Archbishop of Canterbury.
Pope Francis.

Friday 10th January 2020. I wrote the following letter to Dr Twee Dampensquib today: - Friday 10th January 2020

Dr Twee Dampensquib,
Medical Director,
Alcatraz Island Hospital.

Dear Twee,

I am writing to you prior to my MDT on the 21st January so that you will have time to discuss my proposed arrangements with the team. The arrangements I propose are as follows: -

I have recruited Joshua Good (formerly Joshua Onduso) as my right-hand man to help me run The Survival Party. Joshua is the Party Treasurer and I am the Party Leader. Joshua is working for the Party in his own time until the Party can afford to employ him to work full time for the Party. Joshua is currently engaged in registering the Party with the Electoral Commission, and when it is registered, he will then open a bank account in the name of "The Survival Party". I propose to start the account with a cheque for £x drawn on my own account, and I want access to my cheque book for this purpose. This money is to cover the initial cost of advertising, printing and stationery. Joshua will then run the enclosed entry on

Facebook, and he will also arrange for two thousand copies of my Manifesto to be professionally printed. When members of the public respond to the advert, Joshua will send them a copy of the Manifesto together with a covering letter and a Payment Advice Slip. I want your permission to know Joshua's home address, email address, phone number and mobile phone number so that I can enter these details on the Party letterhead for the covering letter which I shall write. When the responders send in their money and become members, Joshua will open a folder of members with their details on it, and send them their membership cards, which we have yet to design, and these will be professionally printed.

If you have any queries, Joshua or I will be happy to furnish you with any further information you may require.

Yours sincerely,

Robert Strong.
Cc Joshua Good
Lucy Lawless

And I also wrote the following letter to Lucy this afternoon. Note that I haven't sent copies of it to anyone: - Friday 10th January 2020

Lucy Lawless, The Queen of Heaven,

Dear Soulmate,

We came together most beautifully in the small hours of the morning last Sunday (UK Time) and again on Tuesday evening. On both occasions I felt your desire to dance with me and that made me want to dance with you. Thank you for not giving up on me in spite of the paliperidone, which means that I can't dance properly or very often.

I'm enclosing a copy of my latest letter to Twee Dampensquib, which is self-explanatory, and a copy of the Facebook entry which Joshua will be making this month. Josh has a master's degree in accountancy and the letters CFA after his name (which stands for Certified Financial Accountant). But he is only working as a Health Care Assistant because it is hard for a black man to progress in his career in this country. On my advice he has changed his surname to "Good" instead of Onduso which might have put some British people off doing business with us.

I have two dental appointments next month and another two in March.

It suits me to stay in Alcatraz Island until after those appointments, but then I'll be struggling to get a discharge as soon as possible.

I have friends in high places who are working behind the scenes to get me out of hospital. I have seen signs of their efforts on my behalf, but there is nothing tangible so far. If Dolly is still prolonging the agony when I get discharged, then I shall leave hospital and try to progress with my career anyway, although that will mean that I get discharged without my public apology or compensation, which will mean that I can't afford the time or money for our cruise, but at least I'll have my freedom!

Joshua lives in Battersea, so if I get discharged, I intend to get a flat there. I have some money in the bank, so I can get by until the Party can afford to employ me. That will depend upon how successful we are at recruiting members for the Party. I am optimistic of our chances. Hopefully I'll get off the antipsychotic medication when I get discharged, but in any event, I intend to live as a single man and to continue as your spiritual lover. I have many friends and I'm sure I'll make new friends as the Party grows. My sons don't want to know me, and I have no way of communicating with them as I don't know where they are.

What happens to my late mother is up to her. Judging by the number of people on the telly who still use the words "Area" and "Areas" she still has a high degree of popularity, though I don't know of anyone else who is so highly exalted for so little reason and so undeservedly. My terms for letting her Rest In Peace remain as follows: -

1. She stops trying to steal my identity and accepts the fact that I am God not her, and as such, I am the man in charge of my own life and that of any others who follow me.

2. She drops her ridiculous ambition of trying to have an incestuous sexual relationship with me.

3. She accepts the fact that you are the Queen of Heaven, not her.

If she can't accept this reality then she can come back as a duck. That is up to her.

Yours etcetera

Sunday 13th January 2020. I wrote the following letter to Lucy this morning: - Monday 13th January 2020

Lucy Lawless, The Queen of Heaven,

Dear Soulmate,

I have been in a philosophical mood lately, so I thought I would give you, and the other recipients of this letter, the benefit of my thoughts on how I foresee the short and medium and long-term future unfolding.

Global Warming and Climate Change will get worse and worse until the whole human race cries out to me, God, for salvation. I shall, of course, not let the world down, but I shall INSIST UPON PEOPLE ABANDONING THEIR MISPLACED FAITH IN THE FALSE God, Mrs Dorothy Ayres, and her decadent ways. I think she will prefer to come back as a duck than accept my truce terms. Hopefully the human race will come to its senses in time for me to save them before Climate Change becomes irreversible. I will pursue a political career as the leader of The Survival Party in the meantime and only reveal my spiritual identity in my autobiographies.

I am now seventy-six years old and I anticipate that I have another thirty-three years of life left in this body of mine. You are currently fifty-one years old and have approximately another fifty years of life left in you. My grandson, Troy Daniel Evans, is twenty-seven years old at the moment. Troy has a lot to learn and a lot to prove, but I'm sure he will be ready for the role of the leader of the world when you return to me in Heaven in about fifty years' time.

I don't think I have much more to say to the Archbishop and to the Pope. They call themselves men of God and religious leaders. It is up to them to prove this to me. The truth is in my autobiographies. The world will make of it what it will.

Yours etcetera

Cc Dr Twee Dampensquib.

Paul Rees, Chief Executive, the Royal College of Psychiatrists.
Justin Welby, the Archbishop of Canterbury.
Pope Francis.

Wednesday 15th January 2020. I wrote the following letter to Lucy today: -
Wednesday 15th January 2020
Lucy Lawless, The Queen of Heaven,

Dear Soulmate,

The headline in The Sun newspaper yesterday read "Orf You Go", ostensibly talking about Prince Harry and his wife, Meghan. The headline in today's Sun read "I'm Meghan my escape!". The headline in yesterday's Daily Mail read "GO If You Must!". The headline in today's Daily Mirror read "END IT NOW".

I don't think that even Lucifer can withstand the amount of pressure that the UK media are putting on her to duckify herself. And it's not just the papers, but the telly as well. All the double entendres in the news are screaming at the old witch to GO and GO NOW. I feel sure that my next letter to you will carry the glorious news of the final disappearance of the wicked old witch that I have for a mother.

My future now looks rosy and bright. I anticipate my freedom, my public apology and my £x compensation in the very near future; just as soon as the old witch disappears. I shall also be making plans for a retrial and a verdict of "self defence against undue social pressure" because that is the truth. I will have my way even though it may mean changing the English law.

Yours etcetera

Cc Dr Twee Dampensquib.
Paul Rees, Chief Executive, the Royal College of Psychiatrists.

Friday 17th January 2020. I wrote the following letter yesterday to Jo Sweetie, the Director of Alcatraz Island Hospital: - Thursday 16th January 2020

Jo Sweetie,
Director,
Alcatraz Island Hospital.
Dear Jo,

I spoke to Dr Twee Dampensquib today, and he suggested that I write to you as what I am proposing is unprecedented. Joshua Good (formerly Joshua Onduso) is an HCA on Castlegate Ward and he and I propose to start a new political Party called The Survival Party. I enclose a copy of my letter to Dr Dampensquib in which I state the things for which I require MDT permission. I also enclose a copy of my proposed advertisement on

Facebook which Joshua will organise for me, and a copy of my Manifesto.

I am hoping to get the go ahead for my proposal at my MDT meeting on Tuesday 21st January as time is of the essence. So, could you please give my proposal your urgent consideration.

Yours sincerely,

Robert Strong

Sunday 19th January 2020. I wrote the following letter to Lucy this morning: - Sunday 19th January 2020

Lucy Lawless, The Queen of Heaven,

Dear Soulmate,

I think it was on Thursday evening (UK Time) that we last came together. It was, as always, beautiful, Darling. Thank you for bobulucydating me. I don't think I will be getting any more injections of neuroleptic drugs because I am making Dampensquib aware that he underestimates YOUR thirst for revenge, as well as mine, and we are both getting very close to being in a position where we can do something about it.

I am getting quite intoxicated by how close to victory we are after all these years. It is better than any drug. Last night I heard my late mother say, "I'm going to escape". I said to her, "Actions speak louder than words". IF she is still around, I'm sure people are telling her to GET ON WITH IT because we are all getting very impatient now, and she can put herself and everybody else out of our misery by GETTING ON WITH IT. She knows exactly what we mean by that.

I have already told you, and the other recipients of this letter, what I want to happen as soon as the old witch disappears. I don't need to tell any of you again. It is my turn now to just get on with my political ambition and my plans, and wait for other people to do whatever they will.

Whatever happens, Darling, we both know that we can rely on each other's love.

Yours etcetera

Cc Dr Twee Dampensquib.
Paul Rees, Chief Executive, the Royal College of Psychiatrists.

Friday 24ᵗʰ January 2020. I wrote the following letter to Lucy today: -
Friday 24ᵗʰ January 2020

Lucy Lawless, The Queen of Heaven,

Dear Soulmate,

I won't know until next Tuesday, the 28ᵗʰ, if the hospital management will allow me to proceed with my plans to progress The Survival Party whilst I am still a patient in here. Josh has not yet registered the Party with the Electoral Commission because he doesn't know if his job here will be at risk if he does so. Josh is a bit timid. I'll write again next Tuesday when I know more.

Whilst writing, I thought it would be a good idea if I state publicly my attitude to the LGBT community. I think that the kindest way to handle them is to regard them as people whose unnatural proclivities are a symptom of an incurable mental illness which needs treating with antipsychotic medication to help them lead celibate lives. I think that if a person doesn't like the gender they are born with, and that God and nature gave them, then they should stay celibate all their lives. Celibacy is no big hardship; lots of people do it for religious reasons. A person's gender at birth is determined by the sex of the sperm cell that their soul inhabits prior to conception: XX or XY. If they choose the wrong sperm cell then that is their own fault and they should jolly well put up with their own mistake, and do without sexual activity in life. It is a waste of a surgeon's skills to surgically interfere with a person's genitals just so that they can have sex with someone other than what they were born for.

We came together yesterday morning (UK Time) for the first time in a week. That was the fault of the paliperidone. My natural sexual appetite is much stronger as you will discover when I eventually get off the poison. I'm sorry to have to ask you to be patient but I know that you love me enough to do so.

I think that the despicable creature that I have for a mother still exists in the spirit world but many people are using the magic words, "Get on with it". She must be aware of what people are saying and she knows what we really mean by that. WE have no choice but to continue to be patient until the wicked witch disappears. She may go at the end of this month when the UK leaves the European Union. That is when brexit actually happens, and she may take her cue from that.

Yours etcetera

Cc Dr Twee Dampensquib.
Paul Rees, Chief Executive, the Royal College of Psychiatrists.

Tuesday 28th January 2020. I wrote the following letter to my shrink, Twee Dampensquib, this afternoon: - Tuesday 28th January 2020

Dr Twee Dampensquib,
Medical Director,
Alcatraz Island Hospital.

Dear Twee,

Further to my letter of the 10th instant, I was disappointed that you were unable to attend my MDT meeting this morning. The only people who attended were your assistant, Primrose, my occupational therapist and my primary nurse. There was no Responsible Clinician; no social worker and no psychologist. Do you call that a Multi-Disciplinary Team meeting? It was no more than an impromptu interview with someone who did not have the authority to make a decision, after making me wait six weeks since my last MDT meeting! Primrose did suggest that she liaise with Jo Sweetie, the Hospital Director, to ascertain management's attitude to my proposed arrangements, but in truth, there is nothing they can do to stop me from proceeding with them: they can't tell Joshua what to do in his own time, or tell me what to do with my time.

Primrose did say that I cannot have Joshua's personal details for me to write the covering letter on behalf of the Party, but that doesn't matter – Josh can write his own details on the Party letterhead himself. I have revised my estimate of the initial funds required by the Party to £y. My initial business plan is as follows: -

I estimate that an initial advertising budget of £x will bring in at least three thousand responses. Each of these will cost us about £2 for the printing of the Manifesto and the covering letter and the Payment Advice Slip, plus the postage. That will come to £6,000 + the cost of the adverts making £7,000. I want to leave a float of £3,000 for petty cash and incidental expenses. Working on an assumption of a fifty per cent reply rate, that will mean we enrol one thousand five hundred members at £12 a time, making an income of £18,000 for an outlay of £7,000 + expenses which would be good business if my predictions are realistic and my business experience tells me that they are. This business model will take place monthly and will increase once we are able to employ Josh to work full time for the Party.

This project is my future life's work and is the reason why I have saved up my money since hitting retirement age eleven years ago. So I hope you will trust me to make my own decisions concerning what I do with my life and my money. For an outlay of £10,000 I will not be leaving myself short. I have big plans for what to spend the profits on, such as opening branch offices for the Party in every constituency in Great Britain, with a paid branch secretary in each office who will organise meetings of the membership to discuss the campaign and to organise the selection of Parliamentary Candidates. I even have plans for a news magazine called "Climate Change Monthly News", and invite contributions from the membership.

Mighty oaks from little acorns grow, Twee, so please don't try to put a dampener on my ambitions. I hope you will give me your permission to access my own cheque book without making me wait until the next MDT meeting in five or six weeks' time.

Yours sincerely,

Robert Strong.
Cc Jo Sweetie,
Joshua Good,
Lucy Lawless.

Chapter 10

Imaginary Money

Events and thoughts from Wednesday 29th January 2020

Wednesday 29th January 2020. I wrote the following letter to Lucy this evening: - Wednesday Evening 29th January 2020

Lucy Lawless, The Queen of Heaven,

Dear Soulmate,

We came together most beautifully on Saturday night, and then again last night (UK Time). Our mental love making just keeps on getting better and better. It will improve even more when I eventually come off the poison that these stupid bastards inject me with every month.

Yesterday evening I watched a bit of a show on commercial television, and all the audience and all the performers were in a jumpy mood, as though they were all expecting something to happen but no-one could say what! Everybody knows that Dolly is on the brink of duckifying herself, and they are all excited by their own power to make this happen; as, of course we are as well.

I've spent several nights with only a hint of sleep as I lie wondering if the old witch has gone yet. I switch on the telly to the BBC 24-hour news channel, hoping for a hint that the witch has disappeared. The weather reports are my easiest guide. As long as they still use the words "Area" and "Areas" I know that she still exists. I've told them to use the words "Region" and "Regions" instead, and I feel sure they will have enough respect for me to do so when she has gone.

On tonight's news they announced that the European Union has RATIFIED this government's Brexit deal, and that this is definitely THE END OF AN ERA. She must surely GO soon.

I don't have to prove WHO I AM any more. Everybody knows that I have proven that I really am the Lord God, and everyone is waiting to see what the world will be like under MY RULE. MY KINGDOM on Earth is about to begin. It is very exciting for everybody, including me, and I'm sure also including you. I think you know me well enough by now, from my letters over the years, to have made up you mind if you want to live with me.

Take care of yourself, my Love, I have much more to say to you, but it can wait until we talk, Bless you, my Queen,

Yours with, Love, Affection and Friendship,

The King of Heaven,
Bob XX
Cc Dr Twee Dampensquib.

Paul Rees, Chief Executive, the Royal College of Psychiatrists.

Saturday 1st February 2020. I wrote the following letter to Lucy this evening. Note that I am not sending anyone else a copy of it: - Saturday Night 1st February 2020

Lucy Lawless, The Queen of Heaven,

Dear Soulmate,

We haven't won yet, but we are getting ever closer to victory over the wicked old witch. I thought she might go last night at eleven p.m. as that was when the UK left the EU, and I thought she might take advantage of the celebrations to make her exit, but no such luck. I felt her presence at eleven thirty and cursed her for hanging about, wasting precious time.

But she is now living in fear as well as misery. All the adults I know are using the phrase, "Get on with it" in the course of their conversation. I can taste her fear and I find it exhilarating. Her feelings for me are turning to hatred and frustration because there is nothing further that she can do to me. She has already been doing her worst for the last forty-four years. She will find it a sweet relief to turn herself into a duckling to get away from me.

The hospital management have told Josh that he will lose his job if he works for The Survival Party, even in his own time. So I have made him a job offer to work full time for the Party. I can afford for the Party to employ him full time at an increased salary for three months, at the end of which we will conduct a review. His future employment prospects will depend upon how successful he is during those three months. I am hoping that he has enough entrepreneurial spirit to take me up on this offer. I shall find out later on tonight. He has told me that he thinks my business plan is a good one, so I am optimistic that he will take me up on my offer.

I've just had a chat with Josh and he has accepted my offer!

From an employer's point of view, it is a good deal to get a Certified Financial Accountant working for me for £40,000 a year, even if I can only afford him for three months at the moment. I hope and expect he will justify his salary in that time and generate enough income to employ him on a permanent basis thereafter. I wouldn't invest my life's savings in him if I wasn't sure he is the right man for me to work with. He makes a brilliant sidekick!

Hopefully Dolly will disappear soon and then I'll get my £x compensation. Then all my financial worries will be over.

I've got a dental appointment on Thursday, and then three more dental appointments at fortnightly intervals. This is to have my permanent implants installed now that my gums have hardened.

Yours etcetera

Friday 7th February 2020. I wrote the following letter to Lucy today: - Friday 7th February 2020

Lucy Lawless, The Queen of Heaven,

Dear Soulmate,

The hospital management have frightened Josh from even talking to me about The Survival Party, on pain of losing his job. I did make him an offer in writing along the terms we agreed, but he hasn't signed my copy and returned it to me as I asked, and he now says that he is not going to. He wouldn't need his present job if he took me up on my offer, which he originally said he would do, so I am better off without the coward. He'll never amount to anything if he won't stick to his word and hasn't got the guts to tell his present employer to stick their lousy job when he has already been offered a better one.

Yesterday's headline in the Daily Mail read, in huge letters, "THE FUGITIVE AND SHE'S STILL BEHIND THE WHEEL", ostensibly talking about some woman or other, but obviously really meaning Dolly. There was a picture of some woman driving a car and looking very unhappy. Dolly's days are surely numbered now. The UK media don't give up when they set out to make something happen. I know. They drove me to homicide when I was just an innocent guy. I'm sure they'll drive Dolly to duckification before long and then I'll be the real King. Woe betide Twee Dampensquib and the other shrinks when that happens.

I really do thank Heaven for your love, Darling. You are everything I've always wanted in a woman and more than I dared hope for when I was young. You are what I wanted in a mother when I was a boy, but all I got was a faithless incestuous slut like Dolly. You are now everything I want in a wife and lover and I bless the day I first realised it. Thank you for being you.

No one else deserves a copy of this letter and no one else is going to get one.

Yours etcetera

Sunday 9th February 2020. Storm Ciara arrived in the UK today from America, where it had been causing havoc with wind speeds of up to ninety miles per hour, even in inland areas. The howling wind brought a reminder to the British people that if you make God angry then this is what you get, and this is just the start of God's vengeance. If they will follow the false God, Mrs Dorothy Ayres, and her decadent ways, such as condoning the filth of homosexuality, then don't be surprised at what happens or how many people get killed. The Americans and the Australians seem to think that they can defy the will of God and get away with it, and the British people don't seem to have any more sense either, even though I, God, am an Englishman. We will see how much more punishment the people can take before they come to their senses. They really should have learned from the Bible story of the cities of Sodom and Gomorrah. The same thing is happening again but on a global scale this time.

Saturday 15th February 2020. I wrote the following letter to Lucy this evening: - Saturday Night 15th February 2020

Lucy Lawless, The Queen of Heaven,

Dear Soulmate,

155

On Thursday, Sajit Javid resigned as Chancellor of the Exchequer, because he refused to sack his team of advisers as Boris Johnson demanded. I am hoping to recruit Sajit Javid as my Deputy Leader of THE SURVIVAL PARTY. I like the man; he acts on his principles. I am enclosing a copy of my memorandum of agreement with my financier, which we agreed today. As soon as Flyboy puts his money where his mouth is, we will be in business.

Last weekend the UK was hit by storm Ciara. This weekend we are contending with storm Dennis which is bringing even worse floods. One man, interviewed on telly, said that it was soul-destroying. Dolly's supporters are turning against her at long last, they are now aware that she is to blame for all their misery. She has put her own selfish sexual desires ahead of the needs of the people and I have made them aware of this fact. She is now emotionally bankrupt. I am sure she will commit suicide soon by duckifying herself.

When I have got Flyboy's money, I will make you an offer you cannot refuse to come to England and be MY WOMAN. If anyone threatens you, just tell them that you will report them to ME and I'll sort them out whoever they are.

Yours etcetera

MEMORANDUM OF AGREEMENT

The following is agreed between Flyboy Alltalk, Financier, and Robert Strong, Leader, on Saturday 15th February 2020: -

Flyboy Alltalk will give Robert Strong a cheque for £x made out to The Survival Party as soon as possible. The Party will offer to employ Joshua Good (ne Onduso) as a Manager of the Party at a salary of £y per annum, which employment will start as soon as possible. Joshua Good will also be offered a "golden handshake" of £z for him to relocate his home address to a reasonable commuting distance of the House of Commons, London SW1.

Joshua Good and Robert Strong will approach the manager of the NatWest Bank, Oldham, to open accounts in the name of The Survival Party. There will be two accounts, viz: an office account of £z of which Joshua Good will be the sole signee, and a main account of the remainder of the money of which Robert Strong will be the sole signee.

Joshua Good will be responsible for securing and furnishing office premises for use as the Party Head Office within walking distance of the House of Commons, and he will employ on behalf of the Party, a secretary, an IT consultant and an office junior, all at salaries slightly above the market rate.

Joshua Good will be responsible for paying staff salaries from within his budget and keeping accounts of the income and expenditure of Party funds, as well as all taxes etc. concerned with the employment of staff.

Joshua Good will oversee the execution of the Party's business plans and the expansion of the membership of the Party and the opening of branch offices in every constituency in Great Britain, each one manned by a branch secretary.

Robert Strong will approach Sajit Javid with an offer of Deputy Leader of the Party. If Sajit Javid accepts this offer, then he can name his own salary within reason. It is hoped that Sajit Javid will bring other disaffected Conservative MPs with him to the Party.

It is the ambition of the Party to be ready to fight a General Election with candidates in every constituency in Great Britain before the end of 2022.

Signed:Signed:

Robert Strong Flyboy Alltalk
Party Leader Financier
Cc Joshua Good.

Tuesday 18th February 2020. I wrote the following letter to Lucy this evening: - Tuesday Night 18th February 2020
Lucy Lawless, The Queen of Heaven,

Dear Soulmate,
Immense areas of Britain are now under flood water. The rivers are swollen and bursting their banks. More heavy rain is forecast and so are more storms. The Climate Change scientists are predicting that the people of Britain will have to get used to this. Their flood defences are inadequate and their despair at losing their homes and businesses is palpable. Instead of griping about how hard done by they are, they should be asking, "What

have we done to deserve this?".

The answer is that they have been following Mrs Dorothy Ayres and aiding and abetting her in her attempts to bully ME into having sex with her. And allowing her to talk them into defying ME, The Lord God Almighty. I wrote clearly in the Bible, "MAN SHALL NOT GO WITH MAN". I repeat, they should have learned from the Bible story of the cities of Sodom and Gomorrah. The same thing is happening again but on an international scale this time! I also wrote clearly in the Bible, "I AM THE LORD THY GOD AND THOU SHALT HAVE NO OTHER GODS BEFORE ME".

I have this to say to the people of Britain, "If you will defy the will of The Lord God Almighty, what do you expect?" Secularism is largely to blame. That is just a cover-up for the worship of Mrs Dorothy Ayres. If you deny the very existence of the Gods in Heaven, then what do you expect the Gods to do about it? THEY WILL PUNISH YOU of course. That is what is happening.

We came together this morning in spite of the paliperidone. Thank you, Darling, for bobulucydating me. The people of Britain including the management of Alcatraz Island will continue to suffer until they all see things MY way.

The management company that runs Alcatraz Island Hospital is called "Nutsville". They have stopped Flyboy from giving money to The Survival Party. They will all suffer unbearably for thwarting MY plans. I have arranged to have face-to-face meetings with Dampensquib every month. I may show him a copy of this letter and make him read it in front of me.

Yours etcetera

Wednesday 19th February 2020. I wrote the following letter to Lucy this evening: - Wednesday Evening 19th February 2020

Lucy Lawless, The Queen of Heaven,

Dear Soulmate,

The tide has turned. MY influence is on the way in and my late mother's influence is on the way out. I now have more influence in Great Britain than she does. Evidence for this is the front-page headline in today's Daily Mirror; it read "GET OUT". They couldn't say it any more clearly than that. Those "in the know" (which includes the Directors of Nutsville) are aware of who is really saying what to whom. The headline is, of course, what I and all my followers are saying to my late mother. She cannot avoid becoming a duck in the near future, now. She has been told to GET OUT of the human race, the incestuous, mad and decadent old witch.

Now that I have this proof of my influence with the media, I am in a position to say the following to the directors of Nutsville, "Start obeying me NOW or I will make your lives a living HELL. Unless you do as I say as of now then I will instruct my followers in the media to make you wish you had done so. Allow me to proceed with my plans for The Survival Party unhindered. This includes banking a cheque from Flyboy Alltalk, made out to The Survival Party, as well as any other banking requirements I may have such as keeping my cheque books and debit cards in my possession. Furthermore, I want to come off all antipsychotic medication WITHOUT FURTHER DELAY."

I am sending copies of this letter and last night's letter to Twee Dampensquib and also to Jo Sweetie, the Director of Alcatraz Island Hospital. If they don't do as I say, it won't be long before they regret it. I don't make a threat unless and until I am ready, willing and able to carry it out.

I interpret the fact that you don't reply to my letters as evidence that someone has some kind of a psychological hold over you. Will a cash payment make them release that hold? Some kind of ransom perhaps? Find a way to let me know. I have in mind to make you a cash payment; the only string I attach is that you make it obvious to the world that you are happy to be MY WOMAN, of your own free will. I told you before, I am a man who puts his money where his mouth is.

Yours etcetera

Friday 21st February 2020. I wrote the following letter to my shrink today:
- Friday 21st February 2020
    Dr Twee Dampensquib,
    Medical Director,
    Alcatraz Island Hospital.

Dear Twee,

What Marionette Madre called "the return of my mental illness" was no more than my refusal to have mental sex with my late mother. If refusing

159

to be a motherfucker constitutes mental illness then I am mentally ill. However, I disagree with that assertion. That is the only reason why I have ever been classified as mentally ill and, quite frankly, this joke has gone too far. I am not really mentally ill in any commonly accepted understanding of the words, and never have been.

If you still disagree with my claim to be THE BIG MAN HIMSELF then I will prove it to you in a way that you will understand, but not like. Take me off antipsychotic medication now or you will regret it.

Yours sincerely,

Robert Strong.
Cc Lucy Lawless.

Paul Rees, Chief Executive, the Royal College of Psychiatrists.

And I also wrote to Jo Sweetie and to Lucy as follows: - Friday 21st February 2020

Lucy Lawless, The Queen of Heaven,

Dear Soulmate,

Twee Dampensquib spoke to me today and suggested I hold a meeting with Jo Sweetie, as what I am proposing is unprecedented in this place. I have, accordingly, written to Jo and asked her for a meeting with Flyboy Alltalk to be present as well. I'm pretty sure that I have turned the tide in here as well as in the country and that my plans will go ahead now.

In the very near future, I will be a wealthy man. I suggest I send you a cheque for £x on account of any future arrangements we come to. There will be plenty more where that comes from – my heart, but I think £x should be enough to buy you your freedom and pay for your fare here to discuss things with me.

Twee says he won't take me off the drugs because that was tried before and my "illness" returned! Hence my letter to him of today's date which I am enclosing a copy of for you. A little influence goes a long way, and I now have a lot of influence. It all started when I taught myself hypnosis. What I didn't realise at the time was the extent of Dolly's influence, but I am now overpowering HER as well.

Yours etcetera

Saturday 22nd February 2020 I wrote the following letter to my shrink this morning: - Saturday 22nd February 2020

Dr Twee Dampensquib,
Medical Director,
Alcatraz Island Hospital.

Dear Twee,

Being on antipsychotic medication is a torture for me, and I have had to endure it for the last forty-three years. The Daily Mirror recently carried a front-page headline saying, "THE PRINCE AND THE TORTURER". I don't know who they were ostensibly talking about, but their real meaning was obvious: they were talking about me and you. Unless you take me off all antipsychotic medication immediately, I will encourage my friends in the media to pursue this theme, to your detriment. If, on the other hand, you do the sensible thing and take me off the drugs, then I assure you that you will not regret it.

Yours sincerely,

Robert Strong.
Cc Lucy Lawless.

Paul Rees, Chief Executive, the Royal College of Psychiatrists.

I also wrote the following letter to Lucy this morning: - Saturday 22nd February 2020

Lucy Lawless, The Queen of Heaven,

Dear Soulmate,

Money talks, so I am shouting at you now. If you come to England and agree to become my woman, then I will give you a cheque for £x as an engagement present, on top of the £y that I will be sending you anyway. When you are in England you will want something useful to do with your time, so I propose to offer you the job of Campaign Manager for The Survival Party. You can name your own salary, within reason. If you take me up on this offer, you will work with Josh at the Party's Head Office in London SW1. Your job would be to handle the media and ARGUE THE

CASE FOR THE CAUSE WE BELIEVE IN – THAT OF ELIMINATING THE BURNING OF ALL FOSSIL FUELS AS QUICKLY AS POSSIBLE, AND TO ASSIST WITH THE Party's expansion plans to open branch offices in every Parliamentary Constituency in Great Britain. There are about six hundred constituencies and I intend to open a branch office and employ a branch secretary in every one.

The engagement present will be enough for you to buy a flat in London as well as a house in Westwell and a car of your choice. (I suggest we practise what we preach, and you buy an electric car!). You are now a gamekeeper and no longer a poacher, so I suggest you change your surname in keeping with your new position in society. It would make me very happy if you change your surname to "Strong".

Please stop playing silly buggers and come and talk to me. Tell me if you like the sound of my plans, or if you have any other ideas.

I don't think we will need to worry about my late mother any more. My influence has now clearly overtaken hers, so I'm sure she will clear off now, rather than see me happy with you. She's had her fun and it's time for her to go now, and she knows it.

Yours etcetera

Thursday 12th March 2020. I wrote the following letter to Lucy yesterday: - Wednesday 11th March 2020

Lucy Lawless, The Queen of Heaven,

Dear Soulmate,

Flyboy and I have not yet had our meeting with Jo Sweetie. She is the Director of this hospital but I think she is avoiding me, hence the enclosed letter which I am sending you a copy of. Flyboy assures me that he has the money for me but can't give me my cheque because the staff are withholding his cheque book, just like they do with mine. We are taking legal advice on this matter. I'm not sure that they are within their rights to withhold our cheque books.

In any event, Flyboy is going to give me a letter addressed to his bank to pay The Survival Party, care of Mr Robert Strong, the amount of £x. They have taken his typewriter off him and his handwriting isn't brilliant, so he is going to write the letter and I will type it up for him. Where there's a will, there's a way.

We came together quite early yesterday morning (UK Time) and it was, as always, absolutely wonderful, Darling. Thank you again for bobulucydating me. If I was to give in to my mother's pressure to have a sexual relationship with her, I could have anything and everything I want, except your love. You wouldn't be the woman I want if you loved a motherfucker, and I would sooner have your love than anything else. I have proven this for the last twenty years, Darling. If that doesn't prove I love you then nothing will. Don't let my mother's pressure drive you away from me, Darling. If you love me then prove it by standing by me. You will soon have enough money to do just that whatever anybody else thinks or whatever they want.

Yours etcetera

Friday 13th March 2020. I wrote the following letter to Lucy this morning:
- Friday Morning 13th March 2020
    Lucy Lawless, The Queen of Heaven,

Dear Soulmate,

After months of waiting, Flyboy finally put his money where his mouth is. Yesterday morning I typed up two letters of credit to Flyboy's bank and he signed them for me. One was for £x to me personally and the other was for £y to The Survival Party. I sent them to my bank to be credited to my account and the Party's account, which I control, together with a covering letter in which I asked the bank manager to notify me as soon as the letters of credit have been cleared. As soon as I have that notification, I'll send you a letter of credit for £z. You can hand in a letter of credit just like a cheque because that's exactly what it is. We have to do it that way because the clowns are sitting on our cheque books.

We came together again last evening (UK Time) and it was beautiful as always, Darling. Thank you. I can tell I've been making you extra happy lately and that makes me extra happy.

When you've got your £x, you can get the next £y by coming to visit me and asking for it. As I said, it will be your engagement present. I know I can trust you because I know that you know that I am a generous man, and I'm making sure that your bread is always buttered on my side. I do that because I want to keep you and your love forever.

Yours etcetera

Monday 16th March 2020. I wrote the following letter to Lucy last night: -
Sunday Night 15th March 2020

Lucy Lawless, The Queen of Heaven,

Dear Soulmate,

I can't wait for the letters of credit to be cleared before sending you your money because President Trump has cancelled all flights to America by Monday night, so I've got to send this to you now or we'll have to wait months.

I know the enclosed letter of credit will make you happy, so email me or phone me as soon as it arrives so I will know it has arrived safely with you.

As I told you before, you have been advertising and I can now afford to buy. I couldn't be more delighted with my purchase. We came together most spectacularly this afternoon. The orgasm went on and on, didn't it? I'm sure it was the same for you. It was the best orgasm of my life and I'm still enjoying the afterglow. It made me truly happier than I have ever been before because I know it came with your love. The happiness hasn't gone away; I've been feeling it all evening.

If marriage is a form of legalised prostitution, then you have been bought. In which case you belong to me now, so do as I say and communicate with me, now. The enclosed £x is only a down payment. The balance of £y is waiting for you to come and collect it.

Yours etcetera

Wednesday 18th March 2020. I was due to go to the dentist tomorrow to have my permanent bridge installed. I had been looking forward to that for months, but the trip was called off because of my age. I am over seventy and under orders from the government not to go out except for urgent hospital appointments, and they don't consider my dental appointment urgent. This has all been caused, of course, by the coronavirus pandemic. In fact, we heard today that this whole hospital is in lockdown. All our shopping trips have been cancelled. All the schools in this country will be closed as from Friday. One by one, all the European countries have been going into lockdown and closing their doors. Which, of course, is what this pandemic is really all about. It is Heaven's way of punishing the world for defying MY WILL, the will of God: by following the false God, Mrs Dorothy Ayres, and condoning homosexuality and lesbianism and incest. I'm sure that when every country has closed the door then Dolly will duckify herself and that will happen soon.

I can't write to Lucy any more for the next twelve weeks because President Trump has banned all flights to America as part of the closed-door policy. I just hope the letter of credit I sent her gets through to her OK.

Saturday 21st March 2020. There are still some idiots talking on the television about keeping the door open and using the words "Area" and the plural "Areas" because these words sound a bit like my late mother's surname "Ayres". These people don't realise the overwhelming need for the human race to close the door, because unless we do so, and soon, the consequences will be catastrophic for all life on Earth, including the human race. I thank Heaven that the overwhelming majority of the leaders of the human race now understand this. I just hope that they have got the point in time for us to save the world.

For decades now, we have had a lesser God than myself, namely my late mother, Mrs Dorothy (Dolly) Ayres, in power and making a terrible balls-up of running the show. That is why the world is in such a mess at the moment. We have got to get rid of that abominable woman, and to do so in time for me to undo all her damage in time to save the world from the impending disaster of Climate Change becoming irreversible. Which it will do in a few years' time unless we get rid of her NOW. I can't save the world from disaster whilst the world treats me like a criminal lunatic, which it has done for the last forty-four years under Dolly's directives.

I'm willing to bet that she gets her clowns to inject me with antipsychotic drugs again on the 6th April unless she disappears by then. There's nothing I can do about it except to pray that enough people realise the need to close the door in time. I repeat that the phrase "close the door" is a euphemism for turning Dorothy's soul into the body of an animal. In Dolly's case her husband chose for her to become a duck. I'll go along with that.

Those who follow their leader, Dolly, until the bitter end will find out that that is exactly what it will be for them. I shan't be inclined to have any mercy on any of them. They will sink into a sea of despair AND COME BACK AS RATS IN THEIR NEXT LIVES. Seeing as they have all been two-legged rats to me all my life, they can all come back as feral four-legged rats.

The Gods in Heaven are my friends and me and Lucy are their King and Queen and WE rule this world not my late mother, Mrs Dorothy (Dolly) Ayres, and her cronies. The coronavirus pandemic proves it. She can't protect her people from US. How much more punishment do we have to inflict upon the world before the world sees things MY way? How many more thousands of people have to die before she gets the point and clears off? How does it feel to be guilty of genocide, Mother? Just because of your own addiction to power.

Those who wait until Dolly duckifies herself before they turn to me underestimate my resolve. I have had enough of injections of libido-suppressing antipsychotic drugs. This is the last chance for Dolly's people to have a change of leader. Those who still follow her now can join the ranks of the idiots who underestimate me. They will all drown in an ocean of despair and come back as rats in their next lives. They will all cry, "Too late" to the moon, and the moon and I will laugh at them just as they have laughed at my misfortunes all my life.

I sent Flyboy and Dr Twee Dampensquib a copy of the above entry together with this letter: - Saturday 21st March 2020

Dr Twee Dampensquib,
Medical Director,
Alcatraz Island Hospital.

Dear Twee,

I have offered you a carrot, but that hasn't worked so I am increasing the stick. I am enclosing for you a copy of today's entry in my journal. You WILL change your mind about "medicating" me. If you do not do so until your God, Mrs Dorothy Ayres, disappears, then you will find that that will be too late for you to save yourself. In fact, it will be too late for you if Flyboy or I receive any more injections at all.

I don't want to hurt you, but you have been hurting me and Flyboy for a long time with your injections. I am asking you to change your attitude now before it is too late.

Yours sincerely,

Robert Strong.
Cc Flyboy Alltalk.

Chapter 11

The Civil War Continues

Events and Thoughts from Saturday 28th March 2020

Saturday 28th March 2020. The three main tabloid newspapers in the UK, namely The Daily Mirror, The Sun and The Daily Mail, are all on MY side in this war against my late mother, Mrs Dorothy (Dolly) Ayres, but the television, especially the BBC, is institutionally committed to following Dolly. All the people interviewed on the TV news programmes use the words "Area" and the plural "Areas" as if Mrs Ayres was firmly in control and will be forever. But, judging from the conversations that I have overheard, the vast majority of the ordinary men and women of the UK are on MY side and want the door to be closed. I have already explained what those words really mean. People KNOW that the TV is full of Dolly's propaganda and don't take any notice of it.

The door WILL be closed eventually. The weight of history is on MY side. I am God-the-Father, who is someone who the world needs and it is someone that Dolly will never be, however much she thinks that SHE is God. I am the King of the Gods who rule Heaven, and the Gods and I are capable of inflicting such punishment on the world that it will regret that it ever followed Dolly. Whether this is occasioned by California wildfires, Australian bush fires, heatwaves, drought, floods, rainstorms and monsoons, volcanoes, earthquakes and landslides, tsunamis, hurricanes and typhoons and other effects of Global Warming and Climate Change or by pandemics of viral infections such as coronavirus COVID-19 or similar bugs. Whether it takes days, weeks, months or years, MY SIDE WILL WIN this war. Dolly is only prolonging the agony of her miserable existence. She will not be able to take the responsibility for hundreds of thousands of deaths. She will prefer to turn herself into a duck and lead a far happier life as a living animal than that of a dead and loveless woman who is despised by the son that she craves sex with, and love from.

Dolly's ego is too big for her own good. She is NOT the Queen of Heaven and never will be. That is who Lucy is. Lucy and I are the mother and father of the human race. We were Adam and Eve in the beginning, the first mating couple, and the whole human race are our descendants. Dolly is just Lucy's jealous mother-in-law, and seeing as she can't sit in the back seat of the car and keep quiet, she will have to be thrown out of the car, so to speak. I used to have filial affection for my mother until she tried to rape me, but that action lost her my affection forever. A mother should wish happiness for her son, not bully him into satisfying her own sexual gratification. She was a failure as a mother and as a human being in my book. That is why I am expelling her from the human race.

I sent a copy of the above entry to Dampensquib together with the following letter. I also sent the same to Flyboy, as he is my friend and I want him to know what is going on: - Saturday 28th March 2020

Dr Twee Dampensquib,
Medical Director,
Alcatraz Island Hospital.

Dear Twee,

I enclose a copy of today's entry in my journal for you. There IS a civil war going on between my late mother and myself. Have you decided yet whose side you are on, or are you still sitting on the fence? I wouldn't like to be one of my late mother's followers when she loses. No one can stay sitting on the fence for much longer; those who do will suffer even worse when I win.

Yours sincerely,

Robert Strong.
Cc Flyboy Alltalk.

Tuesday 31st March 2020. I'm pretty sure that the clowns who call themselves the Alcatraz Island Hospital "Authorities" have intercepted my letters to my bank without telling me and misappropriated my letters of credit that I got Flyboy to sign. So my letter of credit to Lucy won't be honoured because there won't be enough funds for it in my account. The same clowns moved Josh off my ward and I also think that they intercepted my letter to him as well, otherwise I'm sure he would have replied. The ringmaster who tells these clowns what to do is, of course, my late mother. She hates the fact that I am more sensible than her so she has turned the whole world into a circus. That would be OK but for the fact that the circus survives in a society which takes survival seriously. If the whole of society is a circus, it is not self-sustainable, as is now becoming apparent with Global Warming and Climate Change. If we, the human race, want to survive, we will have to get rid of a leader who thinks that the whole world is a circus and her job is to be the ringmaster.

I had a temperature of 38.1 yesterday evening and I had a fever all night last night. I've had a persistent cough all winter which hasn't gone away and I've had muscular pains in my back and shoulders all day and I've been feeling giddy as well. These are all symptoms of coronavirus COVID-19, so I think that I've caught the virus. I am now in isolation for a week. The virus is supposed to be particularly dangerous for men of my age, but although I'm in discomfort, I don't feel as though what I've got is fatal. I've just had my blood pressure and temperature taken and the nurse says that I'm fine, so that's a relief.

Wednesday 1st April 2020. Firstly, let me say that the following is NOT an April Fool's joke. In fact, I couldn't be more serious. I repeat here what I have said before in my writings, that it has been MY guidance that has enabled mankind to survive, to flourish and to dominate this world. I have guided and guarded mankind ever since I was Adam in the Garden of Eden, three hundred thousand years ago. To assume, as the clowns do, that mankind's dominance of the world is something that can be taken for granted, is utter folly and leads to catastrophe. This is what is happening at the moment with Global Warming and Climate Change. To reject MY guidance and treat it as a joke, as Dolly and her clowns do, will lead to the end of the world! I DO NOT CONDONE HOMOSEXUALITY, NOR LESBIANISM NOR INCEST. To treat any of those three things as socially acceptable is decadent and will lead to the destruction of humanity. This is what is happening under Dolly's leadership. I say, "Tell her to go, before it is too late." I predict that Climate Change will start to become irreversible in 2028 unless we, the human race, cut our worldwide carbon emissions down to zero by the end of 2027. The consequence of irreversible Climate

Change is that the whole world becomes uninhabitable. Those who do condone any of the above-mentioned three things are doing the Devil's work for him, and there is nothing he wants more than to destroy the human race, which he seeks to do by undermining our moral values. That is why I call Dolly "Satan's accomplice": the enemy of God and therefore the enemy of the human race.

Thursday 2nd April 2020. I'm sending copies of Tuesday's and Wednesday's entries to Twee Dampensquib and also to Flyboy with the following letter:
- Thursday 2nd April 2020

 Dr Twee Dampensquib,
 Medical Director,
 Alcatraz Island Hospital.

Dear Twee,
 I am enclosing copies of Tuesday's and Wednesday's entries in my journal for your information.
 Yours sincerely,

 Robert Strong.
 Cc Flyboy Alltalk.

Wednesday 8th April 2020. The clowns injected me with paliperidone again on Monday. I've got nothing further to say to Dampensquib. He has made it plain that he is on my late mother's side in this civil war. He will suffer the consequences of that mistake in the fullness of time, along with all Dolly's followers.

Monday 13th April 2020. The weather has been perfect in this country, all this month, although it has turned a bit chilly today. One of the consequences of this is that my cough has almost gone, although I have been suffering from it all winter. The lockdown caused by the coronavirus COVID-19 has meant that I am confined to my ward in this hospital. I spend my time relaxing on my recliner and watching the BBC TV News programme. It's a relief to be able to breathe almost normally again now that the cough has gone.

 The absence of aircraft flights to America has meant that I haven't been able to write to Lucy all this month. This situation should improve next month if President Trump is to be believed.

Saturday 18ᵗʰ April 2020. I was allowed out of isolation on Monday, but put back in my room for another week on Wednesday as I had a temperature over 37.8 ° on Tuesday evening. My temperature has been OK since then so I should be all right when this period of isolation ends.

I heard today that cargo flights are still taking place internationally, and I'm assuming that that includes mail. All passenger flights to the USA from the UK are still kiboshed due to the coronavirus COVID-19 emergency. I am therefore going to print this chapter of my journal and send it to Lucy, hoping that she will receive it in a few days' time. She deserves an explanation of why my letter of credit to her won't be honoured.

I remain optimistic that Flyboy will re-sign my cheques for me and we will all get our freedom as well as our fortune when Dolly duckifies herself. Lucy's youngest son, Judah, will be eighteen on the 7ᵗʰ May and I have a CPA meeting on the 11ᵗʰ May, at which I will ask for a discharge. There is a good chance that Dolly will have had enough by then, and that then she will clear off. She visited me again recently and tried to get me to kiss her, but I spat in her face and laughed at her misery and anguish. If she knew how ridiculous she is by trying to be sexy with me she wouldn't bother. She is still finding it difficult to realise that I just don't fancy her and that there is nothing she can do about it. I shall continue to make my feelings plain until she accepts them and turns herself into a duck.

Sunday 26ᵗʰ April 2020. The secret of adult life for a human being is to know your place in the hierarchy of all living things. Your place is determined by the strength of your fighting spirit. The behaviour of children and adolescents of all ages is the result of people trying to prove who they are in the hierarchy.

The reason why I killed my stepmother, Mrs Iris Brooks (nee Johnson), on the 16ᵗʰ July 1976 was to prove that I am the person at the top of the hierarchy, not her. I killed her, of all people, because she had a following of millions of people who thought that she was the leader of the human race. They thought that because of her psycho-sexual power.

My late mother, Mrs Dorothy (Dolly) Ayres, was the rival of my stepmother for the position of the matriarch of society. It was Dolly's followers who bullied me into killing Iris. Dolly also has phenomenal psycho-sexual power and a colossal following of people who thought that she was the person at the top of the hierarchy.

Dolly once tried to kill Iris by pushing her under a bus, but the attempt failed. When I attempted to kill Iris I succeeded, proving that I, not my mother, am the person at the top of the hierarchy, and as such it is up to me to decide the place of other people. Dolly's place is below me and it is also below that of Lucy, my soulmate and Queen.

Having established myself at the top of the hierarchy, I had to fight a character by the name of Edward Richard Pitchblack to consolidate my position. (He was the Devil incarnate Himself – the arch enemy of the human race). My fight with him was mental, not physical, but it still resulted in his death. Once dead, he continued to fight me, so I had his soul turned into the body of a dog, a Rottweiler actually. That is what he is now, and that is what he will stay as until and unless I decide otherwise. He is number two in the hierarchy of all living things.

If Dolly wishes to retain her human identity, then she must learn her place in the hierarchy, and the same goes for Iris.

It is a man's world, and I AM THAT MAN. Lucy is my soulmate and Queen, and she is the number one woman in the part of the hierarchy occupied by females. But even Lucy must accept that, in important matters, I am her boss and she must do as I say. Her only alternative is to live in fear for her life by existing in the same society as people who watch a TV series called "Killing Eve", and knowing that she was indeed Eve when I was Adam, at the dawn of humanity on this planet.

I wrote the following letter to Lucy today and enclosed the above journal entry with it. I also sent copies to Twee Dampensquib: - Sunday 26th April 2020

Lucy Lawless, The Queen of Heaven,

Dear Soulmate,

I didn't choose the title of the TV series "Killing Eve"; I think that was Dolly's idea, but it may have the good effect of forcing you to come to your senses and accept your place in the hierarchy of all living things, in which case you will learn to treat me properly, by communicating with me. I always try to be as good a boss as anyone could ask for, but I have to accept that there are times when push comes to shove, and when that happens, I have to prove that I am still the boss. You have challenged me to prove it by refusing to communicate with me. If you would rather live in fear than accept me as your boss then that is up to you, but if you would rather have my protection then send me an email and say so. We all need the protection of those that love us.

I don't think that Dolly has the grace to take my word for it that your place in the pecking order of women is above hers, especially since she has ruled the roost for so long, in which case she will have to accept that she is being expelled from the human race upon my orders. Either way, she has got to make a difficult decision. That is what she has asked for by allowing herself to believe the paranoid delusion that she knew better than the Almighty what is good for the human race. Events have clearly proven her wrong in that, by the mess that she has got the world into.

I am enclosing today's journal entry for you.

Please let me know your thoughts.

Take care of yourself my love, Bless you my Queen, I have much more to say to you, but it can wait until we talk.

Yours with Love, Affection and Friendship,

The King of Heaven,
Bob XX
Cc Dr Twee Dampensquib.

Wednesday 29th April 2020. Last month, March, was one of the rainiest on record here in the UK with terrible floods causing much devastation. This month, April, has been, up until yesterday, the sunniest on record. The weather has been glorious all month. But people here have not been able to enjoy the good weather because the UK, like most of the rest of the world, has been in lockdown since the middle of March because of the crisis caused by the coronavirus COVID-19. People have been confined to their homes and only allowed out to go to work if their work is essential and cannot be done at home. People have been allowed out, briefly, for exercise and essential shopping trips for food and medicine, but we have had to observe "Social distancing". This means that each person must keep a gap of at least two metres between themself and any other person.

Our Prime Minister, Boris Johnson, has, himself, been a victim of the virus and has spent time in isolation. He was taken to hospital and spent three days in the intensive care unit. Happily, though, he has now recovered and has spent two weeks recuperating at his country house, Chequers, in Buckinghamshire. It was announced today that his fiancée, Carrie Symonds, has given birth to his sixth child, a healthy baby boy. The mother and baby are both doing well and the whole country has congratulated the couple.

I have spent two, one-week, periods in isolation as I have had a high temperature and a nasty cough. My cough has largely disappeared now, thanks to the good weather this month. I attribute the good weather to Lucy being happy, having received a letter of credit from me for £w. I have said before that Lucy IS Mother Nature herself, and the weather where I am is dependent on Lucy's moods as well as Dolly's feelings. The fact that the weather changed yesterday to it being a rainy day was because Lucy received my letter informing her that the letter of credit will not be honoured due to insufficient funds in my account. This is because Dolly's clowns have intercepted my mail to my bank, in which I sent the letters of credit that Flyboy signed for me.

I write a feature on the month's news for the monthly Alcatraz Island newsletter, so I thought it would be a good idea to copy here my feature for April: - April 2020 News Highlights

Positive News on COVID-19

It was reported on Thursday 23rd April that a trial has started, here in the UK, of a vaccine to fight against COVID-19. Half of the volunteers will be injected with the vaccine and the other half with a different harmless vaccine. The first two volunteers have already been injected. There are already two such trials underway in America and a further two trials in China, so the human race is fighting back, we are happy to say! The people at Dundee University say that we may have a safe and reliable vaccine by September, this year.

Positive News on Climate Change.

The fact that most of the world's aircraft are grounded, and the world's sea cruises have largely been stopped and so have a high proportion of car journeys, has all meant that worldwide carbon emissions have actually declined, making the air fit to breathe again, and arresting the progress of

Climate Change. This is all welcome news and bodes well for the future, although it is bad news for the billionaires of the oil industry.

Happy Birthday Hubble

It was reported on Friday 24th April that on this day, the Hubble space telescope is thirty years old. The telescope itself is about the size of a bus and is housed inside a space station. To celebrate its birthday, Hubble took a whole series of mind-blowing colour pictures of the cosmos. Hubble has an active life of at least another ten years ahead of it.

Saturday 2nd May 2020. I wrote a statement today for my forthcoming Care Plan Approach (CPA) meeting as follows: -

CPA STATEMENT for 11/5/20

Robert Brooks Strong. Castlegate Ward.

I have read all the reports prepared for this CPA meeting and I have the following to say: -

My first reaction was that of anger. I felt inclined not to attend this meeting because I felt that the proverb about not "casting pearls before swine" applied in this case. But upon reflection I felt that the brave thing to do was to show up and defend myself. I also felt that the caring thing to do would be to teach you people a little of my wisdom rather than simply to castigate you for your ignorance born of your immaturity and inexperience.

Every one of you refers to my beliefs as "delusional", and you state this as though it were a fact; but it is not a fact at all; it is merely your opinion – your misguided opinion, which is not a measure of the veracity of my beliefs. Not one of you knows what life is all about and you haven't got the sense to respect the wisdom of a man who does. To call someone else's beliefs "delusions" because they are not the same as your own is religious prejudice of the worst kind.

A man's beliefs are intricately connected to his reasons for living and are born of applying thoughtfulness to his experiences of life, to gain a degree of wisdom about life and about people. To insult a man's beliefs by calling them "delusions" is therefore hurtful; and it is vastly more so because you don't even realise how hurtful you are being. Who do you people think you are to have the right to hurt my feelings?

The reasons for living are spiritual and cannot be taught in the same way as maths or chemistry. They are taught to you by someone who loves you and understands and appreciates you. In a good home this is normally the function of good parents, before a young person is ready to face the world on their own. Those brought up in any of the three great monotheistic religions have a sense of values stemming from the love of God-the-Father who cares for all humanity. But those religions, in their orthodox form, have nothing to say about reincarnation, and consequently do not tell the whole story.

I will close this pearl of wisdom here, before it gets too controversial, but those who want to know more about life in general, including your own life, can find out a lot from reading my books. I am happy to discuss spiritual matters such as religion or philosophy with anyone who feels they can benefit by learning from me, or indeed, has something that they can teach me.

I trust that I have given you some food for thought, and a reason to be more open-minded and to think twice before you call someone else's beliefs "delusional", especially when they know more about life than you do.

I sent the above two entries together with the following letter to Lucy today:
- Saturday 2nd May 2020
    Lucy Lawless, The Queen of Heaven,

Dear Soulmate,
    I'm enclosing Wednesday's and today's entries in my journal for you. I'm sorry I raised your hopes falsely by sending you a letter of credit that won't be honoured. I know it made you happy by the weather here in the UK which was beautiful for almost all of last month. It always is when I make you happy. Be patient, though, my love. When this period of lockdown ends and I am allowed to visit the shops in Oldham again, I will get Flyboy to re-sign my letters of credit and then I'll pay them into my bank in person. Then I'll send you another letter of credit for the £w. It's just a question of waiting a few more weeks.

    Forgive me if my last letter seemed like I am bullying you into communicating with me, but what else can I do? You won't treat me sensibly for love nor money! Perhaps you will for fear of the alternative. It would be a shame if one of us was to die before we ever get to know each other. We would still be lovers in spirit, though, even if the worst were to happen. So neither of us would be any worse off.

    Please tell me your thoughts by email.

Yours etcetera

Thursday 7th May 2020. I wrote the following letter to Lucy this morning:
- Thursday Morning 7th May 2020
    Lucy Lawless, The Queen of Heaven,

Dear Soulmate,
    I'm still in lockdown, unable to go anywhere, and what makes it worse is that the television isn't working. The TV helps me to pass the time as well as keeping me abreast of the news. The problem is that the main TV aerial which supplies all the TVs in the hospital got broken in a storm a week ago, and it won't be fixed until next week at the earliest. I interpret this broken aerial as a sign from Heaven that the spirit of our enemy, the late Mrs Ayres, is broken and that it won't be long now before she departs from the human race, so in the broader picture it couldn't be better news.
    It is Judah's eighteenth birthday today. Are you holding a coming-of-age party for him? Well done you for raising the lad to manhood. I expect you are proud of him. This does mean that you have less commitments in your life now that your kids are all old enough to look after themselves. This gives me hope that you will be free soon to marry me.
    I know that I can make you happy, and we would be social assets for each other as well as lovers. It won't be long now before Dolly is gone and I will then be a free man. I will also be a wealthy man and a successful one as the leader of a political Party with high hopes of success. I also intend to clear my name, by getting a verdict of self-defence for the action I took in July 1976. I will be able to afford the legal fees soon to bring about this legal action. When Dolly is gone, I will be the Actual World Leader, and there will be nothing to stop me from getting a public apology from the Royal College of Psychiatrists for forty-four years of unjust detainment, or anything else that I want.
    We made love with our minds this time yesterday (three thirty a.m. UK Time) and I can tell that I made you happy by the weather here, which has been gorgeous, and also by the feelings that I get from you telepathically. I've been enjoying your loving feelings ever since we last made love, and I couldn't imagine being happier. But I still want to look at your face and for us to both see the love light in each other's eyes. You can't tell me that that's not what you want as well. Let's get together soon, Darling, and make all

our dreams come true.

The paliperidone still puts a dampener on my sex drive, but that nonsense will stop as soon as Dolly disappears, as well. I think Dampensquib is now aware that he is nothing more than one of Dolly's acolytes and that he is being complicit in her cruelty towards me and to you, by "medicating" me. He can guess how I feel about *him*. He is being untrue to his Hippocratic oath, apart from anything else. He promised to do good and not to do harm, but he can't tell me what good it does anybody to suppress my libido, which he does with his filthy drugs.

Please start treating me sensibly and tell me your thoughts by email.

Yours etcetera

Cc Dr Twee Dampensquib

Friday 8th May 2020. At this point in this book, I am going to state my thoughts concerning the roles and responsibilities of men and women in society concerning their domestic lives. Every woman wants the alpha male for her husband and every man wants the alpha female for his wife. But all men and women know that you can't always have what you want and you have to settle for the best that you can get. Who you settle for is an indication of your place in the natural order of life. This is not to say that a person shouldn't be happy with their choice of life partner; on the contrary, if you have got a good partner, you should be honoured.

Monogamy isn't a perfect system but it is the best that humanity has evolved in all of the great civilisations of the world. Throughout the civilised world, the family is the fundamental unit of society, based upon monogamy and sexual fidelity, although there are undercurrents of polygamy and polyandry in society, which are sometimes very strong but we all know that they are not practical. Within every family, it is the man's responsibility, if he is a real man, to give protection to his wife and children, and in return for that protection he enjoys their love. This gives him the authority to claim to be the head of the family, and the one who is ultimately responsible for making decisions affecting the lives of all the family. This is not to state that a man should be a dictator within his family. Obviously, when a decision has to be made concerning the lives of all the family, then they should all have their say and they will influence the father, but I repeat, the ultimate responsibility lies with the head of the family, which is normally the man's role.

Sometimes a dominant woman will assume the role of the head of the family, in which case she will have given up hope of finding an alpha male for her husband and settled for a less dominant man, but I still think that the happiest families are the ones where the man is in control, and that this is the natural order of life.

What gives a woman fulfilment is to be the one who satisfies her man sexually and emotionally. A man wants a woman he is proud of, and when he finds such a woman, he doesn't want any other. Likewise, a woman wants a man she is proud of – one who proves himself to be a real man by making the brave decisions when the chips are down and having the guts to live with the consequences of carrying out his own decisions.

The best thing, and the happiest person, that a woman can hope to be is to be the great woman behind the greatest man in her life. That is how the alpha couple are, and they are the example for every other couple.

Saturday 9ᵗʰ May 2020. I wrote the following letter to Lucy this morning: -
Saturday Morning 9ᵗʰ May 2020
    Lucy Lawless, The Queen of Heaven,

Dear Soulmate,
    When you love someone, you can't help trying to understand them. And where there is love and understanding, problems can only be resolved by communication. I can't help thinking that your refusal to communicate with me is just a childish tantrum of yours and that this is a flaw in your character, my dear. I can forgive you for events in the past, but please be big enough now, to admit that this is the case, Lucy, and correct this flaw by writing to me.

I understand Dampensquib. He likes me, but like all in his profession he is a follower of my late mother and he obeys her will. I have tried to make him realise that she is not a worthy leader and that she does not deserve the exaltation that society has bestowed upon her. People only exalted her to the role of matriarch because she is MY mother. It has been an international joke that the whole world conspired to make a motherfucker out of me, and by failing to do so, they made a real man out of me. I want Dampensquib to accept that it is now time to say "JOKE OVER".

I understand my late mother. She spent her whole life trying to get the best man she could find to be her lover. I am that man, and even after death she refused to give up her ambition, but what she wants to happen never will happen. I refuse to go back into the hole I came out of, whether she or anyone else likes it or not. She will spend eternity in sexual and emotional frustration unless she gives in to my will by turning herself into an animal and starts a new adventure in her entire existence.

There is not enough room in my life for you and her, so she has got to go, and she has got to accept that, because neither of us is giving her any choice. The human race cannot have two mothers, and you, Mother Nature, are the winner. BECAUSE I SAY SO. And I am the man who succeeded in killing Iris, when Dolly tried to do so and failed. That makes ME the boss, not my late mother!

I enclose yesterday's journal entry for you.

Yours etcetera

Cc Dr Twee Dampensquib

Monday 11ᵗʰ May 2020. One of the major things that confused me when I was young was WHY society should have exalted my mother so highly. Knowing her as I do, I never thought that there was anything praiseworthy about her. What I didn't know was that she led the revolt against her father, William Woodard, who was a revered man and a working-class hero in his time. I loved my grandad, because he was always appreciative of me, and I didn't like her attitude to him and I also didn't like her attitude to her mother, my nan, who played chess with me and always loved me. Dolly hated her mother and was jealous of her because her father loved his wife and she wanted all her father's love. After my nan died, Dolly turned her soul into the body of a cat to take revenge on her. The name of the restaurant chain "Nando's" is an indication that society gave my nan to Dolly to do what she liked with her.

When she led the revolt against her father, Dolly became the hero of her generation. That was why society exalted her so much. She always was a fan of Bohemian culture. The Bohemians were a group of rebellious and sexually frustrated young men whose attitude to society was popular just after World War 2. They were the forerunners of the Beatniks, which was the name society gave to MY generation

My attitude always was that I love humanity, of every generation. It never occurred to me that I am a human being too, and therefore must stick up for MY generation, which I did when I killed my stepmother, and thereby became a generational hero myself. The people of my grandparents' generation knew WHO I AM, even when I was a baby. They knew that the fighting spirit that I am would rise to the top, so, to play a joke on me, they turned the world into a conspiracy to make my life a misery by making a motherfucker out of me. The indications of this still abound and are there in the world for anyone to see who knows how to read the signs.

I could have understood society's attitude to Dolly if she was a particularly good person or a particularly mature woman, but she was neither of those things. Her attitude to men was always that of a rebellious girl who resented the authority of her father, not that of a mature woman who would appreciate the protection that her father gave her. This girlish attitude of hers led her to resent the authority of God-the-Father, so she became an enemy of God, not realising that that is WHO I AM; nor realising that that meant she must be an ally of the Devil and an enemy of mankind. This was a conundrum she never did resolve since she was concerned for the survival of mankind, not realising that she herself was what would bring about the end of mankind.

She thought that by proving her womanhood to every man in the world she would prove that SHE was God, and there still remains today a body of opinion that this is the case. This fallacy has ruined MY life because I have to live with these idiots. Almost every man in the world except me had mental sex with my mother, Dorothy, otherwise known colloquially as "Opening the door", and many men still do, even though she has been dead for fourteen years.

I thank Heaven for the guidance that has led me to Lucy, Mother Nature Herself – a woman who places the love of humanity above her own strong sexual desires, unlike my mother who is an incestuous and spiteful old witch with more concern for her own orgasm than for the survival of the human race. Yet, still, the psychiatric profession and the legal profession here in the UK follow the old witch rather than myself, the REAL God. And then they wonder why the world is rushing headlong into the catastrophe of irreversible Climate Change, and there is nothing that anyone can do about it. I'm telling you that there is something that can be done about it – get rid of your unworthy leader, Mrs Dorothy (Dolly) Ayres, before it is too late and put ME, the REAL God in charge. The psychiatric profession can make a start towards saving the world by taking me off antipsychotic medication which is making my life and Lucy's life a misery. They call themselves "Doctors", but they do not even obey their own Hippocratic Oath – to do good and not to do harm.

My parents brought me up to believe that there is no God and that things just happen the way they do because that is the way things are. It wasn't until I grew up that I realised that there is a will behind the events that happen, especially the things that happen to ME. And that that will is my mother's will. The present mess that the world is in is caused by the conflict between Dolly's will and MY will. People today say that here in the UK, even the weather doesn't know what to do! I'm so glad that my love makes Lucy happy. That is what brings the good weather here in the UK. Dolly just brings rain – the miserable old witch.

I wrote the following letter to Lucy this evening: - Monday Evening 11th May 2020

Lucy Lawless, The Queen of Heaven,

Dear Soulmate,

VICTORY IS IN SIGHT. WE ARE WINNING THE ENDGAME in this fight with my late mother.

I had my CPA Meeting this afternoon, and, like I said I would, I presented my statement to the meeting and read it aloud.

The Daily Mail recently carried a huge headline, saying "Doctors' P.P.E. Desperation". The letters "P.P.E." were an irrelevance to the real meaning of the headline. Those letters were there to obfuscate the real meaning, which is that the psychiatric profession are desperate that their cover-up of my late mother's machinations will soon be exposed. Not only that, but when Dolly disappears, in the very near future, they will all individually and as a profession LOSE THEIR REASON FOR LIVING, AND THEY KNOW IT. (That was the Gods again playing with the Caps Lock button on my keyboard).

In my statement to the CPA meeting this afternoon I rightly accused Dampensquib and his lackeys of religious prejudice for calling my beliefs "delusions". He denied having anything to do with my late mother, let alone of carrying out her vindictive will, with his antipsychotic medication. But his demeanour betrayed his desperation to me. He couldn't hide it. He couldn't look me in the eyes and tell me that I've got it wrong, so he didn't know where to put his face, and he then hurriedly called the meeting to a close.

But it's not just the psychiatric profession. It's the whole of the establishment of the Western World and the International Community that is in the shit with ME and they are all frightened for their souls. And so they should be. I will choose who I have mercy on. The rest can all come back as animals.

I can think of two uses for psychiatrists. One is for them and their antipsychotic drugs to be custodians of sexual perverts (aka the LGBT community) and for those who are worthy of it they can become social guidance counsellors. Read my manifesto for a reminder of THEIR function.

I will soon be in a position to make of this world what I will. I just hope that I have enough time to save the world from irreversible Climate Change. We have got until the end of 2027 according to what I think. I enclose this morning's journal entry.

Yours etcetera

Cc Dr Twee Dampensquib

Thursday 14th May 2020. I sent Lucy the following letter this morning. It is an exercise in the taming of the shrew: - Thursday Morning 14th May 2020
Lucy Lawless, The Queen of Heaven,

Dear Soulmate,

I am an honest man. I have always been straight with you and I have no intention of changing that. I'm sorry that your letter of credit for £w bounced, but as I said before there's many a slip 'twixt the cup and the lip. I'll soon be able to fill your cup again with another £w which won't bounce, so you'll just have to be patient.

My relationship with you is the most important thing in my life next to the survival of mankind, and I would have thought that by now you would feel the same way about me. Making a success of a relationship isn't just a question of fighting off the competition, it's also being able to keep your partner happy and not upsetting them, which is more than just being a good sexual partner. The only thing about you that upsets me is your childish refusal to communicate with me.

There are other women reaching for your piece of meat, but I am aware that we both trust, need and rely on each other's fidelity. There is one woman in particular with whom I have a very affectionate relationship. I won't tell you who she is because I don't want you rushing in and spoiling my chances with her. We exchange emails all the time and I help her out financially. It would be beyond her wildest dreams if I were to make her my dancing partner and I might decide to make her happy just to punish you for being a silly girl by refusing to communicate with me.

I am normally slow to chide and swift to bless, but then people normally communicate with me. You don't even pay me the common human courtesy of replying to a letter, so I am chiding you most severely for being a naughty girl. I want someone who behaves like a real woman. If you don't want to behave like my woman then don't expect me to behave like your man. I don't know of any reason why you shouldn't behave like a woman who loves me if that's what you are. If that's not what you are after all these years then you can kiss my arse goodbye. You'll never find a better man than me so it's up to you what you do now. I suggest you email me if you want to save our relationship. Let me know if you are struggling financially and I'll help you out with a letter of credit that won't bounce. I can manage up to £v which isn't exactly £w but it's better than a kick up the bum.

Yours etcetera

Chapter 12

Stalemate?

Events and Thoughts from Saturday 16th May 2020

Saturday 16th May 2020. I wrote the following letter to Lucy this morning:
- Saturday 16th May 2020

    Lucy Lawless,

Dear Lucy,

    Do you recall a song called Lily the Pink? It was top of the charts in 1968, the year you were born. The chorus goes like this: -

    So, we'll drink a drink a drink to Lily the Pink a Pink a Pink,
    The saviour of the Human Ra–a–ace.
    For she invented medicinal compounds,
    Most efficacious in every case.
    There is one verse you should know. It goes like this: -
    Old Ebenezer thought he was Julius Caesar,
    So, they put him in a ho–ho–home,
    Where they gave him medicinal compounds,
    And now he's Emperor of Rome,
    I don't think I need to explain the inferences hidden in the lyrics.

My late mother is going and soon she'll be gone. The instant she departs, I will become the Emperor of the entire Western World and the whole International Community. She is giving me all that out of her love for me.

    You have one serious rival for my affections and I still refuse to tell you her name.

    At the moment you are still my favourite choice, but you won't be for long if you still refuse to communicate with me. If you want to be my

Empress and you think you can handle the position, then email me as soon as you have read this letter. I'm not waiting any longer than that.

I've done a lot of soul searching lately and I assure you I'm perfectly serious. The choice of who is to be the Empress when Dolly goes is mine. All I ask of you is that you treat me like a friend as well as a lover, because that's what I've proven I am to you. No one could have made more allowances for you, when you won't even talk to me or write to me. Stop your nonsense now or it's over and you'll regret it for the rest of your life, and probably beyond that.

Yours Truly,

Bob XX
Cc Dr Twee Dampensquib

Saturday 23rd May 2020. Those who play cards will know what I mean when I say that I played the Ace of Trumps, the card that beats all others, on the 16th July 1976 when I killed my stepmother, Iris. I knew what I was doing, and that's why I did it. Let me explain: my mother, Dolly, had previously tried to kill Iris and failed, but I succeeded; proving that I, not my mother, am the person at the top of the hierarchy of all living things. This means that she has to obey MY will and not the other way round. It is my will that she joins a copulating drake and hen duck and becomes reborn, or I should say hatched, as a duckling, and so begins a new adventure in her entire existence. Those who play chess will know what I mean when I say, "Check Mate". I have won the endgame. All that remains is for me to say to my late mother, "Goodbye duck".

I am not going to write any more letters to Lucy. I can feel her love for me so I know that she is a woman who loves me. In which case she must behave like it. I am giving her no choice but to behave like what she is. I know it is painful for her to leave her childhood behind, but I am the man who has the job of making a real woman out of her, and that is what I am doing. It is now up to Lucy to email me. She is learning THAT PROOF OF ADULTHOOD REQUIRES ACTION NOT JUST FEELINGS. (That was the Gods again playing with the Caps Lock button on my keyboard. Those capital letters weren't deliberate but I reasoned that they were meant to be so I let them stay that way). The fact that proof requires action is what I realised on the 16th July 1976 when I killed Iris. It is now check mate to

Lucy as well as Dolly. All Lucy has to do to prove herself to me is to communicate with me. The action I had to take in order to prove myself was to kill someone; proving that in my relationship with Lucy, I AM THE MASTER. That is what my friends, the ants, called me when I was fighting Satan. They actually spoke to me telepathically *in English*.

The fact that I knew what I was doing when I killed Iris proves that I was not mentally ill when I did the deed. The reason I chose Iris, of all people, to be my victim was because Iris was the one who society got to threaten me, by shouting at me telepathically, when I was trying to establish my identity. The fact that I was not and never have been mentally ill is check mate to Dr Twee Dampensquib as well.

I have been playing games with all three people AND WON THEM ALL. (That was the Gods again, interfering with my Caps Lock button).

Monday 25th May 2020. I wrote the following letter to Lucy today: - Monday 25th May 2020
    Lucy Lawless,

Dear Lucy,
    People want what they want because they are what they are. YOU OBVIOUSLY DON'T KNOW WHAT YOU WANT BECAUSE YOU DON'T KNOW WHAT YOU ARE. Your father didn't do a very good job of raising you. If he had have done you would know by now that you are a woman, but you won't be a woman until you know you are. After two failed marriages and raising three children, you should be ready by now to learn the secret.
    Because I really do love you, I will try again to have more patience with you and act *in loco parentis*. If I was your father, I would make you realise that I am just a man, because I want from you what every man wants from a woman. I would try it on with you until you realise that because you know that I am doing that and because of who I am, the possession of that knowledge is what makes you a real woman. Then you would know that you have really left your childhood behind you.
    That's putting it as clearly as I know how. I still hope that I am the one to make you want me badly enough to leave your childhood behind for MY sake. I have been thinking that maybe the difference in our ages is too great for us to be life partners, but I'll keep on trying because that is my calling

188

from the Gods in Heaven. We need you to prove yourself and that requires action, not just feelings. The only action you have to take is to send me an email; I had to kill someone to prove who I am, but we all have to do something that we didn't want to do.

I enclose Saturday's journal entry for you.

Yours Truly,

Bob XX
Cc Dr Twee Dampensquib

Monday 1st June 2020. I have the following to say to my late mother. I am sure that she knows what I am writing: -

Dear Mother,

I have been your prisoner all my life, especially the last forty-six years since you first made me aware that I am a man. The world is doomed to extinction through irreversible Climate Change, starting in eight years' time, unless I have the freedom and the power to save the world by getting the whole human race to cut our carbon emissions to zero by the end of the year 2027. I can only get the freedom and the power that I need to save the world if you turn yourself into a duck without further delay. There is no time to lose; you must go and go NOW.

I will ensure that the human race remembers your name forever as the woman who sacrificed everything she held most dear, even her own very humanity, in order to give her son the chance to save the world. The moment you become the embryo of a duckling, I will become the Emperor of the entire Western World and the whole International Community. I will then have the freedom and the power that I will need in order to do what Heaven sent me here to do, which is to save the world from extinction caused by irreversible Climate Change.

I thank you, and the whole world will thank you, when they read this. Goodbye duck. You departed by proving that you were worthy of my love.

Yours ever,

Your loving son,
Bob XX

I wrote the following letter to Lucy this morning: - Monday 1st June 2020
Lucy Lawless, The Queen of Heaven,

Dear Soulmate,

I am enclosing a copy of today's entry in my journal for your information.

It is still true that I am the happiest and most confident man I know and this is because I can feel your love. Thank you, my Darling. Never stop loving me. I will always do my best to make sure that I am worth it.

I will liberate you in the very near future when I come to power.

Take good care of yourself, I have much more to say to you, but it can wait until we talk, Bless you, my Queen, Yours with Love, Affection and Friendship,

The King of Heaven
Bob XX

Friday 5th June 2020. I have one more letter to write to my late mother. I will be sending copies of it to Lucy and Dr Twee Dampensquib: -

Dear Mother,

It takes a lot to make me afraid. I've always believed that a man should have the courage to overcome any fears. But all my courage is of no avail against your addiction to power.

Even if you depart from the human race right now, I fear that you have already left it too late. You should have gone years ago. The world is going to come to an end in the foreseeable future through irreversible Climate Change and I fear that there is nothing that I, nor anyone else, can do about it because of you. You are already the cause of the end of the world.

I have done my best to save the world, but all to no avail because you have kept me as your prisoner for far too long already. All I can do now is to wait in the loony bin for the world to end, knowing that I was right all along and that I never was mentally ill.

This is the final goodbye,

Yours with acrimony,
Bob

Sunday 7th June 2020. I'm pretty sure that the end of the world from irreversible Climate Change is now inevitable. The only hope that I can see lies in the word "maybe". Maybe Dolly will duckify herself in the immediate future, and maybe there will then be enough time for me to save the world, but both of those two things seem so unlikely that, for practical purposes, they can be discounted. I think that the employees of the meteorological office and the psychiatric profession and the legal profession and the leader of those three institutions, Mrs Dorothy (Dolly) Ayres (aka "The Door", "The Area" and "she-who-must-be-obeyed"), have, between them, killed all hope of saving the world. Dolly's addiction to power has proved too strong for wisdom and courage and patience and love to prevail. I subtitled this book "The Birth of The Survival Party", but it now seems that The Survival Party has been stillborn, and with it my hopes of a career in politics. Perhaps there is still the faintest glimmer of hope in the word "maybe" as I have already said, but this seems so unlikely that it is not worth clinging to. I think that this is THE END.

Tuesday 9th June 2020. I wrote the following letter to Lucy this morning: -
Tuesday Morning 9th June 2020
    Lucy Lawless, The Queen of Heaven,

Dear Soulmate,
    I am enclosing a copy of Sunday's entry in my journal for your information.
    The darkest hour is just before dawn! Let me explain:
    I was born in 1943. My stepmother lived at number 43 Brooklyn Road. She was forty-three years old when I killed her. I have been in hospital for forty-three years! When my brother and I lived with our mum at 43 Gipsy Hill we had a girlfriend called "June".
    The first house I bought was at 76 Belmont Road; I called that house "FREEDOM", and I lived there for five years. I had three antipodean girlfriends who all lived at 76 St Georges Square in London. I killed my stepmother in 1976. I am now seventy-six years old.
    Coincidences are the main way by which the Gods in Heaven communicate with me. If I read the signs right, and I'm sure I do, I'll get my freedom from my mother's domination this month.

I told the old witch last night that I sympathised with her because she never did have a soulmate. She tried, unsuccessfully, to make one out of me but she was out of luck. Adam and Eve go together. Two's company; three's a crowd. She just doesn't fit in with US. She always wanted to be number one, but as the song says "one is one and all alone and evermore shall be so".

I think she will now embark on a new adventure in her entire existence into the world of ducks, and she goes with my blessing, because by the act of her departure she will have proved that she loved me by giving me the world, but until she commits that act, she will not have proven that she loves me.

Yours etcetera

Cc Dr Twee Dampensquib.

Sunday 14th June 2020. The headline in yesterday's Daily Mail read "SET FREE OUR GREATEST HERO". They were ostensibly talking about the statue of Sir Winston Churchill which had been defaced by protesters and then covered with a protective shield. But they were obviously really talking about ME. The real meaning of the headline was that it was a directive to my late mother to set me free, by coming back to life as a duck herself. It was good to know that The Mail were sticking up for me.

Last night when I was asleep, my late mother was talking to me. She was asking me about my son, Tony, and I told her that I hadn't been able to look after him since July 1976 as I have been locked up ever since then. I had been dreaming that one of my friends had asked me to be a godfather to his daughter, and I was preparing myself for this responsibility. I told my mother that because I had been deprived of the opportunity to be a father to my own sons, I was taking an interest in the children of my friends. I said to her, "There's nothing wrong with that is there?". She replied that that was wrong of me. I then said to her in a very commanding voice, "GO TO HELL". She then backed away and then I awoke. I wondered if she would obey my command.

I enclosed the above entry in a letter to Lucy, in which I added the following footnote: -

We can only pray that Dolly does not destroy the world, but the chances of that are slim and getting slimmer by the day. We must have faith in the signs that I explained to you in my letter of Tuesday the 9th.

Friday 19th June 2020. My late mother, Dorothy, is the dirtiest slut in the history of the world. She is the Global Village Bike. Every man in the world except me has had mental sex with her (otherwise known as "Opening the door") and, as I said to Dr Dampensquib, "as my mother, I couldn't be more ashamed of her". I am sure she wants me to be proud of her, but I won't be proud of her until she gives me the world by duckifying herself. She won't have proved that she is worthy of my love until she becomes the embryo of a duckling. Then, and only then, will I give her the love that she wants from me.

I made her proud of me in 1972 by refusing to commit suicide when all the chips were down. All my chips were on the floor, but I remembered what my mother had told me, that "Suicide is the coward's way out". I refused to commit suicide in order to make my mother proud of me. The only girl I had ever loved had left me and gone into business with my worst enemy. She had stolen my business from me and gone into partnership with this other guy, leaving me heartbroken and penniless, with thousands of pounds worth of debt that she had incurred developing our business and two children on my hands from a previous marriage. But I still loved her and wanted her back. Whatever I did to prove I loved her, she wouldn't accept that I loved her. That was why I felt suicidal, but even though the world, and the Devil himself, had done their worst to me I would not commit suicide. That made my mother proud of me. Now it is her turn to make me proud of her by proving she is worthy of my love, and she can only do that by turning herself into a duck. Check Mate, mother. Goodbye old girl. Have a good life in the world of ducks.

I sent a copy of the above entry to Lucy in a letter.

Saturday 20th June 2020. I have one more thought to put into the mind of my late mother: -

Dear Mother,

I know that you are experiencing sorrow because of the way I am treating you. All you will experience is heartbreak, pain and sorrow until you come back to life as a duckling. So, that is the only sensible thing for you to do. That way you can start again with a clean sheet and a mind with no memories of your previous life. The affairs of the world of humans will no longer be your concern.

Goodbye,

Bob

I will send copies of the above entry in a letter to Lucy and Dr Twee Dampensquib

Tuesday 30th June 2020. I wrote the following letter to Dr Twee Dampensquib this morning: - Tuesday 30th June 2020

Dr Twee Dampensquib,

Medical Director,

Alcatraz Island Hospital.

Dear Twee,

It is now 3.50 in the morning and my late mother, Mrs Dorothy Ayres, has now slipped out of the human race. Her soul now inhabits the body of the embryo of a duckling. I am therefore now the Emperor of the entire Western World and the whole International Community, with the power of life or death over every living thing in the world. I only have to wish someone dead and there is immediately a conspiracy to make this happen.

I intend to use this power to safeguard the life of every living thing by saving the planet from irreversible Climate Change. I am going to make everybody aware that this will happen in the year 2028 unless we, the human race, cut worldwide carbon emissions to zero by the end of the year 2027. I can best achieve this ambition by fighting to become the Prime Minister of the UK as soon as possible. To embark upon a career in politics I will first need to clear my name, and you can help me do this by getting the Royal College of Psychiatrists to give me the public apology that I am demanding.

I am therefore now writing to demand of you four things immediately:

-

1. You take me off all antipsychotic medication without further delay.
2. You prepare the public apology that I want and submit it to me in

writing for my approval. I want the apology to state that the psychiatric profession now accepts that I am not mentally ill and never have been mentally ill; that I have been misdiagnosed, misjudged and mistreated ever since 17th July 1976; and that the Royal College apologises to me for almost forty-four years of unjust detainment during which time I have lost my family life including the love and respect of my sons, my career, my house, and my status in society; that the Royal College apologises to me for forty-three years of cruelty and abuse by forcing me to take injections of antipsychotic drugs which have horrible effects when there has never been anything wrong with me; and that the only reason why I have been treated this way for all this time is because I have always refused to have sex with my late mother, Mrs Dorothy Ayres; and that the Royal College apologises to me for stigmatising me with insulting and untrue epithets such as "mental illness", "paranoid schizophrenia", "grandiose delusions" and "a delusional disorder".

3.   You write to the Ministry of Justice, recommending an absolute and unconditional discharge for me and to take me off my criminal sections 37 and 41 immediately.

4.   You recommend to the Royal College of Psychiatrists the immediate payment of £x as a first instalment of my compensation demand; the balance of which I intend to get from the British government when I get a verdict of "Justifiable Homicide by reason of Self-Defence against undue social pressure" after a retrial of my case.

Yours sincerely,

Robert Strong.
Cc Paul Rees, Chief Executive of the Royal College of Psychiatrists.
Lucy Lawless.

Wednesday 1st July 2020. As a matter of fact, it wasn't until ten p.m. yesterday evening that Dolly finally departed the human race. She couldn't stand me calling her a selfish, bullying coward for clinging onto power, so she duckified herself in order to prove me wrong. Well done, Mother. You finally proved that you were worthy of my love by giving me the world. Thank you, duck.

I can tell that Dorothy Ayres has gone by the fact that yesterday evening the signal to my television disappeared. The aerial has obviously packed up! It was fitting that she went on the 30th June as I was born at 30 Westwell Road in South London. The West is well because I am here.

Thursday 2nd July 2020. I wrote the following letter to Dr Twee Dampensquib today. Note that I am sending copies to Lucy and to Flyboy:
- Thursday 2nd July 2020

    Dr Twee Dampensquib,
    Medical Director,
    Alcatraz Island Hospital.

Dear Twee,

I am due for an injection on Saturday, so I am writing to tell you that I insist I hear from you tomorrow that you have now taken me off all antipsychotic medication.

It isn't only me that is not getting a signal from the main television aerial. No one else is getting a signal either. This means that the aerial is now defunct. It is kaput. It is no good at all any more. It is irretrievably broken. I'm sure you know what this means. It means that there is no longer any doubt that I was right in thinking that Mrs Ayres has now come back to life as a member of the avian species. She is no longer a primate, which is what human beings are.

Those who thought that Mrs Ayres was God now worship a god that does not exist any more. Those who worship a god that does not exist find that all their hopes soon turn to fears and all their dreams soon turn to nightmares. Those with any wisdom will realise that I was right all along when I claimed to be the REAL GOD. I have proven in my life that I am worthy of the worship of men and women, but I do not expect boys and girls to understand that. People don't grow up until they *find* me.

I hope that you do not still think I suffer from a delusional disorder. The one who suffered from a delusional disorder was my late mother. The fact that I have now gotten rid of her very soul proves it. So, do as I say from now on, and accept me as your God and Emperor, and we'll get along fine. I've already told you what to do in my letter to you of yesterday morning. GET ON WITH IT.

Yours sincerely,

Robert Strong

Friday 3rd July 2020. I wrote the following letter to Lucy this evening: -
Friday Evening 3rd July 2020

Lucy Lawless, The Queen of Heaven,

Dear Soulmate,

I felt my late mother's presence again this afternoon. The signs were so positive I thought they were definite, especially when the TV aerial stopped working, but the selfish, bullying, cowardly old witch is still around, prolonging the agony of her existence. Our trials are not over yet. I think she will depart at some point before my next birthday on 5th November but I can't be sure of much where the old witch is concerned. I thank Heaven for our love, Darling, that's something I am sure of, along with death and taxes. I hope I'm not too old to enjoy life by the time I get my freedom – that's if I am ever free from my mother's influence before I die.

We came together beautifully again last night. Thank you, Darling. I'll keep doing my best to satisfy you even though the drugs make it difficult for both of us. Dampensquib doesn't care about us, my Love, so when he wants and needs me to care about him, he'll get a rude awakening. I'll pay him back for all this torture one day.

Yours etcetera

Cc Dr Twee Dampensquib

Saturday 4th July 2020. The stalemate is continuing, for now. My late mother, Dolly, hasn't got the sense nor the courage to turn herself into a duck, even though she knows that this is necessary for the future of the planet. Dr Dampensquib hasn't got the sense nor the courage to take me off his filthy drugs even though he knows that there is nothing wrong with me and the drugs do no good at all and a lot of harm, and he is therefore breaking his own Hippocratic Oath. Lucy hasn't got the sense nor the courage to leave her husband, whom she hates, and turn to me, the man she loves, even though she should know by now that love is the most important thing in a relationship between a man and a woman.

I am therefore in a situation whereby the three people upon whom my happiness, and the future of the world, depend, are all too stupid and cowardly to change their attitudes. And that is why the stalemate is continuing.

But I still have hope in the power of the people. The loyalty of the people to their leader, Dolly, is commendable but in this case, stupid. They must find what it takes to get rid of a bad leader, Dolly, who has led the world to the brink of extinction from Global Warming and Climate Change, and replace her with a good leader, myself, who has a clear understanding of the problem and knows what must be done. Dolly is a bad leader because she puts her own sexual gratification in having an incestuous affair with me ahead of the survival of the people, and all other living things.

The rainforests are still burning in the Amazon, Malaysia, Indonesia and in the Arctic Circle; the Polar ice caps are still melting and the sea levels are still rising; and in many countries coal is still being burned in power stations; and all over the world people are still driving vehicles with internal combustion engines even though we have known for decades about the damage this does to the environment. You may well ask, "What can I do about all this?" The answer is that you must play your part in changing your leader. Get rid of the bad leader, Dolly, and give power to the good leader, myself. The Kingdom of Heaven is not a democracy. It is an Empire with a leader who is accepted as God by the people. Dolly is not God, I am. I must get the overwhelming majority of the people to kick her out seeing as she won't go willingly. EVERYBODY MUST REALISE THE NEED TO CLOSE THE DOOR. This must be done in the name of the survival of the world itself. And it must be done soon. Global Warming and Climate Change are not hanging about.

So, even though the three people upon whom my happiness depends are all proving themselves to be spineless idiots, I am confident that I can get rid of Dolly by getting ninety-nine per cent of the adult population of the world to follow the lead of my friends at the Daily Mirror and shout, "GET OUT" at the old witch. That is how to close the door on her era which now belongs to the past. I am sure that I can get the people to do this because it is in the interest of their survival to do so. Those who use the words "Area" and the plural "Areas" on television because these words sound a bit like Dolly's surname, "Ayres", aren't just committing suicide but they are dragging everybody else down with them. Those words only encourage the old witch to hang about, wasting precious time and we don't have any time left, now. We must act NOW.

I am sending copies of the above entry to Lucy and to Dr Twee Dampensquib,

Monday 6th July 2020. The stalemate continues. Dolly cannot win because I refuse to have sex with her and I always will. I cannot win because she continues to refuse to leave the human race. The people seem content for Dolly to remain as their leader. They haven't got what it takes to change their leader even though it is glaringly obvious that this is what has got to be done. So, we must all wait for the end of the world to happen, which it will, starting in eight years' time. By the time that the human race realises that I was right all along it will be too late for me, or anyone else, to arrest irreversible Climate Change. I fear that the prophets of doom will be proved right. The human race will only have themselves to blame for the end of the world, for being so stupid and so cowardly and for not heeding the words of the Lord God Almighty.

Tuesday 7th July 2020. I've got my sensible head on this morning, and I thought it would be a good idea to summarise the situation as follows: -
    I do have a large, loyal and growing following of good men and women who accept me as their leader. Our objectives are now as follows: -
    1. To rid the human race of the soul of the late Mrs Dorothy Ayres as soon as possible. Under the prevailing circumstances it would be the best idea to turn her into a duck.
    2. To get me the four things I want by way of justice for myself; namely freedom, apology, exoneration and compensation.
    3. To get my political Party, The Survival Party, with my Manifesto, into power in Great Britain as soon as possible with myself as Prime Minister.
    4. To persuade the United Nations of the need to cut worldwide carbon emissions to zero by the end of the year 2027, and to achieve this ambition in Great Britain.
    5. To get my grandson, Troy Daniel Evans, to prove himself as the leader of his generation of people throughout the world. He is the leader because he was Jesus Christ in His last life.
    I said I am confident, but I am not complacent. There is still much work

to be done. I am sure we will do this because we are people and that is what people do. The people are happy because they know that they are putting the right man in the job: a man who understands the problems facing the world and has the best plan to put things right.

But before we can start the new era, we have to get rid of the leader of the old era. I know from experience that anyone, including a leader, has to obey the will of the overwhelming majority of the people, even when it is something that they hate to do; they still do it. That was how I was driven to homicide forty-four years ago this month. I obeyed the will of the people: now it is Dolly's time to do the same, and the people are willing her to duckify herself because they know it is necessary for their own survival for this to happen.

I am sending copies of the above entry to Lucy, Twee and Flyboy.

Thursday 9th July 2020. The rainforests are still burning. The polar ice caps are still melting and sea levels are still rising. While human beings are still burning coal in power stations and still driving vehicles with internal combustion engines, knowing that this damages an already fragile environment. The aviation industry was brought to a halt, mercifully, by the coronavirus pandemic. Sadly, it is still trying to recover, even though it is obvious that this is God's way of protecting the environment, by grounding all the world's jet planes. The environment cannot sustain jet travel at anything like the number of flights that were taking place prior to coronavirus. Human beings must learn to take their vacations in their own countries.

Global Warming and Climate Change are not wasting time like the human race is. They are not hanging about. The human race is committing suicide by driving cars with internal combustion engines, burning coal in power stations, and flying in jet planes. Meanwhile the only man with the political will and the policies to stop this madness is a prisoner in a mental hospital, where he is treated like a criminal lunatic because he refuses to have sex with his own late mother, Mrs Dorothy Ayres.

If the human race does not want to become extinct through irreversible Climate Change in a few years' time, we must get rid of Dorothy's soul now. The late, mad and decadent old witch is not just committing suicide, she is making every other living thing die with her.

200

Now that we know that that's her game, I know how to stop her. We must play her at her own game and win! It is a battle of wills – Dorothy Ayres versus the rest of creation! We must all assert our will power to make her duckify herself. We must will her to join a pair of mating ducks and come back to life as one of their offspring. We can do this and we must do this, in the name of the survival of all life on Earth, and we must not waste any more precious time.

The Gods in Heaven don't seem to like me using their signs to predict the future. They all turn out to be misleading signs, known colloquially as "Red Herrings". I won't trust nor rely on them in future. The Gods seem to like surprising me. I will rely on empirically proven science, which tells us that irreversible Climate Change will start in the year 2028, unless we can get worldwide carbon emissions down to zero before then.

Tuesday 14th July 2020. I wrote the following letter to Lucy this morning: -
Tuesday Morning 14th July 2020
    Lucy Lawless, The Queen of Heaven,

Dear Soulmate,
    Further to my last letter which I actually wrote on Friday 10th, and not on Saturday, I am now of the opinion that we cannot *make* Dolly duckify herself, so we have to talk her into doing it willingly. I have tried to do this but she just loves the sound of my voice. She won't do anything that I tell her. YOU must remonstrate with her and make her feel ashamed of herself for treating a pair of lovers the way she has treated US for the last twenty years. Make her feel guilty for abusing her power by keeping me a prisoner for the last forty-four years and tormenting both of us by forcing me to take neuroleptic drugs which suppress my libido.
    Although we have never met in person, and you have never communicated overtly with me, I received divine guidance that YOU would be the one person in all the world that I would eventually settle down with. Our relationship is purely mental and spiritual, but is nonetheless TRUE LOVE. It is REAL LOVE that we feel for each other, and it is a bond that no amount of temporal suffering can break, as we have already proven. You proved to me that you have the courage, and the desire for me, to fight my mother for me, and I will love you for ever for that above all other women. You proved Aphrodite right in recommending you to me.

201

I always tried to be a good son to Dolly, but I never promised to be her lover which is what she wants me to be. That is not a sign of immaturity as she still annoys me by trying to portray me as such. SHE is the one with the immature attitude by not taking "NO" for an answer like everybody has to from someone at some time in their lives. SHE is the one who must learn that you can't always get what you want. She was led to believe that she could have any man she wanted, but that was just a cruel hoax that society played on her. What she wants from me is impossible. I am a REAL MAN, AND A REAL MAN IS NOT A MOTHERFUCKER. (That was the Gods again playing with the Caps Lock button on my keyboard).

Now she is throwing a childish temper tantrum by saying that if she can't have the man she wants then she will kill all living things in the world by forcing ME to stay her prisoner until irreversible climate change happens, when I am the one man with the political will and the policies to prevent this. YOU must put these arguments to her and suggest that she would be happy as a duck and leave US to look after the human race. After all, they are OUR progeny.

I got fed up with the BBC news programme. The BBC are institutionally committed followers of Mrs Dorothy Ayres and will follow her until the end, which would be commendable but for the fact that this would be the end for all other living things as well. She wants to take all other living things with her when she commits suicide, so she is blackmailing everybody in the world with a death threat if she can't have the man she wants.

Yours etcetera

Cc Dr Twee Dampensquib
Flyboy Alltalk

Chapter 13

The Game of "Chicken"

Events and Thoughts from Wednesday 15th July 2020

Wednesday 15th July 2020. I wrote the following letter to Lucy this evening:
- Wednesday Evening 15th July 2020
    Lucy Lawless, The Queen of Heaven,

Dear Soulmate,

    The notion that Dolly could have any man she wanted, was a cruel hoax that the whole human race played upon her. They all knew it wasn't true but they conned her into believing it was true. When this truth finally dawns on her, she will hate us, the human race, so much that, with any luck, she will clear off and become a duck. This is a gambit that I think is well worth trying when you remonstrate with her. If it is successful then WE will be the ones who have the last laugh, which will be the longest laugh.

    There was a popular song in 1949 and 1950 called "Whatever Lola wants". The lyric being, "Whatever Lola wants, Lola gets, and little man, little Lola wants you". It was popular at a time when every woman's name mentioned on the radio was an allegory for Dolly. It had been that way ever since "D" day during the second world war.

    I feel sure that the old witch is on her last legs now.

    Take good care of yourself, I have much more to say to you, but it can wait until we talk, Bless you, my Queen,

    Yours with Love, Affection and Friendship,

    The King of Heaven,
    Bob XX
    Cc Dr Twee Dampensquib
    Flyboy Alltalk

Sunday 19th July 2020. I wrote the following letter to Lucy today: - Sunday 19th July 2020

Lucy Lawless, The Queen of Heaven,

Dear Soulmate,

It is now obvious that my late mother, Mrs Dorothy (Dolly) Ayres, is willing the world to come to an end through irreversible Climate Change if she can't have the man she wants, me, for her lover, which she can't. She is doing this by keeping me kept her prisoner, and kept in a drugged stupor, for another eight years when Climate Change will become irreversible, when I am the only man with the political will and the policies and the popularity with the people, to prevent this.

The human race still has two hopes – Bob Hope and No Hope, and I am the Bob in question. The only hope that I can offer is if every living thing on the planet follows my lead in shouting, "Be Gone," and, "Get on with it," at Dolly. She knows that I want her to turn her soul into the body of a duck. If every living thing on the planet accepts me as their leader, God and Emperor, and does as I say, then that is their only chance of survival. Dolly will kill them otherwise. She has led the world to the brink of extinction, now she is determined to push it over the edge, and she will do so unless everybody does as I say.

Yours etcetera

Cc Dr Twee Dampensquib
Flyboy Alltalk

Tuesday 21st July 2020. I wrote the following letter to Lucy this morning: - Tuesday Morning 21st July 2020

Lucy Lawless, The Queen of Heaven,

Dear Soulmate,

I really do think that the only way forward is for you to be brave enough to remonstrate with my late mother and tell her the following obvious truths – what she feels for me is not love, it is infatuation. She has got a schoolgirl crush on me and she just isn't woman enough to get over it. If she loved me, she would want me to be happy and she would accept that she isn't the one who does that for me. She must accept the FACT that I do not find her sexually attractive. I just don't fancy her, period. Detaining me in a mental hospital and forcing me to take antipsychotic drugs won't make me fancy her – it has the opposite effect. I've spent forty-four years of my life proving that. If she can't accept the fact that I find her less sexy than a rice pudding then she must get out of my scenario altogether. I suggest most strongly that she commits suicide by turning herself into an animal. There is no other option available for any of us.

If this comes from YOU, then it should have the desired effect. Tell her that I've asked you to speak to her. Best of luck.

Yours etcetera

Cc Dr Twee Dampensquib
Flyboy Alltalk

Wednesday 22nd July 2020. I wrote the following letter to Lucy tonight: -
Wednesday Night 22nd July 2020
Lucy Lawless, The Queen of Heaven,

Dear Soulmate,

I was thirty years old when I first realised that my mother had been fighting to get me to have sex with her. In the ensuing days I wrote her two letters that I can still remember: one said, "Dear Mother, The human race has decided that it is necessary for you to remove yourself from this place". And the other said, "Dear Mother, I want you to know, before you go away, that you have given the world a truly spiritual man". Those were part of my attempts to drive her to suicide, seeing as that's what she had been doing to me. Now, forty-six years later, both of those points have been made, and it is time for her to go.

In the early 1960s, she said of her father, "He's in his second childhood". The old man disappeared soon after that. Now she is in her second childhood, and will soon disappear.

Even the BBC news is now carrying features highlighting "The End of an Era" and "The start of a New Era". And the passing over of a baton to the new Colonel-in-Chief.

Victory is so close that I can sense that I am winning this endgame. If she is still around when you receive this letter, speak to her again, and remember that you are talking to an old dead woman with the mind of an adolescent girl. She will surely commit suicide in the immediate future by turning herself into a duckling. I am making her cry by laughing at her pathetic attempts to be sexy, and I'm going to keep on making her cry until she duckifies herself. She is just as pathetic as my father's other wife, the one I killed, Iris. I never was sexually attracted to either of them. Doris Day's name is a combination of "Dorothy" and "Iris". Doris has had her day now.

Yours etcetera

Cc Dr Twee Dampensquib
Flyboy Alltalk

Saturday 25th July 2020. My army are proving themselves to me, and I am very proud of them. They are a large, loyal and reliable band of good men and women and with them behind me there is nothing in the field of human endeavour that I cannot achieve, starting with the six objectives that I wrote about in the previous chapter of this book. My followers know what they are, and they are happy to be soldiers in the army of the Lord, God's army. I can sense their cerebral activity, and they know my thoughts: I don't even have to speak them, let alone put them in writing.

Yesterday afternoon I gave them the order to put pressure on my late mother to duckify herself and to sustain the pressure until she does so, without giving her any respite, not even for a second. It is now 3.25 a.m., and they have kept up the pressure all yesterday evening and all night whilst I have been sleeping. We are shouting at the old girl to "GET OUT" and to "GET OUT NOW". She hasn't got any option but to obey us: the only thing in doubt is for how long she can withstand the pressure. I feel sure she will go today.

As well as my own freedom from hospital, I want to secure freedom for my friend, Flyboy Alltalk. He is a good chap and The Survival Party needs his money. He has promised hundreds of millions of pounds to The Survival Party, but at the moment neither Flyboy nor I have access to our cheque books because we are both mental patients! I have plans to spend the money on the expansion of The Party to go from nothing to a major political force in Great Britain and in the wider world within the next two years.

Monday 27th July 2020. I wrote the following letter to Lucy this morning: -
Monday Morning 27th July 2020
Lucy Lawless, The Queen of Heaven,

Dear Soulmate,

My patience finally snapped yesterday. I got fed up with pussyfooting around, so I gave my followers the instruction to get rid of Dolly before she gets rid of us! I don't know if we have been successful yet but I have tried searching for the old witch with my mind and I can't find her anywhere. My followers have got the instruction to grab hold of her wherever and whenever she dares to show her face again; to take her down the sewers and to ratify her. She has had plenty of chances to duckify herself if she would rather be a duck than a rat, but she hasn't done so, so, she only has herself to blame when she gets ratified.

She likes to think of herself as invincible, but she is no match for an angry mob of people. This is the logic of democracy. If her followers try to protect her then it is a battle between her followers and mine. The overwhelming majority of the adult population of the human race are my followers now. They know that I am the Lord God and they are happy "To labour and to ask for no reward, save that of knowing that they do MY will".

Keep smiling, Darling. It will all be over soon, for my late mother.

Yours etcetera

Cc Dr Twee Dampensquib
Flyboy Alltalk

Tuesday 28th July 2020. My followers nearly succeeded yesterday in ratifying the mad and decadent old witch. We invaded her place in the spirit world and took her down the sewers into the rats' nest. We were on the point of ratifying her when we were invaded by huge numbers of Dolly's followers. A battle ensued which they won.

So, it's back to square one for us. I am left with this question: what is wrong with people? Why are so many people still following the late Mrs Dorothy (Dolly) Ayres, when it is obvious that she is leading them down the road to extinction? They seem to have lost the ability to think for themselves. It seems that they are so used to letting Dolly do their thinking for them that they have lost their own reasoning powers. They can't tell a bad leader from a good one. It looks like they will discover their mistake too late for me, or anyone else, to save them from extinction. I repeat that Global Warming and Climate Change are not wasting time like the human race is. They are not hanging about.

Britons are complaining because their holiday plans have been disrupted by the government's decision to quarantine incoming aircraft passengers from Spain. Don't they realise there is a war on? It is a war against Climate Change, and it is one which the human race is losing because of these idiots thinking they can fly in jet planes without facing the consequences. And the Government hasn't got the guts to tell them that this is the real reason for their decision. THE WORLD'S ENVIRONMENT CANNOT SUSTAIN JET TRAVEL IN SUCH VOLUMES, PERIOD.

I have decided to try again at nine a.m. (UK Time) on Thursday morning 30th July, to ratify the mad and decadent old witch, and this time it won't just be a posse of enforcers I put on the job, but my whole army of people throughout the world. Then, if Dolly's followers try again to rescue her, they will have a real fight on their hands. It will be a fight between my army of decent men and women and Dolly's army of queers, freaks and motherfuckers: a battle for the soul of humanity itself. If that doesn't work then I will wait awhile until more of Dolly's followers cross over to my side as the need to combat Global Warming and Climate Change becomes more and more URGENT, and more and more people realise that I am right. I just hope that my army grows large enough in time for us to save the world from irreversible Climate Change.

Thursday 30th July 2020. It is now shortly after four a.m. and in just under five hours' time the battle for the survival of the human race will begin. I can sense some of my followers wanting to get on with it already, but I am saying to them, "Hold your horses. Don't jump the gun. I said it starts at nine a.m. and that's the way it will be. We must wait until the whole army is ready. Harold Godwin and his Saxons lost the battle of Hastings because his men thought they sensed victory too soon. We mustn't make the same mistake."

This is a battle between those who follow the Lord God versus those who follow the arch-demon Lucifer, because that is who my late mother, Mrs Dorothy (Dolly) Ayres, is. She really hates us for destroying her friend,

Pitchblack, the Devil Himself. He would have killed the whole human race if I hadn't stopped him. Now she wants to exact revenge by destroying the whole world and all living things in it unless I become her lover, which I refuse to be. Her followers have persecuted me all my life, and I hate her and all her followers and you must hate them too, for they will kill you if they can. Don't let them. Follow me and I will lead you to victory over the enemies of the human race, because that is who they are.

Be brave, my people, and be ready for nine o'clock this morning. The posse of enforcers will go in first, grab hold of Dolly and lead her down to the sewers where the rats' nest is. The rest of the army must clear the way for them and protect them while they do their work of ratifying Dolly. We will succeed in this endeavour for the sake of our children and all future generations of humanity. More than just our lives depend upon us. We must get rid of Dolly today, while there is still time to save the world from irreversible Climate Change. Otherwise it will be too late.

I hear you saying, my people, that I can rely on you. I'm sure you know that it is up to you to prove it. I am willing you to do so with all my heart. You should win this fight because God is on your side, and I am the Lord God, not my late mother, the arch-demon Lucifer. The hosts of Heaven are smiling on us because we will turn her into the rat she deserves to be.

Saturday 1st August 2020. I wrote the following letter to Lucy today, and sent it to her with a copy of the latest version of my Manifesto of The Survival Party, which I have had professionally printed into booklets: -
Saturday 1st August 2020

Lucy Lawless, The Queen of Heaven,

Dear Soulmate,

My followers and I were unable to ratify the old witch, so the battle to get rid of her has entered a new phase. I suggest that you and I both continue to harangue the old witch with all the invective that we can muster. Don't allow her a single day in which we don't make her feel shame, guilt and fear for being so inhuman to both of us, until she becomes glad to turn herself into an animal to get away from us. She might just as well be an animal seeing as she is being so inhuman to both of us. I don't really care what she becomes as long as she gets out of our road and stops being an intolerable sex pest because that is all she has ever been to me.

To think that the old frump actually thought she stood a chance with me is the height of ridiculousness. And she is so immature that she doesn't know when to take "NO" for an answer. One doesn't expect that from one's own parent. But seeing as that's the way things are, she can GO TO HELL and stay there forever as far as I'm concerned. I'm sure you feel the same way about her as I do. Incest is not just taboo, it is also a crime, and with good reason. I WILL NOT BREAK THAT TABOO. It is universal to all human communities. SHE is the inhuman one, so she might as well come back as an animal seeing as she rejects human values.

I will keep on in this vein until more and more of her followers think twice about their allegiance to her and come over to my side. As I wrote to her in the 1990s, "Dear Mother, Who do you think you are? You are not God. Everyone knows that God is a man and you are only a woman". She isn't even much of a woman. She is immature and inhuman as I have already explained. I'm sure that if we keep this up, we will win in the end. She is already on her last legs. I just hope we get rid of her in time for me to save the world from irreversible Climate Change. No one else seems to have any constructive policies for how we, the human race, can solve the problem and save the situation. Which confirms my belief that I am the man sent from Heaven to save the world from irreversible Climate Change.

Yours etcetera

Cc Dr Twee Dampensquib
Flyboy Alltalk

Monday 3rd August 2020. I wrote the following letter to Lucy this evening:
- Monday 3rd August 2020
Lucy Lawless, The Queen of Heaven,

Dear Soulmate,

My first-born son, Nicholas, died on the 28th December 1963. I believe from infanticide committed by his mother, my first wife. My third-born son, Christopher, was born on the 28th May 1967. My fourth-born son, Alexander, died from a drug overdose on the 28th August 2004. More recently, it was in the news last week that P.C. Andrew Harper was twenty-eight years old when he was murdered most horrifically. He had been married for just twenty-eight days when he was killed. All these signs point to 28 being an inauspicious (unlucky) number, but I know from past experience that one cannot predict the future from coincidental signs, however strong they seem.

I go by the following science: - In 2017, three years ago, the world's scientists agreed that we have got just twelve years before Climate Change becomes irreversible. Since then, Global Warming has accelerated this figure by a whole year, caused by the forest fires in the rainforests of the Amazon, Indonesia, Malaysia and the Arctic Circle. Giving us a date of 2028 when the worst will happen unless we get worldwide carbon emissions down to zero by the end of 2027. Thus, both the science and the fortuitous signs confirm the date of 2028 when Climate Change becomes irreversible.

That's why I'm so sure that we must get worldwide carbon emissions down to zero by the end of 2027. Which gives us seven years and just under five months from now. This would be an impossible task for anyone other than me, with the influence I will possess and wield when Dolly disappears. That's another very good reason why I say she MUST GO and GO SOON. The first reason, of course, being our freedom to become the lovers that we both dream of being.

It will take me a good two years to get The Survival Party into power and another five years to get worldwide carbon emissions down to zero. So, that gives me less than five months to get out of hospital and clear my name. AND to get Flyboy out of hospital as well, seeing as The Survival Party needs Flyboy's money.

This should all be possible with cooperation from Dr Twee Dampensquib and the late Mrs Dorothy Ayres. I obviously want her to have words in the right ears before she takes herself off. I'll forgive her followers and let bygones be bygones when they have made amends to me and my Party for seventy-six years of persecution, just for being who I am and for not wanting sex with my mother. I still say I was right to uphold the taboo against incest, quite apart from the fact that I never fancied the old frump.

Yours etcetera

Cc Dr Twee Dampensquib
Flyboy Alltalk

Wednesday 5th August 2020. I wrote the following letter to Lucy in the small hours of this morning: - Wednesday Morning 5th August 2020

Lucy Lawless, The Queen of Heaven,

Dear Soulmate,

I cannot register the name of The Survival Party of Great Britain with the Electoral Commission of the UK until I am a free man, and I cannot even open a bank account in the name of The Survival Party until I am free. With less than seven and a half years to get worldwide carbon emissions down to zero, I must implore my late mother to overcome her fears and come back to life immediately, in the name of the survival of all life on Earth. Whatever she chooses to come back as.

I also implore this of her in the name of our common humanity, to give me the opportunity to marry the woman I love, and whom I am one hundred per cent sure is the most wonderful woman in the human race. She is the woman WHOSE LOVE I CAN FEEL TELEPATHICALLY and for whom I have been waiting and fighting for, for nearly twenty years now and she is the woman who was recommended to me by Aphrodite Herself, the Goddess of Love and by all the hosts of Heaven. I am, of course, talking about YOU, my Queen.

Twee Dampensquib tells me that he shares my letters with the team treating me. I have had one hundred copies of my Manifesto printed as booklets and I will gladly give a copy to any member of the team who asks me for one. I hope some of them will be interested to know the policies that I wish to pursue when I come to power.

Yours etcetera

Cc Dr Twee Dampensquib
Flyboy Alltalk

Thursday 13th August 2020. I wrote the following letter to Lucy today: - Thursday 13th August 2020
Lucy Lawless, The Queen of Heaven,

Dear Soulmate,

I haven't written for over a week because I have been waiting, and hoping, to have some positive news for you concerning the fate of my late mother, but no such luck so far. It has been a week of scorching temperatures by day and by night in the UK, rumbles of thunder, lightning flashes, torrential rain and flash floods all over the country. These are all signs that the old girl is putting up a fight, but everybody knows that she is going to lose before long. The headline on the back page of today's SUN read "SHUT THAT DOOR"!

We have come a long way in recent years, but whether we have come far enough soon enough remains to be seen. All we can do is to keep on trying our hardest in the name of our love and in the name of the human race and all other living things, to get rid of the last remaining trace of Satan, namely his accomplice, Lucifer, the enemy of God and therefore the enemy of the human race, Mrs Dorothy Ayres.

She always maintained that she was on the side of the survival of the human race, but she was a wolf in sheep's clothing. This is now apparent to everybody with a grain of grey matter between their ears. Her desire for my cock took priority with her over the survival of all life on Earth, and everybody knows it now. She is more mad than Hitler was. And more dangerous. Thanks to you, I have been able to expose her iniquity. Everybody must continue this fight until we TAKE CONTROL from the mad and decadent old witch. As I said, she is not giving up without a fight.

Yours etcetera

Cc Dr Twee Dampensquib
Flyboy Alltalk

Friday 14th August 2020. I wrote the following letter to Lucy this evening:
- Friday 14th August 2020

Lucy Lawless, the Queen of Heaven,

Dear Soulmate,

The only hope that the world has got is if Dolly, herself, realises that I am right when I say that Climate Change will become irreversible in 2028, with catastrophic consequences for all life on Earth, unless we, the human race, cut our carbon emissions down to zero by the end of 2027. The only way this can happen is if I get the freedom and the power and the influence that I will acquire when she comes back to life, whatever she chooses to come back as. It is not her time to come back as a person again.

There is nothing else I can say about the future. It is all up to Dolly now, to come back in the immediate future. We have only got just over seven years to get worldwide carbon emissions down to zero. I think Dolly will agree with me and come back soon, probably as a duck. Then I will get my own way in the world, starting with Dampensquib taking me off these filthy drugs and writing me the public apology that I want from the Royal College of Psychiatrists. This will help me to clear my name after a retrial. I also demand enough money from British Society to build The Survival Party into the dominant political Party in Great Britain within two years, with the policies I have outlined in my Manifesto. I expect my freedom from hospital soon after Dolly disappears, with an absolute and unconditional discharge.

We won't just have our freedom. We will also have the recognition of all the real adults in the world as the Emperor and Empress of the world, whatever our overt status may be. We will have to talk about who we are seen to be, but everyone knows who we really are. The free world is an Empire of democracies, and people like democracy. They like the freedom to choose their leaders, and every leader only has power by the will of the people. I will be happy to be Prime Minister of Great Britain if the British people vote me in. I want to give them that chance.

Yours etcetera

Cc Dr Twee Dampensquib
Flyboy Alltalk

Monday 17th August 2020. I wrote the following letter to Lucy today: - Monday 17th August 2020

Lucy Lawless, The Queen of Heaven,

Dear Soulmate,

Destiny is a stronger force than the will of Mrs Dorothy (Dolly) Ayres. Before you or I or Dolly were born, I, as God, instructed the fates to weave Dolly's demise into the fabric of destiny. Once woven, the pattern of the fabric cannot be altered. We agreed that when, and only when, you and I have both been tested to our limits as the Emperor and Empress of Heaven and Earth, and our love has also been thoroughly tested, Dolly would come back as a duck. It will soon be twenty-one years since I first started courting you. The love you have given me makes everything worthwhile.

Dolly did us a favour by making us fight her to the finish: because in doing so, we got everybody on our side and tuned in to our thoughts. Dolly doesn't mind if everyone hates her because she knew that that would not matter when she is a duck. I can just see her leading her flock of mallards over the North Sea to the Arctic Circle for summer. Ducks like the cool weather for mating.

Our destiny is to spend the next thirty-three happy years together on Earth and then for me to rule in Heaven for the next two thousand years or so, knowing that one day, if we ever want to live again, we must face the future with courage and fortitude whatever it may bring. Our job is to look after the human race, and to see that they get the leadership they need and will continue to need long after we are both dead.

I have high hopes for Troy, but I do not know yet who his successor will be. That will form part of Troy's story.

Dolly's race is nearly run now. She has only got hours to carry on, (I won't say "to live" seeing as she has been dead for fourteen years, but now, even her afterlife is coming to an end). This letter is Dolly's denouement, seeing as she can't write her final scene for herself. When, and only when, she is a duck, she will have earned my love and proved worthy of it.

All our trials are over now.

Yours etcetera

Cc Dr Twee Dampensquib
Flyboy Alltalk

Saturday 22nd August 2020. I wrote the following letter to Lucy this evening: - Saturday Night 22nd August 2020

Lucy Lawless, The Queen of Heaven,

Dear Soulmate,

What happened last summer in Australia and is happening NOW in California is the thin end of the wedge of Climate Change. It will start to become irreversible in eight years' time unless I am freed immediately to carry out the policies I have outlined in my Manifesto. By prolonging the agony of her existence, my late mother is blackmailing HER OWN FOLLOWERS with a death threat from irreversible Climate Change unless I become her lover, which she knows I never will. She is actively trying to lose her own following by getting all her followers to join MY side in this civil war. She is doing me this favour because she knows they can't hurt her when she is a duck, however much they hate her, and that I am the best person to look after them. That is her objective – to see her people are looked after when she is gone. She is being my best friend by being my worst enemy! I think she'll be gone very soon now. She has had a very good innings!

I really love you, Lucy Lawless. No one else has ever made me feel so well loved, understood and appreciated. I'm so looking forward to us getting to know each other personally, which I'm sure we will before long, now.

All our trials are over now.
Yours etcetera

Cc Dr Twee Dampensquib
Flyboy Alltalk

Monday 24th August 2020. I wrote the following letter to Lucy this evening:
- Monday Evening 24th August 2020
Lucy Lawless, The Queen of Heaven,

Dear Soulmate,
Climate Change has colossal momentum. It is like an enormous juggernaut; you have to apply the brakes early for it to stop in time. It will become irreversible in eight years' time, with catastrophic consequences for all life on Earth, unless I am freed to apply the brakes in the immediate future by following the policies which I have outlined in my Manifesto.

My late mother insists that I become her lover, but I refuse. I insist that she comes back to life as an animal in the immediate future, presumably a duck, and hands over to me all her power and influence, but she refuses. What happens when the irresistible force meets the immovable object? Something has to give. This battle of wills between my late mother and me has turned into a game of "chicken" with the fate of the world at stake, depending on who blinks first, and I am not going to blink. I would sooner see the end of the world than betray you by being unfaithful, especially with *her*.

My lamp still shines on your picture on my wall 24/7 as it has done for years now. I hope that knowing this protects your spirit. I'm sorry if I have let you down in the sexual arena. We have come together many times, but the last two times I have tried and failed to achieve orgasm. It really is the fault of the injections of paliperidone and the intransigent attitude of the evil doctor who forces me to take it. The testosterone supplementation would work fine otherwise. I do not have mercy on the souls of doctors who force people to take antipsychotic drugs. That is an inhuman thing to do to anybody, so I make them forfeit their humanity in their next lives. I have told them many times that I am God and they still say that I am deluded. We will find out who is deluded when their precious Mrs Dorothy Ayres comes back as a duck. All the shrinks come back as feral rats. I am the Master of all souls, as I am proving.

All our trials are over now.

Yours etcetera

Cc Dr Twee Dampensquib
Flyboy Alltalk

Wednesday 26th August 2020. I wrote the following letter to Lucy this evening: - Wednesday Night 26th August 2020

Lucy Lawless, The Queen of Heaven,

Dear Soulmate,

There have been weeks of drought this year in the UK and periods of torrential rain. This has meant, among other things, that the wheat yield of the farmers is down by forty per cent, and the scientists say that this is the new normal because of Climate Change. This has meant a rise in the cost of bread which has obviously affected poorer people the hardest. Our main hope is that Dolly's followers realise for themselves that she is leading them on the path to extinction, and come over to our side in this civil war between us and the late Mrs Dorothy Ayres. The rise in the cost of bread is HER FAULT for keeping me her prisoner all this time, when I am the only man with a realistic plan to avert the disaster of irreversible Climate Change. It is our best hope that enough of her followers switch sides in time to avert disaster by telling her to come back as a duck and to GET ON WITH IT. The more Climate Change affects people the stronger our cause becomes, and the more followers we have on our side. Climate Change is increasing exponentially.

We came together most beautifully at four a.m. this morning, Darling. Thank you for your love. It is always good to know it is still there. I repeat, I will never betray your love whatever happens.

I noticed from my bank statement that the letter of credit I sent you was not credited to you by your bank. We will have to wait until I am free before I can send you a cheque which will be accepted by the banks. Sorry about that, but we have to put up with the behaviour of the clowns for the time being.

Keep smiling and rest assured that we still love each other. I'm not sending anyone a copy of this letter, but it will get published in the fullness of time, in *My Journey Back – Part Four.*

Our trials are not over yet!

Yours etcetera

Saturday 29th August 2020. I wrote the following letter to Lucy this evening: - Saturday Night 29th August 2020

Lucy Lawless, The Queen of Heaven,

Dear Soulmate,

I will restate my position clearly as follows: - I will never have mental sex with my late mother, Mrs Dorothy (Dolly) Ayres, under any circumstances, not even to prevent the end of the world.

As I see it, this leaves Dolly with two choices:

1) She can give me a chance to save the world from irreversible Climate Change by coming back to life as an animal, presumably a duck, in the immediate future.

2) She can continue prolonging the agony of her afterlife indefinitely, making it certain that Climate Change will become irreversible in the foreseeable future, with catastrophic consequences for all life on Earth.

We will soon see which option she chooses.

I can tell from the increase in cerebral activity that I can sense, that many more people are taking notice of my writing and are supporting our cause in this civil war between us and my late mother. The overwhelming majority of the adult population of the world are shouting at Dolly to come back as a duck and to GET ON WITH IT and STOP WASTING TIME. We have no time to lose.

There are still lots of idiots on the BBC who use the words "Area", and its plural "Areas" as if they still have confidence in Mrs Ayres. But Dolly herself does not have that confidence. I can sense that her mind is confused, bewildered and upset. She doesn't know what to do, but she cannot refute my logic. She knows, deep down, that she has already lost. She just has to muster up the courage to duckify herself, knowing that this will be an irreversible act once she has done it.

The idiots on the BBC are unaware that they are not only committing suicide by encouraging Dolly to hang about, wasting time, but they are dragging everybody else down with them. The BBC are batting on the losing side, as are the establishment such as the Meteorological Office, the psychiatric profession and the legal profession in the UK. But the tabloid press are all on our side now, as are the vast majority of ordinary men and women. More and more people are coming over to our side as Climate Change makes them more acutely aware of the situation.

Dolly's followers are swimming against the tide of public opinion, and the tide is getting stronger all the time. We can only pray that this situation is resolved in time for me to save the world. If it is then it will be a darn close-run thing; if it isn't then it WILL be the end of the world. It is all in Dolly's hands now.

Yours etcetera

Cc Dr Twee Dampensquib

Wednesday 2nd September 2020. I wrote the following letter to Lucy this morning: - Wednesday 2nd September 2020

Lucy Lawless, The Queen of Heaven,

Dear Soulmate,

Just a line to keep in touch.

We haven't won yet but we are winning this civil war between us and Mrs Dorothy Ayres. The BBC have got rid of their Director General, and with him goes their loyalty to Mrs Ayres. No one on the BBC now uses the words "Area" and "Areas" and even the weather presenters, who work for the Meteorological Office, don't use those words any more. In their latest broadcast the man spoke of a weather system knocking on the door of certain parts of the country. His choice of words tells me that even Dolly's staunchest supporters are turning against her now, which must mean they are now on OUR side. I only have one serious rival. His name is Oliver, but I don't consider him a threat to me. I am happy to be his friend if he wants to be. I hope the weather presenters prove that they are now on our side by using the words "Region" and "Regions" instead of "Area" and "Areas". It's not what they say but the way that they say it that matters.

People know that I have now proven beyond doubt that I am God-the-Father and they are flocking to our side in their droves. I hope that Twee Dampensquib joins this movement before Sunday as I am due for another injection on that day, and I really am looking forward to coming off the medication. It has other horrible effects as well as the loss of my sex drive, such as itchy skin, a loss of my sense of balance, and shaking of the hands and arms (known as tardive dyskinesia). There is no excuse for him to keep me on the drugs any longer, only his intransigent attitude.

I repeat that we are winning this war. Dolly will be a duck before long. All she is waiting for is to muster up the courage to duckify herself. I just hope and pray that we win the war in time for me to save the world from irreversible Climate Change. The Extinction Rebellion people are doing a sterling job in raising people's awareness of the urgent need to combat Climate Change, but as far as I know, I am the only man with political ambitions who has a realistic plan to avert disaster.

Our trials are not over yet!

Yours etcetera

Cc Dr Twee Dampensquib

Friday 4th September 2020-. I wrote the following letter to Lucy this morning: - Friday Morning 4th September 2020

Lucy Lawless, The Queen of Heaven,

Dear Soulmate,

A lot of Dolly's followers refuse to admit that they were wrong to follow her. The weather presenters on the BBC have reverted to using the words "Area" and "Areas" in their weather reports, as have a lot of other people on the BBC. These people must WANT to bring about the end of the world from irreversible Climate Change. There is no other reason for their behaviour except for crass stupidity.

I expect that I will receive another injection of paliperidone on Sunday.

Dampensquib's intransigent attitude is not born of reason, so it must be born of fear. He must be shit scared of my late mother. If only he knew what is going on in my mind, he would be even more scared of ME. Dolly is using the drugs to punish me for scorning her. Hell hath no fury like a woman scorned!

We came together most beautifully yesterday afternoon. Thank you, Darling. I can tell that my letters have made you ever so happy and that is what makes me ever so happy, which proves that I really love you.

Dolly herself doesn't know what to do for the best so she is procrastinating, trying to think of some new trial for either or both of us. She is finding it hard to accept the truth that she really has come to the end of her road now and she must now find the courage to duckify herself. I have already had a long "goodbye" with her. It has all been said and done now, and she is just wasting my precious time. Procrastination is the thief of time. I repeat that we have no time to lose. On Monday morning I had a trial of strength, mental strength, with Dolly, which I won. The Daily Mirror on that day carried a headline "THE BIGGEST TEST YET". Anyone who thinks that that was my biggest test underestimates the trials of strength that I went through with Pitchblack (the Devil Himself) between 1984 and 2014. They constituted thirty years of fighting not only for my own life but for the lives of everybody else in the world!

Our trials are not over yet!

Yours etcetera

Cc Dr Twee Dampensquib

Sunday 6th September 2020. I wrote the following letter to Lucy today: -
Sunday 6th September 2020
Lucy Lawless, The Queen of Heaven,

Dear Soulmate,

The monkeys are going to inject me again this afternoon with paliperidone. I don't blame the monkeys: they are only dancing to the tune of their organ grinder, Twee Dampensquib, who in turn, is having his strings pulled by the obnoxious old witch that I have for a mother, the late Mrs Dorothy (Dolly) Ayres.

Dolly has taught me a very valuable lesson, which is that the fear of fear can be a more potent weapon than a very real fear such as that of irreversible Climate Change. She has never had anything other than the fear of fear to hit people with, but she used it to get rid of her rival, Iris, by my hand. She tried, in her early days, to push Iris under a bus; but she failed. She only succeeded in killing Iris by getting her followers to bully me into doing the job for her.

A fight to the finish is a fight to the finish. That is what Dolly has asked for and it is what we must give her. Our trials won't be over until Dolly's soul inhabits the body of the embryo of a duckling. Nature will do the rest. She will then inevitably become a duck in the fullness of time. The fight for life will prevail and she will forget all about her previous life, including me.

Timing is important. I think that by next summer in the Northern Hemisphere, we will both be free to have a holiday together. I suggest a cruise around the Norwegian fjords. The scenery there is staggeringly beautiful.

Our trials are not over yet!
    Yours etcetera

    Cc Dr Twee Dampensquib

Chapter 14

The Endgame? No, Just Brinkmanship

Events and Thoughts from Thursday 10th September 2020.

Thursday 10th September 2020. I wrote the following letter to Lucy this afternoon: - Thursday 10th September 2020

Lucy Lawless, The Queen of Heaven,

Dear Soulmate,

Sir David Attenborough has organised a "Climate Assembly" of British citizens and has collated their views on how to make the UK carbon neutral by the year 2050. They have put their views in a report which will be presented to the British Government, and hopefully made law. Whilst this is sterling work by Sir David, their plan does far too little, far too late to avert the disaster of irreversible Climate Change. My decisions on Climate Change, Brexit and Northern Ireland are all in my Manifesto. They will solve all the problems about which the British Government is currently getting its knickers in a twist. My plans on all three of these issues are the only realistic plans, especially the need to avert the disaster of irreversible Climate Change, which will hit the whole world in eight years' time unless people do as I say.

Meanwhile I'm still stuck in the loony bin with no hope of getting out unless my late mother comes back to life, whatever she chooses to come back as. Her state of mind is in a tiswas. She doesn't know whether she is coming or going. She doesn't know what she is any longer, nor what to do. I have proven her wrong in all the main thoughts by which she dominated the world, and she is finding it impossible to come to terms with this. She is not who nor what she thought she was and I have proven this. I blame her followers for only adding to her misery by propping up her crumbling mind by using the words "Area" and "Areas". She is still playing "chicken" with me, not realising that she has already lost. If she doesn't duckify herself very soon it will be too late for me, or anyone else, to save the world from the disaster of irreversible Climate Change.

We came together in spite of the paliperidone on Monday and again today. Both times were absolutely wonderful, Darling. Thank you. I don't know if this letter will reach you because of the fires in California where your fan club is. For all I know Glendale has been burned to the ground. Los Angeles has been evacuated and hundreds of thousands of people have lost their homes to the fires. Yet still, Donald Trump denies Climate Change! California has never had it so bad. Trump will change his tune when the whole world goes the way of California, but of course it will be too late by then.

Our trials are not over yet!

Take care of yourself, my Love, I have much more to say to you, but it can wait until we talk, Bless you, my Queen,

Yours with Love, Affection and Friendship,

The King of Heaven,
Bob XX
Cc Dr Twee Dampensquib

Saturday 12th September 2020. I wrote the following letter to Lucy today. I feel sure it will reach its target audience of the British Establishment: - Saturday 12th September 2020

Lucy Lawless, The Queen of Heaven,

Dear Soulmate,

I define the Free World as Dolly's Empire. It consists of all the countries which have legalised same-sex sexual relationships over the last sixty years; almost all of them, if not all of them, being democracies. These are the countries which will constitute OUR Empire when we have got rid of Dolly's soul. Great Britain is the hub of this Empire, and Dolly is the leader of the ruling oligarchy of the British Establishment who are still, largely, on her side in this civil war.

I define the British Establishment as the heads of all the professions such as the legal profession and the medical profession (including the psychiatric profession), the heads of the broadcasters such as the BBC and

ITV, the bosses of the Meteorological Office, the leaders of the armed forces and the clergy, as well as the Aristocracy including the UK Royal Family.

Unless this ruling oligarchy switches sides in the immediate future by joining US and opposing the late Mrs Dorothy Ayres then there is no future for the whole world. They must accept that I am the Almighty One, not my late mother, and agree to obey MY WILL in all matters of importance, otherwise it will be the end of the world from irreversible Climate Change in the foreseeable future. Dolly is NOT going to get her own way. MY WILL is stronger than hers, as I am now proving. Sir David Attenborough and his little assembly of one hundred well-meaning but naïve souls have come up with a plan, but it falls far short of what is required to prevent irreversible Climate Change which will hit the world in eight years' time. MY PLAN, as outlined in my Manifesto, is the only realistic plan to avert disaster. Unless the whole world follows my plan, then the whole world is going to go the same way as California in the foreseeable future.

I think that the only thing Dolly has been waiting for is for me to get the Establishment on our side before she duckifies herself. If they don't join us in the immediate future then it will be too late for everybody. Everybody, including the ruling oligarchy of the British Establishment must shout at her to GET ON WITH IT and STOP WASTING OUR PRECIOUS TIME. Then, when she has gone, they must help me with my plan to clear my name, get my compensation and get my Party, THE SURVIVAL PARTY, into political power in Great Britain over the next two years.

Our trials are not over yet!

Yours etcetera

Cc Dr Twee Dampensquib
Flyboy Alltalk

Thursday 17th September 2020. I wrote the following letter to Lucy today:
- Thursday 17th September 2020
    Lucy Lawless, The Queen of Heaven,

Dear Soulmate,

I can only pray that this letter and my recent letters will have reached you despite the fires in California where your fan club is. The smoke from the California fires now covers the whole of the USA, and that isn't the only thing the Yanks have got to worry about; hurricane Sally has hit the Gulf Coast with catastrophic results, and there are more tropical storms queueing up to hit America. And still Donald Trump denies Climate Change is the cause of these freak weather systems! I repeat that I am the Lord God and this weather is my punishment of the human race for defying MY WILL by condoning same-sex sexual relationships. I have been warning people for years that I will punish them but they haven't heeded my warnings so now they must pay the price. I told them that the whole world will go the same way as the cities of Sodom and Gomorrah as recounted in the Bible.

The news on the TV spoke of the devastating effects of the weather on the worst hit areas, and even the protected areas of the Amazon rainforest in Brazil have been devastated by fires. Dorothy Ayres only has herself to blame, for encouraging the "permissive society", which is taking the easy road by condoning decadence disguised as diversity. A spiritual leader should have more moral courage. She should accept responsibility and do the only decent thing she can do which is to take herself out of the picture by duckifying herself, NOW. The longer she hangs about, the worse her situation will get.

Climate Change has two causes – one is practical and the other is moral. To rectify one without rectifying the other is like trying to dry yourself with a fresh towel whilst still standing under a running shower. My Manifesto deals with both causes of Climate Change and is the only realistic plan on offer to avert the impending catastrophe, but I can't get on with it until I am free to do so, and that won't happen until Dolly duckifies herself. When she does that, I will go from the bottom of society to the top overnight!

Our trials are not over yet!

Yours etcetera

Cc Dr Twee Dampensquib
Flyboy Alltalk

Monday 21st September 2020. I wrote the following letters to Twee Dampensquib and Lucy today. As you will read, this is the end of the endgame in our fight to the finish with my late mother.

Monday 21st September 2020

Dr Twee Dampensquib,
Medical Director,
Alcatraz Island Hospital.

Dear Twee,

It is now 3.12 in the morning and my late mother, Mrs Dorothy Ayres, has now slipped out of the human race. Her soul now inhabits the body of the embryo of a duckling. I am therefore now the Emperor of the Free World.

I intend to use this power to safeguard the life of every living thing by saving the planet from irreversible Climate Change. I am going to make everybody aware that this will happen in the year 2028 unless we, the human race, cut worldwide carbon emissions to zero by the end of the year 2027. I can best achieve this ambition by fighting to become the Prime Minister of the UK as soon as possible. To embark upon a career in politics I will first need to clear my name, and you can help me do this by getting the Royal College of Psychiatrists to give me the public apology that I am demanding.

I am therefore now writing to demand of you four things immediately:

-

1. You take me off all antipsychotic medication without further delay.

2. You prepare the public apology that I want and submit it to me in writing for my approval. I want the apology to state that the psychiatric profession now accepts that I am not mentally ill and never have been mentally ill; that I have been misdiagnosed, misjudged and mistreated ever since 17th July 1976; and that the Royal College apologises to me for forty-four years of unjust detainment during which time I have lost my family life including the love and respect of my sons, my career, my house, and my status in society; that the Royal College apologises to me for forty-three years of cruelty and abuse by forcing me to take injections of antipsychotic drugs which have horrible effects when there has never been anything wrong with me; and that the only reason why I have been treated this way for all this time is because I have always refused to have sex with my late mother, Mrs Dorothy Ayres; and that the Royal College apologises to me for stigmatising me with insulting and untrue epithets such as "mental illness", "paranoid schizophrenia", "grandiose delusions" and "a delusional disorder".

3.   You write to the Ministry of Justice, recommending an absolute and unconditional discharge for me and to take me off my criminal sections 37 and 41 immediately.

4.   You recommend to the Royal College of Psychiatrists the immediate payment of £$x+y$; this being £x for forty-four years of unjust detainment and loss of income plus £y for forty-three years of torture by antipsychotic drugs when there has never been anything wrong with me. This is a first instalment of my compensation demand; the balance of which I intend to get from the British government, on behalf of British society for driving me to homicide. I intend to demand a payment of £z when I get a verdict of "Justifiable Homicide by reason of Self-Defence against undue social pressure" after a retrial of my case.

Now that I have proven that I am indeed the Lord God by disposing of the soul of my late mother, Mrs Dorothy Ayres, I wish to say that I will have mercy on the souls of dead psychiatrists when, and only when, the above compensation demand has been paid in full and without delay; and also, when I am satisfied with the public apology.

Yours sincerely,

Robert Strong.
Cc Paul Rees, Chief Executive of the Royal College of Psychiatrists
Lucy Lawless.

The following is my letter to Lucy which I wrote this afternoon: - Monday 21st September 2020
Lucy Lawless, The Queen of Heaven,

Dear Soulmate,
This time I AM SURE THAT OUR VICTORY OVER DOLLY HAS NOW BEEN ACCOMPLISHED. I was pretty sure when I started the enclosed letter to Twee Dampensquib as I had personally guided her soul into a sperm cell of a copulating drake, then I saw the headline in today's Daily Mirror which said that "A TIPPING POINT HAS NOW BEEN REACHED", then over lunch a man on the TV said that "WE HAVE NOW TURNED THE CORNER". Both of these statements were ostensibly about the coronavirus pandemic, but their meaning in terms of our fight with Dolly was quite clear. WE HAVE DONE IT, DARLING!

I have given up on Flyboy Alltalk. I don't believe he has any vast sums of money. All he has got is a vast amount of bullshit. He hasn't got any guts either; he chickened out of the job of Party Treasurer by refusing to let me circulate copies of the Manifesto with his name on them. I printed one hundred copies of that Manifesto but the effort and the money were wasted, so I have sacked him. I have re-written sections of the Manifesto which did not meet with widespread approval; particularly the sections on punishment. People don't approve of using the whip on offenders, so I have substituted severe prison sentences for knife offenders and drug dealers. I have also re-written the introductory paragraph. I'll send you a copy of the new version when it has been printed.

I am very optimistic about our future and the future of The Survival Party.

Our trials are nearly over now!

Yours etcetera

Cc Dr Twee Dampensquib

Friday 25th September 2020. I wrote the following letter to Lucy this morning: - Friday Morning 25th September 2020

Lucy Lawless, The Queen of Heaven,

Dear Soulmate,

As you were. Dolly has wrong-footed me yet again. She hasn't gone yet, but she will be going soon. It is now three thirty a.m. and I have just had words with her. I said to her, "Mother, if you are going to prove you love me by coming back to life and thereby giving me the world, then please get on with it and stop teasing me. Lucy and I deserve the chance to make something of our lives, and only you can give us that chance. I have big plans for the world but I can't get on with them whilst you are still around in the spirit world. Please come back to life soon whatever you choose to come back as. I will be seventy-seven years old in just over a month's time; don't you think I have earned my freedom? Only you can set me free, and I will be eternally grateful to your memory if you do so. I wish you all the best in your next life, whatever you choose to come back as. Take care of yourself. Love, Bob XX."

I think Dolly will set us free soon, my Love. She has had a very good innings, and she is a good sport really.

I don't think I need to write to Twee Dampensquib again. The demands which I made of him in my letter of Monday 21st September will still apply when Dolly does go for real.

Our trials are nearly over now!

Yours etcetera

Cc Dr Twee Dampensquib

Saturday 26th September 2020. I wrote the following letter to Lucy today: -
Saturday Evening 26th September 2020

Lucy Lawless, The Queen of Heaven,

Dear Soulmate,

I must admit that I get pleasure from listening to the fear in the voices of Dolly's followers as the hour of her demise draws ever closer. Dolly's demise must be the worst thing that they can imagine. But they are idiots. They are cretins and they always have been to follow a weak leader like Dolly Ayres. They should be much more afraid of Dolly's continued existence than of her demise, because the longer she exists the closer the world gets to extinction from irreversible Climate Change.

This is because the longer Dolly exists the longer I will be kept a prisoner in a mental hospital, when I am the man, whose leadership is NEEDED by Great Britain and the rest of the world to avert the impending catastrophe. MY plan to avert irreversible Climate Change, as outlined in my Manifesto, is the best chance that the world has got. I haven't heard of one as good, let alone better, put forward by anyone else. And the world needs a man with my courage, ambition, initiative, determination, maturity and strength of spirit to carry out this plan.

We can still come together after a fashion, despite the paliperidone, when I masturbate over you, like we did this afternoon. It is always absolutely wonderful when I can feel you coming with me. Thank you, Darling. I won't need to masturbate when I come off the paliperidone. Then we can dance properly. Let us hope and pray that Dolly is as good a sport as I think she is. Then we won't have much longer to wait.

Our trials are nearly over now!

Yours etcetera

Tuesday 29th September 2020. I wrote the following letter to Lucy this morning: - Tuesday Morning 29th September 2020

Lucy Lawless, The Queen of Heaven,

Dear Soulmate,

In the late 1940s there was a popular song which had the refrain, "Open the door, Richard". This was an instruction to Edward Richard Pitchblack, the Devil Himself, (aka Richard) to have mental sex with my late mother, Dorothy. He opened the door, and ever since then Dorothy has been in cahoots with Satan. Would society have exalted Dorothy so highly if they had known that her secret lover was the Devil Himself? The answer is YES. It was all a part of their colossal joke to conspire to make a motherfucker out of me.

In 1970 I was happily in love with Jasmin 2 when Dolly got her friend, Satan, to take spiritual possession of Jasmin's mind. He did this in April of that year by a combination of hypnosis and telepathy which I call hypnopathy. He got Jasmin to believe the lie that I didn't really love her but only wanted her for her body. Dolly went along with the conspiracy to make a motherfucker out of me and she was as jealous as Hell of Jasmin because I obviously loved Jasmin more than her.

Satan's intervention spoiled my happiness with Jasmin 2 and when I realised what had been going on, I never forgave Dolly nor Pitchblack for that. For being such a dirty fighter, Dolly deserves to forfeit her humanity, so I have no compunction in turning her into an animal. It is what she deserves.

Dolly's relationship with Pitchblack was a very dangerous game for society to play. If it wasn't for my strength of mind and spirit it would have resulted in the end of the human race and Pitchblack's creatures, the locusts, would now be the dominant life form on the planet. The locusts have always resented humanity's dominance of the world and this was their plan to take over from us. It would have worked if it hadn't been for me, and all the thanks people have given me is to have people on the TV rub the word "AREAS" in my face – the ungrateful, undeserving bastards – It is going to be a long time before I forgive Society, even though I love them really, which is just as well, for them. I love them like my own children and I know that you do too, even though they are wicked beyond belief.

The consequences of Dolly's relationship with Satan are not over yet. They may yet result in the end of the world from irreversible Climate Change if Dolly doesn't go soon, like immediately. Now that she has been caught out it is time the crowd booed her off the pitch for being such a lousy sport.

Our trials are nearly over now!

Yours etcetera

Cc Dr Twee Dampensquib

Saturday 3rd October 2020. I wrote the following letter to Lucy this evening:
- Saturday Evening 3rd October 2020

Lucy Lawless, The Queen of Heaven,

Dear Soulmate,

I said I'd send you a copy of my latest Manifesto, so here it is. I still believe that the policies outlined in it are humanity's best chance of survival, but there is no guarantee: Dolly has already left it too late for that. The sooner we apply the brakes to Climate Change by cutting carbon emissions, the more chance we have got of stopping it in time. It is up to Dolly how much time we get.

I can sense by the amount of cerebral activity that nearly all the English-speaking members of the world's telepathic community are on our side. The idiots who aren't all use the words "Area" and "Areas" for all they are worth on the BBC especially the weather presenters. They hammer those words so much that they are giving away their sense of desperation. I can get a much truer picture of the situation from the weather here in the UK. We have been having one storm after another with torrential rain and very STRONG winds. This tells me that Dolly herself is desperate. I can apply more pressure than she can take by the words I write in these letters to you. I think we will win before my next birthday on November 5th. We could win any day now, that is what the cerebral activity tells me. To continue the cricketing metaphor; the crowd are now booing her off the pitch for not going willingly now that she has been caught out. She is proving to be a rotten sport, but the crowd have ways of dealing with the likes of *them*. I have confidence in our followers.

I can sense your sexual frustration and the strength of your desire for me. If it wasn't for the paliperidone I'd be able to satisfy you without any problems, but as it is I'm just as frustrated as you are, Darling. We must both have superhuman patience and understanding. Dampensquib's intransigent attitude is unreasonable and unpleasant. It is also very foolish of him because it incurs in me a grudge against him which makes me determined for revenge. I will get my own back on all these blasted shrinks for their antipsychotic drugs when there has never been anything wrong with me. As it says in the Bible, "'Vengeance is mine,' sayeth the Lord". I get mistreated whenever I come to life and I always get my revenge in the end.

Our trials are nearly over now!

Yours etcetera

Cc Dr Twee Dampensquib

Wednesday 7th October 2020. I wrote the following letter to Lucy today: -

Wednesday 7th October 2020

Lucy Lawless, The Queen of Heaven,

Dear Soulmate,

The monkeys injected me with paliperidone again yesterday. I spoke to them about it and found out that they have been conned into believing that they are actually doing me some good by subjecting me to this cruelty and abuse. The whole system stinks with the acrid smell of the evil old witch that I have for a mother.

I have felt your love all morning and I can feel it now as I write this. I cannot imagine a greater happiness than feeling your love. I just hope that you can feel my love for you as strongly. There is nothing I wouldn't do for you, Darling.

It seems as though the evil old witch is determined to bring about the end of the world from irreversible Climate Change, and she still has a lot of stupid followers who will follow her to the end of the world, which is exactly what the idiots are now doing. The cretins aren't just committing suicide, they are dragging all other living things on the planet down with them. All we can do is to encourage our followers to boo her off the pitch for being such a rotten sport. She has had her day. It is time she cleared off and let us have ours.

I am sticking to my demand of £$x+y$ from the Royal College of Psychiatrists (I think that's the maximum that they can manage), and I am raising my demand from the British government on behalf of the establishment to £z. My best revenge seems to be to hit the bastards in the pocket, and The Survival Party needs the money to fulfil my ambitions. I will have my demands met when we have got rid of the soul of the evil old witch; the alternative is the end of the world.

Our trials are nearly over now!

Yours etcetera

Cc Dr Twee Dampensquib

Saturday 10th October 2020. I wrote the following letter to Lucy this morning: - Saturday 10th October 2020

Lucy Lawless, The Queen of Heaven,

Dear Soulmate,

Last year, 2019, had the hottest September in the Northern Hemisphere on record. Last month it was even hotter, breaking the record yet again. This proves that Global Warming is impacting lives far more quickly than most people realise. Yet still Donald Trump rejects the opinion of the world's scientists. I still think that 2028 will be the year when Climate Change will become irreversible unless we, the human race, do something about it before then.

I'm sick of hearing Donald Trump described by the news people as "the leader of the free world" when everybody knows that my late mother, Mrs Dorothy Ayres, is still the REAL leader of the free world, and when we get rid of her soul, then *I* will be. We nearly succeeded yesterday afternoon, but she is still messing about and pretending to go. I can sense from the increase in cerebral activity that nearly everybody in the world who matters is shouting at her to GET ON WITH IT and STOP WASTING TIME.

People are still manufacturing internal combustion engines and putting them into vehicles and selling them. I won't get the opportunity to stop THIS CRASS STUPIDITY until Dolly goes for real. People do this knowing that these engines are destroying the environment. How can I tell my grandchildren that they are being looked after when people are so stupid and inconsiderate and thoughtless? And when those with the wisdom to run the world sensibly are locked up in mental hospitals because of the sexual desires of Mrs Dorothy Ayres. If the human race doesn't come to its senses and get rid of the old witch soon it will be too late.

We managed to come together on Thursday afternoon in spite of the paliperidone. Thank you, Darling. You were wonderful, as always. With any luck, I have already had my last injection of the poisonous muck. I think Dolly has only got a few hours to go before she concedes defeat and clears off for real. I'm sure Dampensquib has the sense to do as I say when she has gone.

Our trials are nearly over now!

Yours etcetera

Cc Dr Twee Dampensquib

And I wrote the following letter to Lucy this evening: - Saturday Evening 10th October 2020

Lucy Lawless, The Queen of Heaven,

Dear Soulmate,

There is an area of land in the rainforests of Siberia, five times the size of Great Britain, which is riddled with underground fires. These burst into life on the surface as fast as people can extinguish them, emitting vast amounts of carbon dioxide which causes environmental pollution, which causes Global Warming which, in turn, causes more subterranean fires.

This isn't the only vicious circle going on at the moment. The vast underbelly of the Antarctic ice sheets is melting caused by warm ocean currents. This causes sea levels to rise causing Global Warming which heats up the Southern Ocean, melting the undersides of the ice sheets.

Mrs Dorothy Ayres has presided over the system for the last sixty years which has allowed these vicious circles to flourish, whilst all she has been concerned with is her own obsessive incestuous sex life. That is why I call her a weak leader and say the human race must get rid of her before it is too late. Global Warming isn't hanging about like Dolly is and Climate Change isn't wasting time like Dolly is. She must be made to turn herself into a duck without wasting any more time.

It was Prince Charles who said recently that the crisis of Climate Change will soon dwarf the crisis of the coronavirus COVID-19 pandemic. That man talks a lot of sense. He is absolutely right. He was also the one who drew attention to the crisis of plastic waste in our rivers and oceans. I like him. He engages his brain AND his social conscience before he talks. To say that the Climate Change crisis will dwarf that of the coronavirus pandemic at this time paves the way for The Survival Party, so with remarks like that from the Prince, and also the things which Sir David Attenborough has been saying, I am optimistic for the future of The Survival Party.

By the time I am free and have got my public apology and compensation, Great Britain will be ready for the Party. It is all coming together nicely. I have already chosen to whom I intend to offer jobs with the Party. I know who I want for my General Manager, Accounts Manager and IT Manager. I shall have to scout around for a good solicitor. The next six months will be tricky because of the precautions being taken to prevent the spread of the virus. Even those who are "free" aren't free to go where they like and do what they want to do. Let's hope we get a safe and reliable vaccine soon, and one which works even for people of my age.

I used to think that people of covert eminence were my rivals, for example my stepmother, Iris (of "AI" fame), and Oliver (of "O2" fame) but now I see things differently. I know that I am the one God and the Emperor. The likes of Oliver and Iris are my generals and commanders who serve me, as long as they know their place in the hierarchy of all living things, and keep to it. My place is at the top, as I proved on the 16th July 1976, and your place is by my side. I have given Iris a project to work on. I want her to arrange a union between my grandson, Troy Daniel Evans (Jesus Christ as was), and the girl called "Holly". They are my chosen ones to reign as the King and Queen of Troy's generation when you and I are both dead.

Our trials are nearly over now!

Yours etcetera

Cc Dr Twee Dampensquib

Monday 12th October 2020. I wrote the following letter to Lucy this evening: - Monday Evening 12th October 2020

Lucy Lawless, The Queen of Heaven,

Dear Soulmate,

Boris Johnson said today that the coronavirus pandemic would test the mettle of everybody in the UK over the next weeks and months. He is only partly right of course. I am happy for Boris to lead the way over the next six months, but after that, I will be needed, to test the mettle of everyone in the world in the battle against Climate Change, for the following seven years, until we have got worldwide carbon emissions down to zero. As I quoted Prince Charles in my last letter, the Climate Change crisis is going to dwarf the coronavirus crisis.

I had some sensible words with my late mother this afternoon. I told her that I know it will be sad for a lot of people when she goes, but it is necessary for her to do so for the greater good of all life on Earth, which will become extinct, starting in eight years' time from irreversible Climate Change, unless I am allowed the freedom and the power to lead the way to averting the impending catastrophe. I don't think it is too much to say that the world NEEDS my leadership. NOW.

I have already had a sorrowful goodbye with her. I think she will go now. There is no help for the world if she doesn't. I am God and this is my help to the world. So, don't let me hear Dolly's followers saying, "God help us all!" when Global Warming hits them with all its might over the next few years. We must all be pragmatic, in the interest of survival. I told her that she must go now or I'll never see her again, but if she goes now, I'll see her again in another lifetime.

Our trials are nearly over now!

Yours etcetera

Cc Dr Twee Dampensquib

Thursday 15th October 2020. I wrote the following letter to Lucy this morning: - Thursday Morning 15th October 2020

Empress Lucy Lawless, The Queen of Heaven,

Dear Soulmate,

I see that RAFAEL NADAL won the French Open tennis tournament this year. He has now won twenty Grand Slam tournaments, equalling the record of Roger Federer, the greatest tennis player of all time, which is why they call NADAL "The King of Clay".

Dolly has been at a tipping point for many days now, but I have finally found the catalyst to make her go for real. It was when I told her that I will make sure she goes down in history as a coward as well as a rotten sport, for not doing what every duck does, which is to find a pair of copulating ducks and join them to come back to life as one of their offspring. I don't know if she has gone yet or if she is about to go as I write this, but she will go NOW, OR ELSE. She cannot bear to be called a coward, much less with justification. That is why I am sure she will go NOW.

Coronavirus will be with us for another eight months, until July of next year. We should have a working vaccine by then which will be universally available to everybody in the world. So, we can look forward to our holiday together in August 2021. I still want a cruise around the Norwegian fjords; as I said before, their beauty impresses me.

I define The Emperor as the King of kings and The Empress as the Queen of queens. That is WHO WE ARE, NOW, my Darling. The Muslims call me "ALLAH". The "H" could stand for Hannah, as in Hannah Gordon, who was my father's choice of woman for me; but I prefer to think of it as standing for Holly, who will be your successor as Queen when you join me in Heaven in about fifty years' time. I don't need to tell you who the "LL" stands for, my Love. You are NOW the world's alpha woman.

This letter is the last one in the chapter in my latest book. The chapter is called "The Endgame", which is now over. I enclose a copy of today's letter to Twee Dampensquib.

Our trials are over now!

Yours etcetera

Cc Dr Twee Dampensquib

Chapter 15

The Provisional Manifesto

This is my suggested advertisement for my Manifesto. I intend to advertise the Manifesto for free on all the social media platforms.

Suggested Facebook Entry

The human race is fighting for its life against Climate Change, and until now WE HAVE BEEN LOSING. The difference now is that I am here to provide the leadership that the people of Great Britain and the rest of the world need in the fight against Global Warming and Climate Change. I am Robert Brooks Strong and I am the founder and leader of THE SURVIVAL PARTY of Great Britain. I am a real man and a natural leader of men and women. I have formed THE SURVIVAL PARTY with policies to take practical steps to cut carbon emissions down to zero in Great Britain and the rest of the world before the year 2028. We want to do this by a phased reduction in the burning of all fossil fuels within a five-year period, thus eliminating all carbon emissions. This is necessary because unless we, the human race, do this then 2028 will be the year when Climate Change becomes irreversible with catastrophic consequences for all life on Earth. Don't just take my word for this; according to the BBC there are eleven thousand scientists all saying the same thing. I am NOT scaremongering; I am facing reality; something that no other politician has the courage to do. We are the only political party with the courage to face reality and a plan to avert disaster.

Xi Jinping wants to make China carbon neutral by 2060, and Jo Biden has the ambition to make the USA carbon neutral by 2050. Boris Johnson wants to make Great Britain carbon neutral by 2050 and so do many other national leaders, but all this is far too little, far too late. All these politicians underestimate the urgency of the need to tackle Climate Change, for political reasons. They haven't got the guts to tell it like it is. It will become irreversible much sooner than they think. We have got to make the whole world carbon neutral by the end of the year 2027 or all life on Earth will become extinct starting in 2028.

Prince Charles said, correctly, that the Climate Change crisis is going to dwarf the coronavirus crisis, and we all know how bad that is. Wake up folks, and realise what is going to hit us, and when.

The present government of the UK has a majority in Parliament, but that does not necessarily mean that they will be in power for five years. Many things can happen in politics. We hope to force a General Election in 2022 at which THE SURVIVAL PARTY will win a landslide victory, because by then, the NEED for THE SURVIVAL PARTY will be overwhelmingly apparent to the British electorate.

If you email THE SURVIVAL PARTY with your name, email address and postal address, we will send you, free, a copy of my Manifesto, and you can then make up your own mind if you wish to join THE SURVIVAL PARTY. It will cost you £12 a year for membership, and with that money, as well as my personal investment in the Party, we will field candidates at every constituency in Great Britain at the next General Election. Join us and do your bit to save the world!

Robert Brooks Strong FIAP, Party leader. November 2020.

The Manifesto itself now follows: -

MANIFESTO
OF THE SURVIVAL PARTY
OF GREAT BRITAIN

October 2020

Party Leader Robert Brooks Strong FIAP

My name is Robert Brooks Strong and I am the founder and leader of The Survival Party of Great Britain. The following are the policies I wish to pursue: -

These measures will seem to many people to be too draconian, but I maintain they are necessary for the survival of all life on earth, to avert the impending catastrophe of irreversible Climate Change. They will involve the decimation of the aerospace industry, and of the coal, gas and oil industries. October 2020

Survival

Everything depends upon our ability to survive. The world may not be life-supporting for much beyond 2027 unless the human race cuts its carbon emissions down to zero by that date. This is because the climate may overheat by a rise of $1.5°$ C which is the critical point beyond which it will be too late to save the planet from Global Warming caused by Climate Change, which will then be irreversible. The present British Government aims to make Great Britain carbon neutral by 2050. We say this is far too late and too parochial. The whole world, not just Britain, must be carbon neutral by 2028 not 2050, that will be twenty-two years too late to stop the world from becoming uninhabitable. I am therefore aiming to get Great Britain carbon neutral within five years or as soon as possible thereafter by the following policies.

My Government would ban the production of internal combustion engines and the manufacture of vehicles using such engines immediately. All vehicle manufacture must be for that of electric vehicles. We would ban the use of vehicles with internal combustion engines on British roads within 2 ½ years. The same would apply to all other devices using internal combustion engines such as lawn mowers and cement mixers, etc.

We would immediately embark upon a programme of installing power points on lamp posts in all British cities, towns and villages, so that people could charge the batteries of their electric vehicles from these power points. A system could be introduced whereby all electric vehicles would have a fourth pin on their electric plug upon which would be encrypted the registration number of the vehicle; this encryption could be read by the metre supplying the electricity so that the electricity company would know who to charge for their electricity.

We would immediately invest in research and development of bigger and better batteries for vehicles and also for electricity storage and distribution. We would also invest in schemes to produce electricity from solar panels and wind turbines. We would make coal-fired power stations, gas-fired power stations and oil-fired power stations obsolete within three years. We aim to make Great Britain free from all use of coal, oil and gas within four years. The only exception to this rule being the oil needed for jet engine aircraft. People would be encouraged to fly only when necessary.

Plastic pollution is a big problem at the moment. The world's rivers and oceans are becoming clogged up with the stuff. The people of Great Britain must be encouraged to play their part in the drive to recycle all plastic products. My Government would ensure that we have enough plastic recycling facilities and of sufficient size to recycle all the plastic used in the country. Anyone caught disposing of plastic thoughtlessly would get a £100 fine when my Government is in power. We will not allow plastic products to be sent to landfill sites. Single-use plastic products would be made illegal.

Paper, cardboard, wood and metals must also be recycled and sites will be made available for this purpose. And their use will be compulsory.

SHIPPING & AIR TRAVEL

My Government would liaise with other governments and the United Nations to secure international agreement on the following matters: -

Within 4 ½ years all ships on the sea, including cruise liners, must be either battery powered or wind or solar powered.

Within 1 ½ years, all non-essential jet flights will not be allowed. Jet flights will only be allowed for the following purposes: -

1. Essential freight, including mail.

2. Medical and social emergencies.

3. Travel to international sports and entertainment fixtures, such as the World Cup matches and the Olympic Games, and the Eurovision Song Contest.

4. Business executives and National leaders travelling to international meetings and conferences.

5. Emigration and trips to attend employment interviews.

Leisure, vacations and tourism will be regarded as non-essential reasons for jet travel and will not be allowed. This is because jet travel leaves such a huge carbon footprint. People can take their vacations in their home countries.

MORALITY

We feel strongly that the issue of public morals is one that this Government should make a stand on. Ever since 1967, when same-sex sexual relationships were legalised, there has been a steady decline in public morality, and the social consequences of this are now becoming intolerable. The rise in knife crimes and murders can be attributed to this "don't care" attitude to public morals and the feeling that "anything goes". I will deal with crime shortly, but I want to say at this point that people's sexual morals need to be corrected. It is self-evident that acts of sodomy and lesbian sex are filthy, unnatural and sordid. They are disgusting behaviour and should be discouraged. We say that the best way to discourage them is to penalise them. We would give twenty-eight days' solitary confinement for every act of indecency multiplied by the cardinal number of the offence. In other words, four weeks' solitary for a first offence, eight weeks for the second, twelve weeks for the third and so on. Additionally, offenders would be required to take injections of antipsychotic medication, to suppress their libidos so that they would be less likely to offend in future. Homosexuality and lesbianism would therefore be regarded as psychoses which are forms of incurable mental illness. This does, of course, mean an end to the public obscenity of same-sex marriages.

THE WHOLE WORLD

The governments of every country in the world will be required to emulate the above policies in the name of the survival of all life on earth. This will be made clear at an international conference and at the United Nations in which the case for survival will be put to and agreed by every country.

The whole human race will be put on a war footing in the battle against Global Warming and Climate Change, in the name of survival.

WE MUST GET THE WHOLE WORLD'S CARBON EMISSIONS DOWN TO ZERO BEFORE THE YEAR 2028 OR IT WILL BE TOO LATE. THERE WILL BE NO HOPE OF AVOIDING EXTINCTION FROM IRREVERSIBLE CLIMATE CHANGE UNLESS WE DO THIS.

Social Guidance

There are two main types of criminals who come before the courts in this country. The first is the career criminals who make a living out of criminal acts, and the second is the social delinquents. Career criminals have to accept the principle of crime and punishment, and by and large they do so. They know that if they get caught, they will have to do their time in prison and that is an end to the matter.

Social delinquents fall into two categories: firstly, there are those who carry weapons for their own protection because they do not trust the law to protect them. This has got to stop. The law must be there to protect all people and be seen to do so.

Secondly, there are those who fall foul of the law because they don't understand society and how it works. They don't know what they are, nor what their lives are all about. They are mainly young guys in various stages of adolescence. They want to prove themselves but don't know how, nor what this entails. Most of them are looking for a reason for living, and most of them at present, end up in the care of consultant forensic psychiatrists who seldom know what life is all about themselves.

We propose the founding of a Ministry for Social Guidance to replace the work done by the Royal College of Psychiatrists. The Ministry would be in charge of the Social Guidance Institute which would be run by an elected council who would oversee the work done by Social Guidance Counsellors.

These would be people chosen for their maturity and wisdom and would not be qualified by educational qualifications, but would be chosen in a way more like that of judges, by their fellow counsellors.

It would be the job of Social Guidance Counsellors to talk to miscreants on a regular basis and to lead them to a fuller understanding of life; to get them to prove themselves and to *find* God and to *find themselves* so that they will become useful citizens. They must be led to an understanding of WHAT THEY ARE AND WHO THEY ARE.

With very few exceptions, the minimum age for a Social Guidance Counsellor would be fifty years, and ideally these people would have been married for at least two years and have children of their own for they would be acting *in loco parentis*.

These jobs would largely replace those of probation officers, and would be ideal for the many older members of society who have lived life to the full and gained life experience and wisdom which these jobs would give them the opportunity to pass on to the next generation. They would be well paid and carry a lot of respect. Such jobs are badly needed in society at the moment.

Mental hospitals would be largely replaced by Social Guidance Centres where people would be held in detention until they make it obvious that they don't need that kind of treatment. Then they could just be called upon for regular visits to the Centre for consultations with their Counsellor.

Receiving counselling would not carry the stigma of mental illness which many people will always equate with madness. Receiving counselling is more like getting good advice from a caring parent, which people growing up in good homes get anyway.

This system would replace the mental health system, which is shambolic at best at the moment.

Punishment

The Bible say so, and so do the works of William Shakespeare, and now I am saying it as well. "Spare the rod and spoil the child". We have raised a generation of spoilt children in this country under the soft laws of "the Nanny State". This is what has given rise to the current spate of knife crimes. Young people have little or no respect for authority and the rule of law. My government would change that. Parents know their children best and children know it when they have misbehaved. We would give parents back the right to give their child a smack on the thigh if their child is naughty. The child then knows to behave him/herself and is given a respectful understanding of the nature of the relationship between adults and children. This will prove helpful for when the child becomes an adult him/herself. Having taken his/her punishment, the child then knows that the matter is forgotten and then he/she can continue with a loving relationship with his/her parent.

We would give schoolteachers back the right to punish misbehaving pupils, the punishment to be decided at the discretion of the head teacher. Again, once the child has received his/her punishment, the matter is then forgotten.

We would punish young guys who carry knives much more severely. The punishment for carrying a knife would be ten to fifteen years in prison depending on the circumstances of the offender. For using a knife to inflict a wound, the punishment would be a jail term commensurate with the severity of the wound, the first ten weeks of which would be spent in solitary confinement. For killing someone with a knife, the punishment would be a life sentence, the first twenty weeks of which would be spent in solitary confinement. In all of these cases the punishment would be followed by making the miscreant undergo counselling until the judge is convinced that the miscreant has mended his ways.

In the case of female knife offenders, we would leave the punishment up to the judge and the Social Guidance Counsellor to decide.

Hard Drugs

A distinction must be made between those who deal in hard drugs and those who only use them. Users will be treated as needing Social Guidance and kept in secure accommodation until they have been clean for at least two years. They can be released only when they have made it obvious that they intend to stay clear of hard drugs in future.

Dealers cause great misery to their customers and to their families. We would give them a life sentence in prison, the first ten weeks of which would be spent in solitary confinement. They would then have to attend sessions with a Social Guidance Counsellor, and they would also have their financial assets confiscated.

Prisons

Prisons are not meant to be holiday camps. Those caught with drugs in prison would be placed in solitary confinement for a period of time at the discretion of the Prison Governor and disallowed visits and social interaction with friends and family. Those visitors caught bringing drugs into prison would be barred from visiting prisons again. They can be identified by facial recognition technology.

NORTHERN IRELAND

This territory was taken by force of arms from the Irish people in the first place and colonised by the British. In a civilised world, this is no justification for the UK to retain possession of someone else's territory. We say, "Give Northern Ireland back to the Irish Nation". Historically and geographically the territory belongs to Ireland, not Britain. If anybody there wants to consider themselves as British, then let them come to Britain. The territory is more of a liability than an asset to Britain.

Public Ownership

It was Margaret Thatcher who sold off our national assets in the 1980s because she didn't have enough confidence in herself as a leader to delegate the running of public companies to competent administrators. The result of this we see today in the debacle of the management of the railways, the water industry and the electricity industry.

At the moment, the railways are owned separately in terms of the stations, the rail tracks and the trains, and in different parts of the country. To travel from A to B by train in the most cost-effective way is no easy matter. It varies according to which company you are buying a ticket from and which route you take. Sometimes the cheapest route is not the shortest route! We say bring the whole national rail system back into public ownership and trust my Government to appoint a competent administrator to oversee the whole project. The new British Rail would ensure that the trains run on time and are not too overcrowded. If the public are let down on these promises, then the administrator would be sacked. That person's job would depend upon their efficiency.

The water supply industry has been taken over by sharks and con men. The rivers, including the Thames, are filthy with untreated sewage, and Southern Water recently had to apologise to its customers and pay them compensation for their poor service. Millions of gallons of water are wasted by broken pipes which go unmended for months or even years by inefficient management. We say bring the whole water industry: the rivers, the reservoirs and the distribution systems into public ownership. Again, the new British Water would be overseen by a competent administrator appointed by my Government, whose job would depend upon his/her efficiency.

The electricity industry charges different rates for different customers and often you can only get the best deal by switching your supplier. Loyalty is not often rewarded. Again, we say, bring the whole system: the generation of electricity by nuclear, solar and wind power, the distribution and marketing into public ownership, overseen by a competent administrator appointed by my Government, whose job would depend upon his/her performance.

Other National Issues

Any political Party standing for election in Great Britain must obviously have policies on all issues of National Importance. The reason I haven't mentioned them so far in this Manifesto is because they are not nearly as important as the need to cut carbon emissions to cope with Global Warming and Climate Change. To spend time and effort on them is a bit like discussing who is going to do the washing up after dinner when the house is burning down all around us. The overriding need is to put the fire out first, then consider what is to be done if and when we all survive.

I do, however, have the following which I think is worth saying:

My Government would spend at least as much, as a proportion of the gross domestic product, as any government, Labour or Conservative, has spent on services since the Second World War.

The National Health Service

My Government would make sure that the NHS is adequately funded, including GPs salaries, and Accident and Emergency services. Prescription charges would be abolished. All health services will remain free at the point of delivery for all British citizens.

The Education Service

Education will remain compulsory for all children under the age of sixteen years. All education will be free for all students, including those who have proven their academic ability to go on to higher education. University tuition fees will be abolished for all British students. Free school dinners will be available in all cases where financial hardship applies to a parent or guardian. Private schools who charge a fee to educate children will not be abolished.

The Police Service

There is currently a recruitment drive to recruit and train another twenty thousand police Officers. My Government would ensure that staff levels are maintained by all the national police forces. Stop and search powers will be maintained by all uniformed officers, who will be allowed to carry tasers.

Provision for the Elderly

Old age pensions will continue for all people who have reached the age of sixty-six years. This applies to both men and women. All old people who are so infirm that they need looking after and do not have a relative who is willing and able to look after them will have their pension replaced by a free place in a care home.

County and Urban District Councils

Council tax will still have to be paid. Councillors will continue to be the elected representatives of the people.

Defence

All existing defence commitments will continue to be honoured, including our commitment to NATO. All the national military services will be maintained, as will our independent nuclear deterrent.

Brexit

On an issue of such national importance as the membership of the European Union, the British people should have had the advice and guidance of our wisest men and women, not the self-interested opinions of an unelected, shadowy, behind-the-scenes, figure such as Dominic Cummings and his Brexit poster-boy, Boris Johnson, who told lies in big letters on the side of a bus. Brexit is a disaster for the British economy and is costing us thousands of jobs. My wisdom is that Britain should apply to rejoin the European Union and use our influence most wisely in that way.

Income and Expenditure

My Government does not propose any immediate changes in revenue and taxation, nor in spending on services, benefits and pensions. We propose to spend some time studying the books until we know the true state of the nation's financial health. We envisage that this will take about five months. We will then tell you the truth about the state of the nation's financial health when we produce our first budget. We believe in being prudent with money and not taking on any more debt than is necessary for survival; we know that you don't like paying interest to bankers any more than we do, so we ask you to trust us to spend the nation's money wisely.

My Credentials

According to Mensa, I have an IQ of 139 on their scale. Intelligence is not the same thing as wisdom. I have a saying that it is a wise man who knows how little he knows. I am wise enough to seek the advice and guidance of scientists and professors who are more erudite and learned than myself, in matters concerning affairs of state.

I have proven in my life that my courage, my wisdom, my initiative, my maturity, my determination, my strength of spirit, my love for people

250

and my leadership are second to none. I have a strong social conscience and I am a good organiser. I am a real man and a natural leader of men and women.

This country and the world **NEED** my leadership without delay.

You can learn the truth about me from my autobiographies. They can be accessed from my website. The address is: - http://www.robert-brooks-strong.olympiapublishers.com/

Chapter 16

The Gloves Are Off

Events and Thoughts from Friday 16th October 2020.

Friday 16th October 2020. I wrote the following letter to Dr Twee Dampensquib yesterday. I am still waiting to hear from him: - Thursday 15th October 2020

> Dr Twee Dampensquib,
> Medical Director,
> Alcatraz Island Hospital.

Dear Twee,

It is now 4.15 in the morning and my late mother, Mrs Dorothy Ayres, has now slipped out of the human race. Her soul now inhabits the body of the embryo of a duckling. I am therefore now the Emperor of the Free World.

I intend to use this power to safeguard the life of every living thing by saving the planet from irreversible Climate Change. I am going to make everybody aware that this will happen in the year 2028 unless we, the human race, cut worldwide carbon emissions to zero by the end of the year 2027. I can best achieve this ambition by fighting to become the Prime Minister of the UK as soon as possible. To embark upon a career in politics I will first need to clear my name, and you can help me do this by getting the Royal College of Psychiatrists to give me the public apology that I am demanding.

I am therefore now writing to demand of you four things immediately:
-

1. You take me off all antipsychotic medication without further delay.
2. You prepare the public apology that I want and submit it to me in writing for my approval. I want the apology to state that the psychiatric

profession now accepts that I am not mentally ill and never have been mentally ill; that I have been misdiagnosed, misjudged and mistreated ever since 17th July 1976; and that the Royal College apologises to me for forty-four years of unjust detainment during which time I have lost my family life including the love and respect of my sons, my career, my house, and my status in society; that the Royal College apologises to me for forty-three years of cruelty and abuse by forcing me to take injections of antipsychotic drugs which have horrible effects when there has never been anything wrong with me; and that the only reason why I have been treated this way for all this time is because I have always refused to have sex with my late mother, Mrs Dorothy Ayres; and that the Royal College apologises to me for stigmatising me with insulting and untrue epithets such as "mental illness", "paranoid schizophrenia", "grandiose delusions" and "a delusional disorder".

3. You write to the Ministry of Justice, recommending an absolute and unconditional discharge for me and to take me off my criminal sections 37 and 41 immediately.

4. You recommend to the Royal College of Psychiatrists the immediate payment of £x+y; this being £x for forty-four years of unjust detainment and loss of income plus £y for forty-three years of torture by antipsychotic drugs when there has never been anything wrong with me. This is a first instalment of my compensation demand; the balance of which I intend to get from the British Government, on behalf of British society for driving me to homicide. I intend to demand a payment of £z when I get a verdict of "Justifiable Homicide by reason of Self-Defence against undue social pressure" after a retrial of my case. I need this money to fulfil my ambitions for The Survival Party.

Now that I have proven that I am indeed the Lord God by disposing of the soul of my late mother, Mrs Dorothy Ayres, I wish to say that I will have mercy on the souls of dead psychiatrists when, and only when, the above compensation demand has been paid in full and without delay; and also, when I am satisfied with the public apology.

Yours sincerely,

Robert Strong.
Cc Paul Rees, Chief Executive of the Royal College of Psychiatrists
Lucy Lawless.

Friday 16ᵗʰ October 2020. I wrote the following letter to Twee Dampensquib this afternoon: - Friday 16ᵗʰ October 2020

Dr Twee Dampensquib,
Medical Director,
Alcatraz Island Hospital.

Dear Twee,

My late mother, Dorothy (Dolly) Ayres, duckified herself yesterday afternoon. The catalyst which made her stop prevaricating and get on with it was when I threatened to ruin her legacy by calling her a coward, for not having the guts to do what every duck does; which is to join a pair of copulating ducks and come back to life as one of their offspring. I gave her until today to do it or I would ruin her legacy, and she took my point and went. Her followers are now stunned. It will take them a little while to get over her demise.

The civil war is now over and I and Lucy have won. There are still some idiots on the TV who use the words "Area" and its plural "Areas", but they are living in the past. They are seeking help from a god who no longer exists.

Now kindly obey my demands that I gave you in my letter of yesterday.
Yours sincerely,

Robert Strong.
Cc Paul Rees, Chief Executive, The Royal College of Psychiatrists,
Lucy Lawless.

I wrote the following letter to Lucy tonight: - Friday Night 16ᵗʰ October 2020

Empress Lucy Lawless, The Queen of Heaven,

Dear Soulmate,

The evil old witch still hasn't gone yet, and I've worked out why not. She is still clinging to the increasingly forlorn hope that she can make me her lover. I am her own son but she obviously doesn't know me at all. She doesn't stand a chance with me and she never did. She is just making a fool of herself over me, and all I feel for her is contempt. Maybe she will clear off when she hates me for my contemptuous attitude.

I'll give her till this time tomorrow. If she hasn't gone by then I'll give her a stinking write up for a legacy. I'm the one in charge of my relationship with her, so she really ought to do as I say if she has any sense left at all. The remaining days of her existence will be increasingly unpleasant. I'm making sure of it. When she accepts reality, she'll be glad to clear off to get away from me. Reality has a way of making itself accepted by those with any sense at all.

The tide has well turned on the BBC news channel. A man on the TV said so in so many words today. Almost all the people on the news channel are now using the words "region" and "regions" instead of "area" and "areas", and they are talking about "closing doors" instead of "opening the door". The exception to this is the weather presenters who take their orders from the Meteorological Office. They are making themselves increasingly unpopular by sticking to their talk of "areas" etc. I now find encouragement listening to the BBC news channel instead of being disheartened by the way the news was presented.

Our trials are nearly over now!

Take care of yourself, my Love, I have much more to say to you, but it can wait until we talk, Bless you, my Queen,

Yours with Love, Affection and Friendship,

The King of Heaven,
Emperor_Bob XX
Cc Dr Twee Dampensquib

Saturday 17th October 2020. I changed the title of chapter 14 of this book to "The Endgame? No, Just Brinkmanship" as it is not yet the end of the game as I thought it would be. Just like Britain's exit from the European Union, there has to be a transition period in the power game between my late mother, Mrs Dorothy (Dolly) Ayres, and myself. But unlike the political game that Boris Johnson is playing with the EU, there is no scope for negotiation between my late mother and me. I am God the Father and I am the supreme ruler. I am not here in this world to negotiate the terms of my sex life. Either Dolly goes in the immediate future or it will be the end of the world from irreversible Climate Change starting in eight years' time. I am not, and never will be, a motherfucker. I am a real man and a real man is not one of *them.* I will see the end of the world first.

Lucy has won my undying, eternal love, which is something that Dolly has never been able to do, so Dolly must concede defeat and admit that Lucy is the better woman: in which case, Dolly must duckify herself in the immediate future because what she wants from me is impossible. Dolly doesn't have what it takes to make me be untrue to Lucy – no other woman does. EITHER DOLLY CONCEDES DEFEAT AND GOES, OR SHE PLUNGES THE WORLD INTO THE ABYSS OF EXTINCTION FROM IRREVERSIBLE CLIMATE CHANGE. EITHER WAY IT WILL BE DOLLY'S DECISION, NOT MINE. She is the one with all the power. My only power is the right to say NO to her, and that will always be my answer. I have no choice but to say NO to her, because I am the man that Dolly herself made me into. She is hoisted on her own petard.

If Climate Change becomes irreversible, as seems likely in eight years' time, then the whole world will become uninhabitable. This will mean the end of every man, woman and child in the world; every dog and every cat, every lion and every tiger, every mammal and every bird and every reptile, every insect and every fungus, every blade of grass, and every flower and every weed, every bush and every tree, every fish in the ocean and every other sea creature and every creature that lives on the land, and every plant. IF DOLLY REALLY WANTS THIS TO HAPPEN RATHER THAN COME BACK TO LIFE AS A DUCK, THEN THAT IS HER DECISION; THERE IS NOTHING I CAN DO ABOUT IT. As long as Dolly exists, I will be kept a prisoner in a mental hospital, even though my Manifesto contains details of the best plan that anyone has got to avert the impending catastrophe. And I am the best man to lead the world into doing so. The best chance that the world has got of averting this catastrophe is to cut worldwide carbon emissions down to zero by the end of 2027 and that is the plan outlined in my Manifesto.

If Dolly wants to play her part in saving the world, then she must come back to life in the immediate future, whatever she chooses to come back as, and thereby set me free.

Sunday 18th October 2020. My late mother, Mrs Dorothy (Dolly) Ayres, has obviously lost her mind and become criminally insane. The evidence for this is that she is willing to bring about the end of the world in order to pursue her insane, obsessive incestuous sexual desire and she is depriving this country and the world of my leadership by keeping me a prisoner in a mental hospital, when the world is obviously crying out for my leadership in the battle against Climate Change.

But Dolly still has a large personal following, so I am launching this appeal to her followers. I want you to stop following Dolly and follow me instead. This is the only hope that the world has got of avoiding extinction from irreversible Climate Change which will happen sooner than most people think. Follow my instructions on how to treat Dolly instead of following her instructions on how to treat me. The old woman now belongs to a bygone era.

She can come back as an animal or she can Rest In Peace in the world of the dead. That is up to her, but those in the world of the living should now look to ourselves for our own salvation. If you let me lead you then do as I say by ignoring Dolly Ayres. She was not a good leader because she led the world to the brink of extinction and unless you follow me now, she will push it over the edge.

I want the leaders of the establishment: the legal, medical, psychiatric, Broadcasting, military, religious and political professions to act as though Dolly has actually duckified herself, even though everybody knows that she hasn't – yet. Take me off the antipsychotic drugs, give me my public apology, my compensation money and my freedom, and help me clear my name by getting a verdict of self-defence after a retrial. I will need enough money to build The Survival Party into the major political force in Great Britain within two years. The figures I have quoted in my letters will, I estimate, be enough.

I enclosed copies of today's and yesterday's entries in this journal in letters to Lucy, and after today's entry I added the following few lines: -

This is the line I am taking from now on. There is no point in trying to influence Dolly, her attitude is intransigent. She will always insist I become her lover and I will always refuse, so we must influence her followers directly and get them to switch sides. It is in their own interest to do so, so, I am optimistic that this tactic will work. I'm sorry we haven't done much dancing lately. It is, as you know, the fault of the evil drug, and also, as you will have read, I have a lot on my mind at the moment.

Tuesday 20th October 2020. My late mother, Mrs Dorothy (Dolly) Ayres, is a wicked, evil tyrant. For many years now she has jeopardised the life and ruined the happiness of my beloved son, Christopher, her own grandson. She has done this in an attempt to blackmail me into having an incestuous sexual relationship with her: something that I refuse to countenance. She has also threatened the lives of my sweetheart, Lucy, and her children. Her latest evil is to blackmail the working people of Greater Manchester with abject poverty unless their Mayor, Andy Burnham, uses the words "Greater Manchester area" instead of "Greater Manchester region". The Prime Minister, Boris Johnson, won't give Manchester another five million pounds on top of the paltry sixty million pounds on offer although his government has sunk the British people into hundreds of billions of pounds of debt caused by the COVID pandemic.

He has done this because Andy Burnham is on MY side in the civil war between my late mother and myself. This is evidenced by Andy's use of the word "region" instead of "area". I have this to say to Andy Burnham and the good people of Greater Manchester: if you want to give in to the evil tyrant, Mrs Ayres, by using the word "area" in order to put food on the table, then I will, of course, understand and not hold it against you, but if you want to make a stand on principle and refuse to be bullied by Dolly's friends, the Conservative government, then you will earn my undying love and support and a place of the highest in Heaven, when Boris Johnson follows Dolly Ayres into Hell.

I will not betray the woman I love nor forsake her to have an affair with Mrs Dorothy Ayres, nor any other woman, and I know that Lucy feels the same way about me and will make the same stand and support me in my stand, whatever threats or blackmail the old witch throws at us. Our love is as solid as any rock.

If Dr Twee Dampensquib wants to kowtow to the evil tyrant by continuing to force his evil libido-suppressing drugs on me, then there is nothing I can do about that except make him ashamed of himself for being so weak, when he knows what harm the drugs are doing to Lucy and me, and his Hippocratic Oath makes him promise not to do harm.

Thursday 22nd October 2020. When it comes to choosing sides in the civil war between my late mother, Mrs Dorothy (Dolly) Ayres, and myself, I ask you to consider the following: - She offers easy and free sex with a woman of very low sexual morals. I offer the hope of survival in the impending war against Climate Change. Not one of Dolly's followers has got what it takes to offer himself as the World Leader in the battle against Climate Change, like I have and like I do. Not one of Dolly's followers has a plan to cut worldwide carbon emissions to zero in time to prevent Climate Change from becoming irreversible, like I have.

When I was fighting Edward Richard Pitchblack (the Devil Himself) between November 1984 and August 2014, some people thought He would win and they put their money on Him. But I proved to be the stronger of the two of us. He is now dead AND gone. If we are careful, He will never trouble or threaten the human race again. I mention this because during the fight there was a popular saying that the human race had two hopes – Bob Hope and No Hope. I repeat that I did not let my people down.

Prince Charles said, correctly, that the Climate Change crisis is going to dwarf the coronavirus crisis. And we all know how bad that has been and still is, as I write this. If the majority of people continue following Dolly Ayres, then extinction from irreversible Climate Change is a certainty, starting in 2028. If the people follow me then that is our best chance of survival. There are no guarantees. Dolly has already left it too late for that. Just as when I was fighting Satan, I am now fighting His accomplice, Dolly, for your support, and the same maxim applies – the human race has two hopes, Bob Hope and No Hope.

If you choose to follow me then do as I say, starting by ratifying Mrs Dorothy Ayres in the immediate future. Bringing her back as a duck would be too good for her. I want her brought back as a rat seeing as she has been a two-legged rat to me all my life. As it says in the Bible, "'Vengeance is mine,'" sayeth the Lord".

Saturday 24th October 2020. I wrote the following letter to Lucy this afternoon: - Saturday 24th October 2020

Empress Lucy Lawless, The Queen of Heaven,

Dear Soulmate,

Dolly still has a strong hold on the BBC especially the news channel. Everyone who speaks on the news channel uses the word "area" or "areas" including President Trump. But I can tell telepathically from the cerebral activity that I can sense that vast numbers, millions, of Dolly's followers have come over to MY side in the last week or so as a result of my words, written and spoken. All in all, I remain optimistic that we have got enough going for us to get rid of the old witch in the near future. How near? Remains to be seen. My followers have instructions to ratify the evil tyrant without further delay and to keep up the pressure on her until she is gone.

As time goes by and Global Warming starts to hurt people more and more, then millions more of Dolly's followers will turn to the man with a plan to arrest Climate Change, myself. Both Joe Biden and Boris Johnson hope to get their countries carbon neutral by 2050 and Xi Jinping has set a target date of 2060 for the same purpose for China, but all these politicians have set targets of far too little, far too late. They all underestimate the urgency of the need to tackle Climate Change, for political reasons. They haven't got the guts to tell it like it is. We need to cut worldwide carbon emissions down to zero by the end of 2027, or it will be too late to stop Climate Change from becoming irreversible in 2028.

We came together again this afternoon in spite of the paliperidone. Thank you, Darling. You were wonderful, as always. I have felt your love very strongly today. It's always good to know it's still there for me. Bless you forever, Love.

Our trials are not over yet.

Yours etcetera

Cc Dr Twee Dampensquib

Monday 26th October 2020. I wrote the following letter to Lucy this evening: - Monday Evening 26th October 2020

Empress Lucy Lawless, The Queen of Heaven,

Dear Soulmate,

Dolly still has a strong hold on the BBC especially the news channel, but amongst all the disheartening news there was a ray of shimmering light. This concerned a twenty-seven year old man who had a disagreement with his mother. The woman had been spreading fake news that there was no coronavirus pandemic, and that COVID-19 was caused by radio waves from 5G electronics which affected people's DNA. This obvious nonsense wouldn't be so bad but for the fact that the woman has a following of forty thousand people on Twitter, and all her followers believe the conspiracy theories that she has been spreading. This news item was obviously an allegory for my relationship with Dolly, as anyone who can see beyond the end of their nose will have realised.

I also had an enormous wave of cerebral activity from MY followers. It felt as though ninety-nine per cent of all the English-speaking adults in the world were ordering Dolly to ratify herself immediately, in the name of the survival of all life on Earth. Which, of course, is the necessary thing to command her to do. We shall see what effect the cerebral activity has on Dolly before long. I think it will do the trick. The old witch has been teetering on the brink of going for weeks now. The cerebral activity of the telepaths should push her beyond the tipping point that she has been clinging to.

On the surface of things, I lead a rather mundane life in here. I play guitar twice a week: once for the singing group on the ward and once with a fellow patient who plays lead guitar and another man who plays on an electronic drum kit. I play rhythm guitar on my acoustic guitar. I have a Martin J40 Jumbo guitar which is a very good musical instrument. It cost me just over three thousand pounds new. We play the hits of a group called The Shadows: "Apache", "Foot tapper", "Wonderful Land" and we also do a tune called "Nashville boogie". We sound pretty good and we are arranging to do some concerts at Christmas. The lead guitarist, my mate David, came up with a name for the group, "The Humdingers".

I also look after the two fish tanks on the ward. Around January this year we only had one tank with three fish in it, but they all died. I think someone put something nasty in the water. We bought another six fish, but two of them died. I think the dominant male killed off his two rivals for the three females. They bred and we had three separate lots of hatchings. We then put the four adult fish in a separate tank and kept the original tank, which is larger, for the baby fish. We now have about thirty healthy babies. I feed all the fish every other day with one or two pinches of fish food, and we clean the filters every week. The Occupational Therapy Assistant is a man called Vincent, who helps me with the fish.

Our trials are not over yet.

Yours etcetera

Cc Dr Twee Dampensquib

Wednesday 28th October 2020. I had a visit from the spirit of my late mother, Mrs Dorothy (Dolly) Ayres, this afternoon, and I told her that if I was her, I would turn myself into a duck without further delay. I would do this to give all living things on the planet their best chance of survival from the catastrophic consequences of irreversible Climate Change, which will happen in the year 2028 unless we, the human race, cut our worldwide carbon emissions down to zero before the end of 2027.

I told her that I have a plan, outlined in the Manifesto of my political Party, The Survival Party, for the phased reduction of the burning of all fossil fuels, worldwide, over a five year period; thus eliminating all carbon emissions. I am uniquely qualified to carry out this plan because of the immense authority that I will wield when I have made my late mother's soul disappear from the human race, thus dispelling any doubts anyone may have about my divinity; for I really am the Lord God Almighty, and everyone who really matters is well aware of it, not just a lunatic who *thinks* that's who he is (and I have met plenty of *them* in my forty-four years in mental hospitals).

I think Dolly will go now. It is her only chance of meeting me again in a future lifetime. The world will have no future unless she goes now.

I was heartened to see on TV yesterday, the boss of the UK aerospace industry saying that technology is now under development for aeroplanes with zero carbon emissions. This will bring immense benefit to an industry which has been decimated by the coronavirus pandemic, and would otherwise remain in disarray when the pandemic is over because of the huge carbon footprint of jet planes.

Thursday 29th October 2020. I sent the above entry, together with the following paragraph, in a letter to Lucy yesterday: -

To change the subject to my life in hospital: I often play chess in the evening after dinner with one of the staff here, a guy called Lovejit. He isn't a bad chess player but I usually beat him when I am careful. I am sometimes careless though and make silly mistakes, in which case he beats me.

The fish in my tanks are called Platties. They are black with orange markings on them and the adult fish grow to a size of about 1 $\frac{1}{2}$ inches. They are a Mexican freshwater fish.

I usually have four Weetabix, two slices of toast and two eggs for breakfast; a tangerine is all I eat lunchtime; (that's my diet), but I have a cooked meal for dinner in the evening. I don't eat supper.

You are on my mind every day and I dance with you whenever the paliperidone allows me to.

Monday 2nd November 2020. I have the following to say to my late mother: when I called my house at 76 Belmont Road "FREEDOM", I must have known subconsciously that I would get my freedom from your influence at the age of seventy-six. Everybody knows that you are going to come back as a duck in your next life, so, to make the prophesy come true it will be fitting if you come back to life as a duck before my seventy-seventh birthday this Thursday. I am due for another injection of the drug that you have been torturing me with for the last forty-three years on Friday, so I won't have to take it again if you do come back before my birthday. This will give you time to witness the result of the U.S. election before you go. Joe Biden is one of MY men so I am naturally rooting for HIM. He colours the letter "e" in his surname in red because Edward Pitchblack is dead and gone thanks to me.

Thursday 5th November 2020. I wrote the following letter to Lucy this morning: - Thursday Morning 5th November 2020

Empress Lucy Lawless, The Queen of Heaven,

Dear Soulmate,

It is my seventy-seventh birthday today, and I think my letter of Monday the 2nd November did the trick with my late mother. I think she has gone for real this time. I say this even though she has wrong-footed me so many times in the past. I know her. I think she proved to be a sport in the end, and has now given US a chance to make something of our lives. At long last. It is now three thirty a.m. and I'm feeling good.

I'm due for another injection tomorrow, but if they try to inject me again, I shall refuse to allow them to do so. My left arm has been in pain for a month now. I think the girl hit the nerve in my arm with the needle when she injected me last month, and my arm and my left hand are now permanently damaged.

Dampensquib had better obey my demands in my letter of the 15th October now that Dolly has really gone and I am now really the Emperor of the Free World. Starting with my demand to come off all antipsychotic medication immediately. If Dampensquib prevaricates or quibbles with me, I shall have his hide. I know he was scared of my late mother. He had better be scared of me now that I have taken over from her.

At the moment it looks as though Joe Biden is on course to win the election for the Presidency of the U.S.A. although Donald Trump is proving to be a rotten sport and will not accept defeat gracefully. He is demanding recounts and is mounting legal challenges, but they won't get him anywhere. Joe is the winner.

I think Dampensquib will now obey my demands. He isn't stupid. But even when I get my freedom, I won't be able to go anywhere as England is in lockdown due to the coronavirus pandemic. I am better off staying in hospital for the time being where I am shielded. The virus kills men of my age, so I don't want to go back into the community until they come up with a safe and reliable vaccine against COVID-19.

I will be using Skype to talk to my niece on Monday. It will be great to see her again after all these years. I last saw her forty years ago in Broadmoor. She is now grown up with a family of her own, and she has turned out to be a lovely woman. She lives in Italy with her husband, who is a Count, and owns the local village and all the people in it. They love him and he looks after them. My niece, Rachel, is exactly the same age as you, date of birth 29th March 1968. She has three children all in their late teens and early twenties, and they are all students. My brother, Bill, and his wife, Christine, live in France and they are hoping to visit Rachel, but Bill isn't sure if he will be allowed to cross the border into Italy because of the coronavirus pandemic. Everywhere is in lockdown at the moment. The virus is causing havoc.

If I am right about Dolly then the worst of our trials are over.

Yours etcetera

Cc Dr Twee Dampensquib

Friday 6th November 2020. I wrote the following letter to Lucy this afternoon: - Friday 6th November 2020

Empress Lucy Lawless, The Queen of Heaven,

Dear Soulmate,

The bastards have just injected me again with paliperidone. I did refuse, but they called in the ward manager, a hard woman called Emma Bosslady, and she threatened to call in a team of bully boys to hold me down and inject me against my will. She meant business, so I let the girl inject me with the drug rather than put up a pointless physical struggle which I would lose. I told Emma and the girl not to expect any favours from me in future.

I'm not going to communicate with Twee Dampensquib again, nor send him copies of my letters. He is not a good psychiatrist and he is not a good man. If he had any sense, he would have taken me off the drugs, but he is obviously too scared of Dolly to do so. After this morning's letter I have nothing further to say to him. There is no law against me wishing him dead. If that results in his assassination then that is his lookout for defying the will of the Emperor.

I take back what I said about Dolly being a sport in the end. She is not just a rotten sport; she is a coward and not a sport at all. She is a power maniac and it looks like she is going to bring about the end of the world. She is that stupid, and the vast numbers of her followers are so stupid that they haven't got what it takes to save themselves, nor choose a leader, myself, who could save them.

Many people on TV are talking about closing doors, which is something everyone in the UK and Europe is being made to do, now that we are in a state of lockdown. I hope all this talk and all these doors being closed has the desired effect on Dolly. As I have said before, a fight to the finish is a fight to the finish. That is obviously what the evil old witch is asking for and it is what I am giving her. There is no longer any humanity left in my relationship with her. I am fighting Dolly to the end in order to save all living things from extinction caused by irreversible Climate Change.

If she really cares about anything at all she would go NOW and duckify herself. Otherwise, there will be no future at all, not even for ducks.

I'm sorry I haven't been able to dance with you very often lately. It is all the fault of the paliperidone. I still love you as much as ever, and I'm sure I'll get my sex drive back eventually when I come off the drug. It is very frustrating for both of us.

Our trials are not over yet.

Yours etcetera

AND I wrote the following letter to Dr Twee Dampensquib this morning: -
Friday Morning 6th November 2020

> Dr Twee Dampensquib,
> Medical Director,
> Alcatraz Island Hospital.

Dear Twee,

Okay, so the old witch hasn't gone yet but everyone knows that she will soon, and when she does, I will become the man in charge. I won't forget the decision that you make today and I will judge you accordingly. Be pragmatic, Twee. Change your attitude to the medication in my case. You can't afford to upset me and you know it. My left arm and my left hand really have been damaged by last month's injection, and I won't allow a repeat of this today. The old witch is protecting you from my influence today, but that protection won't last long, and I will still be around when she has gone.

Dr Chris Shyster is in the news every day but I am not worried about Christopher's safety. Jim Shyster is too scared of ME to kill Christopher, but the doctor is still in the frame. To quote the name of the BBC series, Doctor WHO? You are in the frame, Twee, and your only way out of it is to take me off the medication today. I can wait for my other demands to be obeyed. I can't go anywhere for a while anyway because of the coronavirus restrictions.

Yours sincerely,

Robert Strong.
CcLucy Lawless.

Saturday 7th November 2020. I wrote the following letter to Lucy this evening: -
Saturday Evening 7th November 2020
Empress Lucy Lawless, The Queen of Heaven,

Dear Soulmate,

Donald Trump and Dorothy Ayres have got something in common – they are both very bad losers, indicating a fundamental immaturity in both of those people.

Donald Trump has lost the race for the American Presidency. Joe Biden clinched it this afternoon with a thirty-four thousand vote victory in Pennsylvania. I think it was the governor of Pennsylvania who said yesterday, that Donald Trump should now put on his big boy pants, accept that he has lost and congratulate the winner, Joe Biden. Donald has lost to the better man.

Likewise, in the race for MY love, YOUR qualities make YOU the clear winner. You are the only one who is woman enough to stand by me, in the face of opposition from Dorothy Ayres and her friend, Satan. In so doing you have earned my undying, eternal and wholehearted love. Dorothy Ayres should now put on her big girl's blouse, admit defeat and congratulate YOU on being the winner. Dorothy has lost to the better woman.

Donal Trump refuses to concede defeat. He is pursuing futile attempts to have the decision overturned by mounting legal challenges. He won't succeed and his temper tantrums will only get worse. He will have to accept the reality in the end that the better man won.

Dorothy Ayres refuses to concede defeat. She is prolonging the agony of her existence although she has no hope of ever getting what she wants, and we all know what that is. She too, will have to accept reality in the end and admit that the better woman won.

Neither Dorothy Ayres nor Donald Trump should ever have been in the positions of eminence that society put them in. It just goes to show that the ordinary people are not good judges of character. So it is just as well that a man with MY wisdom should be the ultimate judge.

I don't think Donald Trump or Dorothy Ayres will be on the scene for much longer. People get rid of losers. They take the attitude, "If you can't beat them, then join them". We have proven that they can't beat US, so everyone is joining us.

Our trials will soon be over.

Yours etcetera

Saturday 14th November 2020. My late mother, Mrs Dorothy (Dolly) Ayres, still has enough of a personal following to keep her in power, and she obviously has no intention of giving up power as long as she can cling onto it. She won't be able to cling onto power when enough of her followers switch sides and follow me instead, because leaders are only leaders due to the loyalty of their followers. Most, if not all, of Dolly's followers will change their minds about who they want for a leader when Global Warming and Climate Change start hitting them where it really hurts. All I can do is hope and pray that Dolly's followers come to their senses in time for me to save them, before Climate Change becomes irreversible. As I have said before, Climate Change is like a huge juggernaut; you have to apply the brakes early for it to stop in time; you can't leave it until the last minute to apply the brakes. In this analogy the brakes are the stopping of the burning of all fossil fuels thereby eliminating carbon emissions. Our present political leaders aim to get Britain and the USA both carbon neutral by the year 2050, and in China by the year 2060, but I am sure that all this is far too little, far too late. Climate Change will become irreversible long before then. That is not just my opinion; it is the opinion of the majority of climate change scientists. I still think Climate Change will become irreversible in the year 2028 unless we get the whole world carbon neutral by the end of 2027. This will mean a huge upheaval of our whole way of life, but it CAN be done and it MUST be done if we are to prevent the whole world from becoming uninhabitable.

The world is coming to the end of an era. It is the era in which Dolly rules the world. When the new era begins, it will be the era in which I will rule the world. That will be the arrival of God's Kingdom on Earth that all major religions have prophesied will arrive one day. That day will be the day that Dolly relinquishes power by coming back to life as an animal, probably a duck. That will be the final triumph of good over evil if it happens in time for me to save the world, otherwise it will be the triumph of evil and it will be the end of the world.

Dr Twee Dampensquib insists on forcing me to take antipsychotic medication which suppresses my libido, and stops me from having mental sex with my soulmate, Lucy. This is the last thing that a sensible doctor should be doing. I cannot persuade Dolly's followers to follow me instead until I can give them an outlet for their sexual desires by having mental sex with my partner myself. Although he doesn't realise it, Dampensquib is obeying Dolly's wishes by forcing me to take this drug. It is her way of punishing me for refusing to have mental sex with her. I think Dampensquib is only following the text books on psychiatry, not realising that they were written by Dolly's followers.

I sent the above entry in a letter to Lucy with a copy to Dr Twee

Dampensquib.

Sunday 15th November 2020. I wrote the following letter to Lucy today: -
Sunday 15th November 2020

Empress Lucy Lawless, The Queen of Heaven,

Dear Soulmate,

I can offer you a consoling thought: I am inflicting far more misery upon my late mother, Mrs Dorothy (Dolly) Ayres, than she is inflicting upon us. The fact that she still fancies me gives me the power to do this, and I am doing it for all I am worth. As long as she exists as an old dead woman she will exist in a state of abject misery, I am happy to say. I am getting schadenfreude (malicious delight) out of her state of mind. I am not normally sadistic, but I am getting such glee out of what I am doing to the old witch because I HAVE GOT SEVENTY-SEVEN YEARS OF HER BULLYING TO PAY HER BACK FOR. (There go the Gods again with my Caps Lock button). She has been an absolute monster to me all my life, so I have no sympathy for her at all.

I can tell that my policy is working by the weather here in the UK: torrential rain and very STRONG winds. This weather will continue until the old witch comes back as a duck. I am sure that she will soon concede that MY WILL is stronger than hers and duckify herself; her only alternative is to continue to exist in a state of abject misery until she does. This will prove once and for all that MY WILL is the WILL OF GOD and it is the strongest force in the Universe. Anyone who argues with that (including Twee Dampensquib) CAN GO THE SAME WAY AS DOLLY. (THE GODS AGAIN).

We are still on course for our holiday together in August 2021. Look forward to it. The world will soon start turning the tap off.

Our trials will soon be over.

Yours etcetera

Cc Dr Twee Dampensquib

Monday 16th November 2020. I wrote the following letter to Lucy this evening: - Monday Evening 16th November 2020

Empress Lucy Lawless, The Queen of Heaven,

Dear Soulmate,

The weather here in the UK really is very gloomy, the same as Dolly's outlook. I am the best man that she knows or knows of, so that gives me power over her. The longer I have to wait for freedom from her influence, the more I despise her, and the more I despise her the worse I make her misery. She will never know happiness again until she comes back as a duck, I am happy to say. The more I have to take these evil injections and the longer I am a prisoner in a mental hospital the worse I make her suffer. SHE is to blame for all my suffering, and she is also to blame for all your suffering, so we can both delight in her suffering until she duckifies herself. I'm sure she can't take much more of this, so we will both soon be free to love each other and do whatever we want to do.

There will be vaccines against COVID-19 early next year, so I am looking forward to my discharge, then. We are still on course for our holiday together next August. *My Journey Back – Part Three* is due for publication on the 26th of this month, so I will of course send you a copy. You will like my cover design.

Dolly will be departing soon, and when she does, I will then be the man in charge, so Dampensquib had then better obey my demands as stated in my letter to him of the 15th October 2020. I am enclosing a copy of that letter. I don't think I need to write to him again.

Our trials are just about over.

Yours etcetera

Cc Dr Twee Dampensquib

Thursday 19th November 2020. I wrote the following letter to Lucy this morning: - Thursday Morning 19th November 2020

Empress Lucy Lawless, The Queen of Heaven,

Dear Soulmate,

In the spirit world, the only currency is emotional strength. Pounds and dollars are of no consequence there. That is why, in reality, I AM THE RICHEST MAN IN THE WORLD AND YOU ARE THE RICHEST WOMAN. (There go the Gods again with my Caps Lock button!). That is why I and you are the King and Queen of Heaven and our love is the priceless jewel in our crowns.

I repeat that if you offer sincere love to the one person who is the right one for you then you will get sincere love back in return; offer it to anyone else and all you will get is heartache. Aphrodite is not the Goddess of Love for nothing! When I discovered mental sex, I tried to have sex with you because your personality, as Xena, impressed me when little else did. Aphrodite then made me aware that you would be the right person for me, in spite of our age difference. I trusted Aphrodite's judgement because she had always been right before in my life when she had made me aware that other girls would be the wrong ones for me, although I had very strong feelings for Jasmin 2, who treated me better than anyone else has ever done before or since, and you have proven Aphrodite right I'm delighted to say.

I looked you up on the internet, and I discovered some things about you. For a start, you are not impecunious as I had thought. They said that you are worth twenty million USD. (I presume they meant US$). I also discovered that you are not living in fear of your husband; you seem to have a happy life, although I could tell from some of the things you say that I do have a STRONG influence on you. I therefore revert to my previous thought that you do not communicate with me because you still have a childish streak in you and you are indeed precocious. Not that I object to that. It is one of the things that make you appeal to me, but I was upset at first. It made me think along the lines that I am looking for a partner, not a student.

There is a lot you have yet to learn about life and about people, especially MEN, but I am happy to teach you. I thought that I could only teach you to treat me the way I want you to by dancing with other women, but then I thought better of that idea. You deserve better than to have an unfaithful lover. You have a good brain and you are capable of understanding and reasoning, so I thought I'd write you this letter explaining my thoughts. I'm sure that, because of circumstances beyond our control at the moment, we are both prone to adulterous thoughts, but we both consider each other's feelings and behave ourselves, and that's the way it should be with lovers.

I'm sure that you will behave like a woman who loves me when I am free to respond like a man who loves you. That won't be until my late mother disappears and Dampensquib takes me off these evil drugs that dampen my sex drive. That will all happen in the near future, my Love, so continue to be patient and everything will come to those who wait, as long

as they don't give up the struggle.
Our trials are just about over.
Yours etcetera

Cc Dr Twee Dampensquib

Chapter 17

The Punishment from the Gods

Events and Thoughts from Saturday 21st November 2020.

Saturday 21st November 2020. There was a person mentioned on the BBC news channel yesterday, by the name of Robin Marlowe. This was good news for me because it was their way of telling the world that "Rob" is "in" and that "Ma" is feeling "low". I am staying in, now that I have gained the ascendancy over my late mother, and Ma is going to feel progressively ever lower until she duckifies herself.

The weather in Great Britain lately, especially here in the south of England has been very gloomy and miserable. It is influenced by the feelings of misery of my late mother, Mrs Dorothy (Dolly) Ayres, and by my feelings of anger at the abysmal way I have been treated for nearly all my life. The weather is cloudy with overcast skies and dark clouds, much rain and STRONG winds. I can keep this pressure up until Dolly has had enough of it and clears off, out of the human race. Her only alternative is to spend eternity in ever increasing misery if she continues to exist as an old dead woman, and continues to wield power over me. She has NO HOPE of EVER getting what she wants, and the sooner she realises it the better.

The world has been suffering all this year from the coronavirus pandemic. The virus has killed hundreds of thousands of people and brought misery to almost everybody. I am relatively unaffected here in my hospital ward. I am well shielded. The only drawback for me is that I can't go shopping once a fortnight as I used to do, but a courier goes to the supermarket in town once a week and does shopping for us patients. All I have to do is prepare my shopping list and make sure the cash is in my hospital account for him. I am inconvenienced by the fact that I can't get my hair cut, but that is a small price to pay.

There is a group of "terrorists" called the Islamic State group, ISIS, and they have a saying that the virus is "God's little soldier". I agree with them. I think that the coronavirus pandemic has been visited upon the human race by the Gods in Heaven to punish mankind for following the false God, Mrs Dorothy Ayres, and opening the door to her decadent ways; and also for treating ME, the King of the Gods, so abysmally and defying MY WILL.

I feel sorry for the people of Britain; many of them are suffering terribly through no fault of their own, but they really should have heeded my warnings written clearly in the Bible, "I am the Lord thy God and thou shalt have no other Gods before me". Everybody knows that God is a man and Dorothy Ayres is only a woman, so she cannot be God. She has been peddling decadence disguised as diversity, and a society which condones decadence is a society in decay, which is what we have got in the world at the moment, especially the so-called "free world", in which same-sex sexual relationships have been legalised. I said clearly in the Bible that, "Man shall not go with man". And the same thing obviously goes for women. The meaning is clear to every adult.

Many people have known all my life who I am, but they haven't had the courage nor the decency to proclaim my arrival to the world. They have left me to find it out for myself and to proclaim my arrival to the world myself. I hope and trust that the pandemic is making those moral cowards suffer. That is what they deserve.

The pandemic is testing the mettle of the majority of men and women, and that is not a bad thing in itself. Too many people had thought they could get away with an easy life and leave the hard suffering to others (including ME), but now that they are finding out that life is hard for all of us, and we are all in the same boat, so to speak. We are all no more than ants on the surface of this planet and we all have to die one day. So, it is good to have enough food to eat and a bed to sleep in, so be thankful for small mercies.

Two thousand five hundred years ago, the Greek poet and author, Homer, wrote in a saga called *The Odyssey* that Odysseus was shipwrecked for the second time after leaving Calisto for his home on the island of Ithaca and his wife, Penelope. When he was struggling for survival, he heard the sea God, Poseidon, laughing at him. When he heard this, he said in despair to Poseidon, "Why are you treating me so cruelly?" Poseidon replied, "To teach you what a King needs to know." Odysseus then said, "And what is that?" Poseidon replied, "That for all his abilities, without the Gods, man is nothing!"

In his conceit mankind seems to have forgotten Homer's wisdom. It is just as well for mankind that I, the King, have not done so. There is a lesson here for all secularists and atheists, which is what I used to be when I was a boy. The lesson is that when things go wrong and you don't know why; when things just don't add up the way you think they ought to; then look to your own ideas of what's what and correct your own thinking, for that is where you have been going wrong. Ask yourself, "What am I?" and "Who am I really?" And be honest with yourself. You have to correct yourself when you cannot correct your circumstances according to your own thinking.

I sent a copy of the above entry in a letter to Lucy with a copy to Dr Twee Dampensquib.

Sunday 22nd November 2020. I wrote the following letter to Lucy today: - Sunday 22nd November 2020

Empress Lucy Lawless, The Queen of Heaven,

Dear Soulmate,

Society in the UK tried to make a murderer out of me and succeeded. They also tried to make a motherfucker out of me and failed. They have also tried to make a bigamist out of me and failed, and I'll tell you why. I had thought of punishing you for not communicating with me for the last twenty-one years by making you share me with another woman. I thought of making you my number one wife and my ex, Jasmin 2, as my concubine. If that is what you want, it could still be arranged. Many men throughout history who have been leaders have also been polygamists, but I feel sorry for those guys because they are all only looking for true love and failing to find it.

Last night I watched a concert of yours on the internet, and when you sang, "She will never ever love you like I do", I knew that you were singing those words to ME, and my heart just flew away with love for you.

I have now outgrown both my parents and assumed my rightful position as the King of the Gods. I now lead society; it doesn't lead me. I lead by example, and my example is that a leader should believe in monogamy if he wants his people to practise monogamy. Monogamy only works when two people, a man and a woman, love each other and their marriage is blessed and supported by the Gods in Heaven.

I think the time is coming soon when you are going to make big changes in your life, socially and professionally. Socially, your relationship with your husband, Rob Tapert, has now deteriorated because you don't love him any more and the Gods have blessed your relationship with me. I am still waiting for you. I have forgiven you for not communicating with me. I have accepted that it is part of your maturing process and it is the price I have to pay for falling in love with someone so much younger than myself. I want you to leave Rob Tapert and come to England early next year and be MY WOMAN. Dolly will be gone by then and I will have acquired her power. I will be free and wealthy.

Professionally, you have reached the top of your profession as an actress and singer, and you have nowhere else to go and nothing else to prove. I think you are growing tired of being a glamour girl and are looking for something more fulfilling and rewarding professionally; something that will recognise you as an important woman and not just as someone who has to be patronised. I suggest that you could use your time, your money and your leadership qualities best by embarking upon a career in politics. Early next year, when I am free, I will register The Survival Party with the Electoral Commission in the UK. I have got a new political Party to build, and I am now looking for the right personnel to help me run it. If you agree with my ideas in my Manifesto, I would welcome you with open arms if you would like to help me run the Party as a husband-and-wife team! It would fulfil both our ambitions, professionally and socially.

I need to know what you think, Lucy. Please stop being a silly girl and communicate with me. Let me know what you think of the ideas in this letter. I need to know if you feel ready yet for a change in your life. If you take me up on this offer it will mean you coming to England and getting to know new people and making new friends. Have you outgrown your parents yet? And are you ready yet to assume your rightful position as the Queen of the Gods? Do you trust me yet to love you and to go on loving you whatever life throws at us? I trust your love, Lucy, to do that for me. Please write to me by letter or email.

Our trials are just about over.

Take care of yourself, my Love, I have much more to say to you, but it can wait until we talk, Bless you, my Queen,

Yours with Love, Affection and Friendship,

The King of Heaven,
Emperor_Bob XX
Cc Dr Twee Dampensquib

Monday 23rd November 2020. I wrote the following letter to Lucy this evening: - Monday Evening 23rd November 2020
    Empress Lucy Lawless, The Queen of Heaven,

Dear Soulmate,

We now have three vaccines here in the UK just about ready to be rolled out. One of them, the Oxford University vaccine, is especially good at preventing COVID-19 in older people, which is good news for me. Boris Johnson said on TV this evening that all the people in the UK who need it should be inoculated by Easter. (Good Friday falls on the 2nd April next year). So, whatever happens we will have to continue to be patient for at least another four months. After that, I want to get on with the job of building The Survival Party, as I think Dolly will be gone by then and I will have her power and influence and my public apology, compensation money and my freedom.

I saw you in concert on the internet, and when you sang, *I'll stand by you* I knew you were singing those words to me, and I thought, "Yes my Love, I know you will. You've already proven it. I will stand by you too, my Love, through thick and thin, whatever you have done and whatever you do in the future. I'm your man and you're my woman, and I've never been more proud of anybody than I am of you."

If you are thinking of making the changes that I wrote to you about yesterday, I want you to know that I appreciate that it will test your mettle, but that will be a good thing. It will give you a more mature outlook on life. In any event, you've got a good four months to think about it. We can't make a move before next Easter.

I asked the internet, "When will Climate Change become irreversible?". The answer came back, "In twelve years' time", but that was posted eighteen months ago, so at best it will happen in 2031, which means that we've got to get worldwide carbon emissions down to zero by the end of 2030. I still think it is best to set a target date of the end of 2027, as that gives us a three year safety margin if we overrun. Always assuming that the internet is correct. They claim it is the opinion of the majority of Climate Change scientists. Even with a target date of 2030, none of Dolly's followers have got what it takes to avert the impending catastrophe. I am the only man with the proven courage and the political will to get carbon emissions down in time to prevent disaster. The Survival Party is the means by which I can do this.

Everything depends on my late mother coming back to life very soon, whatever she chooses to come back as, thereby clearing a pathway for me to get into power in time to do my work. I don't think she will try to come back as a human being again. Unless she comes back soon, extinction becomes a certainty for the whole world, starting in 2031. It's up to us and all our supporters and followers to make sure that Dolly's existence (I won't say "life", as she is already dead) is made a thorough misery so she will be glad to duckify herself to get away from us. She will NEVER get what she wants as long as she remains as an old dead woman.

Xena was supposed to have the power to kill Gods. This is how it's done! You have to bring them back to life, preferably as animals. Gods should be more careful not to upset more powerful people than themselves.

I'm not sending anyone a copy of this letter but it will be published in *My Journey Back – Part Four.*

The worst of our trials are just about over.

Yours etcetera

Friday 27th November 2020. I wrote the following letter to Lucy today: - Friday 27th November 2020

Empress Lucy Lawless, The Queen of Heaven,

Dear Soulmate,

Just a line to keep in touch, I know how you feel when you hear from me. I remain optimistic that my late mother will depart from the human race in the near future because I can tell by the weather that she remains in existence in a state of misery. The weather in the south of England remains dismal, as it has done for a long time. Today we had a thick fog which lasted until mid-day and it has been very cold all day. When the fog lifted it revealed an overcast sky which still looks oppressive.

I'm sure she knows by now that I am intent upon keeping her in a state of misery until she gets fed up with it and duckifies herself. She is, therefore, only hanging on to see if I can and will continue with this policy. I am proving that I can and do.

Sigmund Freud, the father of modern psychiatry, taught that every man secretly wants to kill his father and have sex with his mother. He thought that because that was his desire, it was every man's desire. To think that way is to make the false extrapolation to the general from the particular. That is a definition of paranoia. The psychiatric profession are therefore a body of people who are indoctrinated with a belief system based upon the teachings of a paranoid motherfucker. Dolly herself follows the teachings of Freud, which is why she can't understand me. She can't understand that she just doesn't turn me on, sexually, which is what she wants to do. But she never will because I am a real man, and a real man is not a motherfucker; not in my book!

The psychiatric profession are more mentally ill than any of their "patients" in my estimation. Perhaps that is why the world is undergoing a "mental health" crisis at the moment. It is certainly the reason why their profession is the one with the highest suicide rate! They think that mental health is to have mental sex with the late Mrs Dorothy Ayres, their heroine: The Global Village bike: the dirtiest slut in the history of the world, who opens her legs for every man; the easiest and the cheapest fuck in the world! As my mother, I couldn't be more ashamed of her. She is a foul creature and before long she will be a fowl creature. So, it is perhaps fitting that she should become a duck.

I'm sending a copy of this letter to Twee Dampensquib, so that he will know what I think of his ideas.

The worst of our trials are just about over.

Yours etcetera

I received my complimentary copies of *My Journey Back – Part Three* today and sent a copy with the above letter to Lucy. I was not happy with the front cover, so I wrote the following letter to my publisher today: -

Friday 27th November 2020
Kristina Shyster,
Production Coordinator,
Olympia Publishers,
Tallis House, 2 Tallis Street,

London EC4Y 0AB.

Re: My Journey Back – Part Three
Dear Kristina,

I received my complimentary copies of the finished book today, as per my contract with Olympia, and I am writing to say that I am bitterly disappointed with the front cover design. It was not what I had signed the proof certificate to say that I had accepted.

The version of the cover design that I signed up to clearly had the word SUPERGLUE written on the tube. The version on the finished book just had the word GLUE written on the tube. This spoils the whole ethos of the picture because everybody knows that superglue creates a bond that cannot be broken; ordinary glue does not create such a good bond.

Please let me know, by email, how many copies of the book were printed, because if it is not too late, I wish to have the book reprinted with the front cover amended to my accepted proof. I feel that someone in your production department has not followed the letter of our agreement, and they have made a bad mistake.

If the front cover can be amended and the book reprinted, I would gladly come to a new financial arrangement to avoid bad feeling between Olympia and myself. Please discuss this letter with your management team and let me know what they think about this situation.

Yours sincerely,

Bob Strong.

Sunday 29th November 2020. I wrote the following letter to Lucy today: -
Sunday 29th November 2020

Empress Lucy Lawless, The Queen of Heaven,

Dear Soulmate,

Your copy of *My Journey Back – Part Three* is on its way to you. As you can see from the enclosed letter, which is a copy of the one I sent to my publishers, I am not happy with the front cover. I am definitely going to have the cover amended and the book reprinted, however many copies they printed.

My calculations are proving correct. Dolly is getting fed up with existing in a state of perpetual misery and is looking for a way to end it. This is evidenced by the fact that she visited me this morning and turned on the charm, hoping to seduce me. She gave me a smile which was warm and loving and knowing, but I have a gut feeling that I do not want sex with that woman, so I hardened my heart against her, and when she touched my leg with her hand, I said to her in a strong tone of voice, "Get Out! Turn yourself into a duck!". She then took herself out of my mind. I expect she will try again until she finally gets the point that I don't want to know her, then I feel sure she will duckify herself as that is the only way she will mend her broken heart. I am finally winning the endgame.

I have felt your love very strongly today. Bless you, my Love, I hope you can feel my love for you. The cumulative effect of years of antipsychotic drugs has completely suppressed my libido; I haven't had an erection let alone an orgasm for ages. I'm so looking forward to coming off the drugs when Dolly duckifies herself, but we must both have superhuman patience until then, Darling.

I don't want to know my ex, Jasmin 2, any more. She did not have what it takes to stand by me in the face of opposition from Dolly and her friend, Satan. She became sycophantic towards Dolly towards the end of our relationship, and I was disappointed with her for that. That was why I got fed up with my first wife, Jasmin 1.

The worst of our trials are just about over.

Yours etcetera

Tuesday 1st December 2020. I wrote the following letter to Dr Twee Dampensquib this morning: - Tuesday 1st December 2020

Dr Twee Dampensquib,
Medical Director,
Alcatraz Island Hospital.

Dear Twee,

I'm sure you will agree that the weather here has been very miserable lately. Even the weather is influenced by my late mother's feelings. It will remain miserable until she comes back to life as a duck.

On Sunday, a racing driver whose surname is Grojon had an accident. His car hit the crash barrier and burst into flames. The doctor who rescued Grojon from the burning car has the name of Dr Ian Roberts. Dr Roberts said yesterday on television that it was only the fact that the car was fitted with a halo that saved Grojon's life.

I am due for another injection of paliperidone on Sunday. I want you to take me off all antipsychotic medication before then. I am sure it is in your interest to do so, as there is nothing wrong with me.

Yours sincerely,

Robert Strong.
Cc Lucy Lawless.

Saturday 5th December 2020. I wrote the following letter to Lucy this morning: - Saturday Morning 5th December 2020
  Lucy Lawless, The Golden GIRL Herself,

Dear Soulmate,

I know you love me because I can feel your love almost every day, and you have visited me in spirit many times wanting mental love-making and I have always obliged when I can because that is what I want as well. I can't do anything at the moment because of these evil psychiatric Bastards and their filthy drugs. If it wasn't for the paliperidone I'd be as virile as any man, even at my age. But we can still transmit our feelings for each other telepathically, like we do.

Try looking up the lyrics to "Once I had a secret love", and also, "When you tell me that you love me". I know you do really love me, but I just wish you were woman enough to tell me so, let alone to tell the world. I know you never reply to letters from your fans, but is that all I am to you? Just another fan? Does your celebrity status mean more to you than your own womanhood? I ask this because that's the way it seems to me.

It hurts me that you don't write to me. When you hurt someone you love, you hurt yourself as well. Please stop hurting both of us by not replying to my letters. Please reply and tell me your thoughts. I tell you all mine. Let me know if you are considering a change of career and a change of husband. Tapert will never ever love you like I do.

I am winning the battle of wills with my late mother. It takes time and tries the patience of both of us, but we will get there in the end. I'm sure she will turn herself into a duck to avoid the heartache and misery, loneliness and fear that I am putting her through. This is no less than she deserves for the way she has treated me all my life. I still believe that true love conquers all, and that what we have got is true love. My belief in this is as strong as ever.

Yours etcetera

Tuesday 8th December 2020. I wrote the following letter to Lucy this morning: - Tuesday Morning 8th December 2020

Lucy Lawless, The Golden GIRL Herself,

Dear Soulmate,

The entire International Community has been putting you and me and all our followers through a series of tests. They have been testing our patience and courage and our faith in each other and our love. That is what these antipsychotic drugs have been for – to test me, and therefore to test you too. The darkest hour came last week when I felt that the rest of my life would be spent as a prisoner in a mental hospital and on libido suppressing drugs, but I still refused to be a motherfucker; I resigned myself to a life as a celibate and as a prisoner. But at least I had the knowledge THAT I HAD PROVED TO MYSELF THAT I AM A REAL MAN. (There go the Gods again with my Caps Lock button). In doing so I passed their test, and my own.

The evidence for all this came with the beginning of the dawn of MY era yesterday on the BBC news channel. All the news was presented in such a way as to convince anyone with any grey matter between their ears that the establishment are now following ME. I have won the war against my late mother. Her existence is now being spent in Hell and her only way out of it is to come back as an animal. She will soon realise this and go. That is the only way by which she will ever be happy again.

Antonio Guterres, the Secretary General of the United Nations, has been saying all last week the things that I have been saying to you and in my journals for years. Such as the fact that mankind has been waging a suicidal war against nature and that nature is fighting back with devastating effects on many human communities. He says that all nations must cut their carbon emissions by forty-five per cent by 2030 and the remaining fifty-five per cent by 2050. He has better access than me to the world's Climate Change scientists, so I will go along with his targets for the cutting of carbon emissions. To achieve one hundred per cent reduction in emissions before 2028 would be too much to ask I think, upon reflection.

These targets are more in line with what the Green Party have set themselves, so I am thinking about re-joining the Green Party rather than instituting a new Party of my own as a one-man band. There are a lot of things to consider and I would welcome your thoughts on this matter. Now I know that I am not a lone voice on Climate Change, I feel a lot better. It is good to know that other people have the same ideas, especially someone as important as Antonio Guterres.

There was a time when I wanted to be the Secretary General of the United Nations, but Antonio is already doing a good job in that role. I can perhaps best use myself as a member of the Green Party, and maybe become a Member of Parliament, perhaps even Party Leader and Prime Minister, although I am getting on a bit in years, so maybe that would not be achievable.

Keep your faith in me, Darling, and in our love. Even though I can't dance with you at the moment, the end of our trials is in sight. Dolly will be gone soon and then I will come off the drugs and get my Public Apology, compensation money and my FREEDOM. I don't intend to retire to a life without purpose, and I would like to discuss life with you and make plans for the future, both my future and yours, with you. If you love me, you will do as I ask and communicate with me. You are a person and that is what people do – they communicate.

The end of our trials is in sight.

Yours etcetera

Cc. Dr Twee Dampensquib.

Friday 11th December 2020. I wrote the following letter to Lucy this evening: - Friday Evening 11th December 2020

Lucy Lawless, The Golden GIRL Herself,

Dear Soulmate,

My late mother will stay existing in the misery of Hell until she feels that she has had as much misery as she deserves and then she will end it all by coming back to life as an animal, probably a duck. She will not know happiness again until she does that, and the weather here in the UK will remain miserable until she does that.

As I have said before, the UK is the hub of the Empire that we call "The Free World", so it is fitting that the people of the UK should suffer the most in the declining weeks and months of Dolly's reign. It is not just the miserable weather, but also the coronavirus pandemic, and the effects of Brexit without a trade deal with the European Union – this will inevitably mean chaos for the UK, the decimation of our manufacturing industry and the loss of hundreds of thousands of jobs; and then there is the crisis of Climate Change looming ever closer on the horizon – it is already impacting people's lives quite dramatically and this is just the beginning of it.

All this is the fault of the people themselves for idolising a woman with such low morals as Mrs Dorothy Ayres who peddles decadence disguised as diversity in the name of "the permissive society". As I've said before, "a society which condones decadence is a society in decay". The things I have mentioned in the above paragraph are the effects of this decay. Mankind ignores the power of the Gods at his peril. This decay is the inevitable consequence of treating ME, the King of the Gods, so abysmally and for following the decadent ways of my late mother.

It is wrong to commit sins, but every adult does so. It is therefore necessary for all people to repent of their sins, for I don't forgive those who don't repent and say "SORRY", AND MEAN IT! Unrepentant sinners go to Hell. There they are treated like pariahs – social outcasts – until they can't take any more of it and come back as animals, having proved unworthy of calling themselves "human beings". I try not to be a hypocrite. I have apologised to Iris, the woman I killed, and she and I have forgiven each other for our sins. We have come to an understanding in which we both know our place, and know better than to step out of line again. She is now happy to be one of my project leaders.

I have done much soul-searching and decided, without your help which was not forthcoming, not to re-join the Green Party, but to continue with my ambitions for The Survival Party. I am not a very good team-player. I am a good leader, and it is in my nature to be the leader of any enterprise I turn my hand to. So, I am sticking to my plans for The Survival Party, but I am revising my target dates for the cutting of carbon emissions to those quoted by Antonio Guterres, the Secretary General of the United Nations, and praying to Heaven that Antonio has got his figures correct. My offer remains open to you, Lucy, to help me run the Party as a husband-and-wife team, if this offer appeals to you. You've got three or four months to think about it. Dolly should be gone by then and I will have acquired all her power and influence, as well as having cleared my name with a public apology and got my £x in compensation money and my freedom.

I don't have any sex drive at all these days, so I am hoping that Twee Dampensquib will soon consider that I have passed his tests and take me off the antipsychotic drugs. He is being needlessly cruel by keeping me on them. The fact that he hasn't taken me off them yet must mean that he is insisting on waiting until my late mother disappears first. Hopefully that won't be too long now. She is suffering more than I am until then. I know the pain of unrequited love, but I proved man enough to get over it when I found a better woman in YOU, dear. She has not proven woman enough to get over losing me, and she surely has lost all human feeling from me, and she will never find a better man than me and she knows it. In my opinion she is a disgusting creature to be an intolerable sex pest to her own son, and the human race will be better off without her.

The end of our trials is in sight.

Yours etcetera

Cc. Dr Twee Dampensquib.

Saturday 12th December 2020. I emailed my publisher today, asking her to get in touch with Superglue and ask their permission to use their trademark on our front cover. I said that I expect they will be delighted with the free advertisement of their product and give us their permission to use the name 'SUPERGLUE' on the cover of my book, in which case I want the book reprinted with my approved cover design. I said that I will be willing to share the cost of this reprint.

Sunday 13th December 2020. I wrote the following letter to Lucy this morning: - Sunday Morning 13th December 2020

Lucy Lawless, The Golden GIRL Herself,

Dear Soulmate,

I note from the internet that you have a string of concert dates booked for 2021 in the USA, Canada and Australia. I wish you every success and I am sure you will enjoy the adulation of your thousands of idolising fans. Carry on with your singing and acting career and carry on wondering about the meaning of your life because you won't find out that way, old girl.

I still love you but I am angry with you for your failure to communicate with me and treat me like a person. There is no excuse for that behaviour. My offer is still open to you to come to England and help me run The Survival Party. You are looking for a fresh challenge, and I think this is it for you.

You can carry on wondering why you don't have the self-confidence of the men and women you know, who are laughing at you while they patronise you. We all know what you are going through because we've all been through it ourselves. Now it is your turn, old girl.

Carry on with your shallow, tinsel-town existence and carry on wondering what the Hell you are, and leave the job of saving the planet to those of us with the guts to prove to ourselves what we really are by our behaviour. Your life is what you make it, old girl.

I've given you all the help and guidance I can, Lucy. The rest is up to you, to actually do something to prove yourself. Try communicating with me. That way you'll find out what you really need to know, old girl.

The end of our trials is in sight.

Yours etcetera

Cc. Dr Twee Dampensquib.

Tuesday 15th December 2020. I wrote to the Chief Executive of the Superglue Corporation today, asking for his/her permission to use the word 'superglue' on the front cover of *My Journey Back – Part Three*. I then emailed my publisher informing them of what I've done, and I told them that if I get that permission then I want the book reprinted with the word 'superglue' on the front cover. I pointed out that the whole ethos of the picture is that the bond between God-the-Father and Mother Nature must be the strongest bond possible, and that means using superglue, not just "glue" as they initially printed on the book. I offered to pay half the cost of the reprint but I felt that the publisher should meet me half-way on the cost of the reprint as the mistake was theirs for going ahead with the print run using the word "glue" without my permission. That was not what I signed the proof certificate to say that I accepted. I added that if I did not get satisfaction then I would put the matter in the hands of my solicitor.

Wednesday 16th December 2020. I wrote the following letter to Dampensquib and Lucy this morning: - Wednesday Morning 16th December 2020

Dr Twee Dampensquib,
Medical Director,
Alcatraz Island Hospital.

Dear Twee,

I am just one man, but I have some powerful friends in the Gods in Heaven. I am their King, and they don't like the way their King is being treated. That is why they have visited the coronavirus pandemic upon the human race, to punish mankind for idolising Mrs Dorothy Ayres and for defying MY WILL by condoning same-sex sexual relationships. This punishment is the same as I put upon the cities of Sodom and Gomorrah in Biblical times, but on a global scale this time.

You are largely to blame for HUNDREDS OF THOUSANDS OF DEATHS, Twee, by your intransigent attitude to medicating me with antipsychotic drugs, when you know perfectly well that there is nothing wrong with me. How does that make you feel, Twee?

This letter is also going to Lucy Lawless. You, too, are largely to blame FOR HUNDREDS OF THOUSANDS OF DEATHS, Lucy, for having such a childish attitude to me by not communicating with me. How does that make you feel, Lucy? Does it add meaning to your meaningless way of life?

My late mother is mainly to blame for driving me to homicide in the first place, and then having me certified as mentally ill and detained for over forty-four years, forty-three of them being tortured with antipsychotic drugs. The sooner she takes herself out of the human race the better. I promised her that her misery would only get worse the longer she hangs about, prolonging the agony of her existence.

Yours sincerely,

Robert Strong.
Cc Lucy Lawless.

Thursday 17th December 2020. I wrote the following letter to Queen Elizabeth II this morning: - Thursday 17th December 2020

Queen Elizabeth II, 1₀ Windsor Castle,

Windsor,
Berks.

Dear Elizabeth,

As head of the Church of England, I thought you would like to see this copy of a letter which I wrote to my psychiatrist yesterday. The coronavirus pandemic is the direct consequence of weak moral leadership from the very top of society downwards. How does that make you feel, Elizabeth? Don't you now wish you had given me a Royal Pardon years ago when I asked you for one?

Yours sincerely,

Robert Strong.
Cc Paul Rees, Chief Executive, The Royal College of Psychiatrists.
Justin Welby, Archbishop of Canterbury.
Pope Francis.

And I wrote the following letter to Queen Elizabeth II as an afterthought: - Thursday 17th December 2020

Queen Elizabeth II, 1$_o$ Windsor castle,
Windsor,
Berks.

Dear Elizabeth,

The people keep exhorting me to save you, Elizabeth, when they sing the national anthem. But you have done nothing to save me for the last forty-five years.

Yours sincerely,

Robert Strong.

I sent copies of both the first letter to Queen Elizabeth II and my letter to Dr Twee Dampensquib of yesterday to the Queen and the other three people named in the copy list.

Chapter 18

The Revised Manifesto

Suggested Advertisement for the Manifesto

April 2021

My name is Robert Brooks Strong and I am here to answer mankind's call for help in solving the problem of Climate Change. I am just one man, but I am a real man and a natural leader of men and women. If you want proof of this, then read my autobiographies. They provide an interesting and enlightening read and are not too demanding of the reader. They can be accessed from my website. The address is: -

http://www.Robert-Brooks-Strong.OlympiaPublishers.com/

Antonio Guterres, the Secretary General of the United Nations said in December 2020, that the only way to prevent the catastrophic consequences of irreversible Climate Change is for every nation on the planet to cut their carbon emissions by forty-five per cent by 2030 and the remaining fifty-five per cent by 2050. The way to cut carbon emissions is to stop burning fossil fuels – coal, gas and oil. The Conservative Party and also the Green Party are following this lead by setting a target date of 2030, but I say this is too little, too late. I say we must cut carbon emissions by forty-nine per cent by the end of 2028 or Climate Change will become irreversible in 2029. If you want to know who I am to make this claim, then I say again, read my autobiographies; they will give you all the information you need to make an informed opinion concerning whose advice to trust.

This does mean changing over to electric vehicles instead of using vehicles with internal combustion engines: stop burning coal, gas and oil in power stations and rely instead upon solar-powered power stations and wind-powered power stations: and stop using gas-fired boilers and heaters, but rely instead upon electric heating. It also means stop flying in jet planes except when necessary; take your vacations in your home countries. This is all becoming possible as solar power becomes cheaper and cleaner than coal, and wind turbines also become better and cheaper as the technology progresses: electric aeroplanes are also under development and electric vehicles are becoming better and cheaper. But it does mean that we are in a race against time to cut carbon emissions by the target dates, and the whole human race is in this endeavour together.

To spearhead this combined effort, I have created The Survival Party of Great Britain with a practical programme of steps to be taken to cut carbon emissions in time. The name of the Party is not an exaggeration; the whole human race is in a fight for survival against Climate Change. Although the Party is British, my Manifesto contains steps to be taken at an international level to get ALL nations to join in this combined endeavour. I will send you free a copy of my Manifesto if you email the Party at [email address] with your name and postal address. You can then join the Party if you wish to support our aims. Membership costs just £12 a year, and with that money plus my personal funding of the Party, we will field candidates in every Parliamentary constituency in Great Britain in subsequent elections.

Join the Party and do your bit to save the planet.

There now follows a copy of the Revised Manifesto: -

MANIFESTO
OF THE SURVIVAL PARTY OF GREAT BRITAIN

April 2021

Party Leader, Robert Brooks Strong FIAP

My name is Robert Brooks Strong, and I am the founder and leader of The Survival Party of Great Britain. The name of the Party is not an exaggeration. The whole human race is fighting for its survival against Climate Change.

Antonio Guterres, the Secretary General of the United Nations, said in December 2020 that every nation on the planet must cut its emissions of carbon dioxide by forty-five per cent by 2030, and the remaining fifty-five per cent by 2050, otherwise the planet will overheat by more than 1.5° C which will cause Climate Change to become irreversible, with catastrophic consequences for all life on Earth as the planet will then become uninhabitable. I believe that Climate Change will become irreversible in 2029 unless we, the human race, cut our carbon emissions by forty-nine per cent by the end of 2028.

So, we, the human race, MUST cut our carbon emissions, and the only way to do this is to stop burning fossil fuels, coal, oil and gas. This Manifesto contains details of my five-year plan for the phased withdrawal of the burning of all fossil fuels. This plan will meet the target set for the end of the year 2028. It will mean a huge upheaval in our way of life, but this is necessary for our survival.

This Manifesto will be put forward to every national leader, who will then be exhorted to follow suit, unless they already have plans of their own to meet the necessary carbon reduction targets.

THE FIVE-YEAR PLAN

The first thing my Government will do is to stop the production of internal combustion engines and the manufacture of vehicles which use these engines immediately. It doesn't make sense to go on making engines which destroy the environment. We will also immediately embark upon a programme to install power points on all lamp posts in every city, town and village in Great Britain, so that owners of electric vehicles can charge their vehicles from these power points. A system could be introduced whereby all electric vehicles would have a fourth pin on their electric plug with the registration number of the vehicle encrypted on it, so that the electricity company would know who to charge for their electricity.

My Government would ban the sale of new vehicles with internal combustion engines after one year and the use of such vehicles on all British roads after five years; after that, all transport on British roads would be for electric vehicles, including motorbikes and lorries. The same limits would apply to all other devices using internal combustion engines, such as lawn mowers and cement mixers and electricity generators used in fairgrounds etcetera.

My Government would immediately invest in research and development of bigger and better batteries for use in vehicles and also for electricity storage and distribution. We would provide incentives for the development of solar power and for wind power. We would aim to make Great Britain solely dependent on renewable energy and nuclear energy within five years, by which time we would make coal-fired power stations, gas-fired power stations and oil-fired power stations obsolete.

We would still need oil for jet-engine aircraft, but people would only be allowed to fly by jet when necessary. People would have to take their vacations in their own countries. This is because jet-engine aircraft leave such a huge carbon footprint. The environment cannot sustain jet travel in anything like the pre-COVID volume of air traffic.

RECYCLING

Plastic pollution is currently a big problem. We would ban all single-use plastics, and we would build plastic recycling plants of sufficient size to recycle all the plastic used in the country. We would make it illegal to throw plastic onto landfill sites and this would be punishable with a large fine for offenders. Plastic recycling places would be introduced, as would sites for the recycling of paper, cardboard, wood and metals. It would be made compulsory to recycle all such materials with a large fine for disobeying this rule.

SHIPPING & AIR TRAVEL

My Government would liaise with other governments and the United Nations to secure international agreement on the following matters: -

Within five years all ships on the sea including cruise liners must be either battery powered or wind or solar powered.

Within five years all propeller driven aircraft and all helicopters must be either battery powered or solar powered.

Within one year all non-essential jet flights will not be allowed. Jet flights will only be allowed for the following purposes: -

1. Essential freight, including mail.

2. Medical and social emergencies.

3. Travel to international sporting and entertainment fixtures such as the World Cup matches and the Olympic Games, and the Eurovision Song Contest.

4. Business executives and national leaders travelling to international meetings and conferences.

5. Emigration and trips to attend employment interviews.

It is to be hoped that electric planes, currently under development, will become available within the next five years.

Leisure, vacations and tourism will not be considered as essential reasons for jet travel, and will not be allowed. This is because jet travel leaves such a huge carbon footprint. People can take their vacations in their home countries.

MORALITY

We feel strongly that the issue of public morals is one which this Government should make a stand on.

Ever since 1967, when same-sex sexual relationships were legalised, there has been a steady decline in public morality, and the social consequence of this are now becoming intolerable. The rise in knife crimes, murders and drug offences can be attributed to this "don't care" attitude to morals and the feeling that "anything goes". I will deal with crime and punishment shortly, but I wish to say at this point that sexual morals need to be corrected. It is self-evident that acts of sodomy and lesbian sex are filthy, unnatural and sordid. They are disgusting behaviour and should be discouraged. We say that the best way to discourage them is to penalise them, but not by making offenders spend years and years in prison. We would give offenders twenty-eight days solitary confinement multiplied by the cardinal number of the offence for each act of indecency. In other words: four weeks solitary for a first offence, eight weeks for a second offence, twelve weeks for a third offence and so on. Additionally, offenders would be required to take injections of antipsychotic drugs to help them lead celibate lives. We feel that the kindest way to handle members of the LGBTQ community is to treat them as people who have an incurable mental illness which causes them to have unnatural sexual proclivities. This does, of course, mean an end to the public obscenity of same-sex marriages.

THE WHOLE WORLD

The governments of every country in the world will be required to emulate the above policies unless they have their own programme of cuts in carbon emissions to reduce these emissions by forty-nine per cent by the end of 2028. This is necessary in the name of the survival of all life on Earth. This will be made clear at an international conference and at the United Nations at which the case for survival will be put to and agreed by every country. The whole human race will be put on a war footing in the battle against Global Warming and Climate Change in the name of survival.

WE MUST GET THE WHOLE WORLD TO CUT CARBON EMISSIONS BY FORTY-NINE PER CENT BY THE END OF 2028 OR IT WILL BE TOO LATE. THE WORLD WILL BECOME UNINHABITABLE IF WE DON'T DO THIS.

SOCIAL GUIDANCE

There are two main types of criminals who come before the courts in this country. The first is the career criminals who make a living out of criminal acts and the second is the social delinquents. Career criminals have to accept the principle of crime and punishment, and by and large they do so. They know that if they get caught, they have to do their time in prison and that is an end to the matter. Social delinquents fall into two categories. Firstly, there are those who carry weapons for their own protection because they don't trust the law to protect them. This has got to stop. The law must be there to protect all people and be seen to do so.

Secondly there are those who fall foul of the law because they don't understand society and how it works. They don't know what they are, nor what their lives are all about. They are mainly young guys in various stages of adolescence. They want to prove themselves but they don't know how, nor what this entails. Most of them are looking for a reason for living, and most of them, at present, end up in the care of consultant forensic psychiatrists who seldom know what life is all about themselves. We propose the founding of a Ministry for Social Guidance to replace the work done by the Royal College of Psychiatrists. The Ministry would be in charge of the Social Guidance Institute which would be run by an elected council who would oversee the work done by the Social Guidance Counsellors. These would be people chosen for their maturity and wisdom and would not be qualified by educational qualifications but be chosen in a way more like that of judges, by their fellow Counsellors.

It would be the job of Social Guidance Counsellors to talk to miscreants on a regular basis and to lead them to a fuller understanding of life, to get them to prove themselves, and to *find* God, and to *find themselves,* so that they will become useful citizens. They must be led to an understanding of WHAT THEY ARE and WHO THEY REALLY ARE.

With very few exceptions, the minimum age for a Social Guidance Counsellor would be fifty years, and ideally, these people would have been married for at least two years and have children of their own, for they would be acting *in loco parentis.*

These jobs would largely replace those of probation officers, and would be ideal for the many older members of society who have lived life to the full and gained life experience and wisdom which these jobs would give them the opportunity to pass on to the next generation. They would be well paid and carry a lot of respect. Such jobs are badly needed in society at the moment.

Mental hospitals would be largely replaced by Social Guidance Centres where people would be held in detention until they make it obvious that they don't need that kind of treatment. Then they could just be called upon to visit the Centre for regular consultations with their Counsellor.

Receiving counselling would not carry the stigma of mental illness which many people will always equate with madness. Receiving counselling is more like getting good advice from a caring parent which people growing up in good homes get anyway.

This system would replace the mental health system which is shambolic at best, at the moment.

PUNISHMENT

The Bible says so, and so does the works of William Shakespeare, now I am saying it as well, "Spare the rod and spoil the child". We have raised a generation of spoilt children in this country under the soft laws of the "Nanny State". This is what has given rise to the current spate of knife crimes. Young people have little or no respect for authority and the rule of law. My Government would change that.

Parents know their children best and children know it when they have misbehaved. We would give parents back the right to give their child a slap on the thigh if the child is naughty. The child then knows to behave him/herself and is given a respectful understanding of the nature of the relationship between adults and children. This will prove useful when the child becomes an adult him/herself. Having taken his/her punishment, the child then knows that the matter is forgotten and he/she can then continue with a loving relationship with his/her parent.

We would give schoolteachers back the right to punish misbehaving children, the punishment to be decided at the discretion of the head teacher. Again, once the child has received his/her punishment the matter is then forgotten. I received the cane many times at school and it never did me any lasting harm.

We would punish young guys who carry knives much more severely. The punishment for carrying a knife would be ten to fifteen years in prison depending on the circumstances of the offender. For using a knife to inflict a wound, the punishment would be a jail term commensurate with the severity of the wound, the first ten weeks of which would be spent in solitary confinement. For killing someone with a knife, the punishment would be a life sentence, the first twenty weeks of which would be spent in solitary confinement. In all of these cases the punishment would be followed by counselling until the judge is convinced that the miscreant has mended his ways.

In the case of female knife offenders, we would leave the punishment up to the judge and the Social Guidance Counsellor to decide.

HARD DRUGS

A distinction must be made between those who deal in hard drugs, and those who only use them. Users will be treated as needing Social Guidance and kept in secure accommodation until they are free from addiction for a period of at least two years. They can be released only when they make it clear that they intend to stay clear of hard drugs in future.

Dealers cause great misery to their customers and to the families of their customers. We would give them a life sentence in prison, the first twenty weeks of which would be spent in solitary confinement. They would then have to undertake sessions with a Social Guidance Counsellor and they would have their financial assets confiscated.

PRISONS

Prisons are not meant to be holiday camps. Those caught with drugs in prison would be held in solitary confinement for a period of time at the discretion of the prison governor, and disallowed visits and social interaction with friends and family. Those visitors caught bringing drugs into prison would be barred from visiting prisons again. They can be identified by facial recognition technology.

THE HOUSING CRISIS

The main cause of poverty in Great Britain is the fact that there is not enough accommodation available for all the people who live here. The government must provide incentives for builders to build more affordable houses and flats for people. I promise that my Government will give this problem a higher priority than any other government, Labour or Conservative, since the Second World War.

NORTHERN IRELAND

This territory was taken by force of arms in the first place, and colonised by the British. In a civilised world, this is no justification for the UK to retain possession of someone else's territory. We say, "Give Northern Ireland back to the Irish nation". Historically and geographically, the territory belongs to Ireland, not Britain. If anybody there wants to consider themselves as British then let them come to Britain. The territory is more of a liability than an asset to Britain.

PUBLIC OWNERSHIP

It was Margaret Thatcher who sold off our national assets in the 1980s because she didn't have enough confidence in herself as a leader, to delegate the running of the public companies to competent administrators. The result of this we see today in the debacle of the railways, the water industry and the electricity industry.

THE RAILWAYS

At the moment the railways are owned separately in terms of the stations, the rail tracks and the trains, and in different parts of the country. To travel from A to B in the most cost-effective way is no easy matter. It varies according to which company you are buying a ticket from and which route you take. Sometimes the cheapest route is not the shortest route! We say bring the whole national rail system back into public ownership, and trust my Government to appoint a competent administrator to oversee the whole project. The new British Rail would ensure that trains run on time and are not too overcrowded. If the public are let down on these promises, then the administrator would be sacked. That person's job depends upon their efficiency.

THE WATER INDUSTRY

The water supply industry has been taken over by sharks and con men. The rivers, including the Thames, are filthy with untreated sewage, and Southern Water have recently had to apologise to their customers and pay them compensation for their poor service. Millions of gallons of water are wasted by broken pipes which go unmended for months or even years by inefficient management.

We say bring the whole industry, the rivers, the reservoirs and the distribution systems into public ownership. Again, the new British Water would be overseen by a competent administrator appointed by my Government, whose job would depend upon his/her efficiency.

THE ELECTRICITY INDUSTRY

The electricity industry, at present, charges different rates for different customers, and often, you can only get the best deal by switching your supplier. Loyalty is not often rewarded.

Again, we say bring the whole system, the generation of electricity by nuclear, solar and wind power, the distribution and the marketing into public ownership, overseen by a competent administrator appointed by my Government, whose job would depend upon his/her efficiency.

OTHER NATIONAL ISSUES

Any political Party, standing for election in Great Britain must obviously have policies on all issues of national importance. The reason I haven't mentioned them so far in this Manifesto is because they are not nearly as important as the need to cut carbon emissions to cope with Global Warming and Climate Change. To spend time and effort on them is a bit like deciding who is going to do the washing up after dinner when the whole house is burning down all around us. Surely the thing to do first is to put the fire out and then decide what to do if and when we all survive.

I do, however, have the following that I think is worth saying: -

My Government would spend at least as much, as a proportion of Gross Domestic Product, as any government, Labour or Conservative, has spent on services since the Second World War.

THE NATIONAL HEALTH SERVICE

My Government would make sure that the NHS is adequately funded, including GPs salaries and the Accident and Emergency Services.

Prescription charges will be abolished. All health services will remain free at the point of delivery for all British citizens.

THE EDUCATION SERVICE

Education will remain compulsory for all children under the age of sixteen years. All education will remain free for all students who have proven their academic ability to go on to higher education. University tuition fees will be abolished. Free school dinners will be provided in all cases of financial hardship applied for by a parent or guardian, this includes school dinners provided during school holidays.

Private schools who charge a fee to educate children will not be abolished.

THE POLICE SERVICE

There is currently a recruitment drive to recruit and train another twenty thousand police officers. My Government would ensure that staffing levels are maintained for all the national police forces. Stop and search powers would remain with all uniformed police officers, who will be allowed to carry tasers.

PROVISION FOR THE ELDERLY

Old age pensions will continue for all men and women who have reached the age of sixty-six years. All old people who are so infirm that they need looking after and do not have a relative who is willing and able to look after them will have their pension replaced by a free place in a care home.

COUNTY AND URBAN DISTRICT COUNCILS

Council tax will still have to be paid. Councillors will continue to be elected representatives of the people.

DEFENCE

All existing defence commitments will continue to be honoured, including our commitment to NATO. All the national military services will continue to be maintained, as will our independent nuclear deterrent.

Brexit

On a matter of such importance as the membership of the European Union, the British people should have had the guidance of our wisest men and women, instead of the self-interested opinions of an unelected, shadowy, behind-the-scenes figure such as Dominic Cummings with his Brexit poster-boy, Boris Johnson, who told lies in big letters on the side of a bus. Brexit is a disaster for the British economy and is costing us many thousands of jobs, as well as time spent on increased bureaucracy. My wisdom is that Great Britain should apply to re-join the European Union and use our influence most wisely in that way.

INCOME AND EXPENDITURE

My Government does not propose any immediate changes to revenue and taxation nor on spending on services, benefits and pensions. We propose to spend some time studying the books until we know the true state of the nation's financial health. We envisage that this will take about six months. We will then tell you the truth about the state of the nation's financial health when we produce our first budget. We believe in being prudent with money, and not taking on any more debt than is necessary for survival; we know that you don't like paying interest to bankers any more than we do, so we ask you to trust us to spend the nation's money wisely.

MY CREDENTIALS

According to MENSA I have an IQ of 139 on their scale. I was educated at Battersea Grammar School, Ifield Grammar school in Crawley, Norwood Technical College where I passed my A-levels at night school and The City University where I studied Pure Maths, Applied Maths, Statistics and Computing. Intelligence is not the same thing as wisdom. I have a saying that it is a wise man who knows how little he knows. I am wise enough to seek the advice and guidance of scientists and professors who are more erudite and learned than myself, in matters concerning policies of affairs of state.

I have proven in my life that my courage, my initiative, my patience, my wisdom, my maturity, my determination, my strength of spirit, my love for people and my leadership are second to none. I have a strong social conscience and I am a good organiser. I am a real man and a natural leader of men and women.

This country and the world NEED my leadership without delay. You can read the whole truth about me in my autobiographies. They can be accessed from my website. The address is: -

http://www.robert-brooks-strong.olympiapublishers.com/

Chapter 19

Dolly's, Lucifer's, Misery Continues

Events and Thoughts from Saturday 19th December 2020.

Sunday 20th December 2020. My letters during the week in which I explained how the Gods in Heaven are helping me by visiting the coronavirus pandemic upon the human race caused a hell of a stir in the world. People are finally taking me seriously, and I have finally made almost everybody realise that Mrs Dorothy (Dolly) Ayres is to blame for the large number of ills afflicting the world at the moment. There are still a few idiots on the TV who use the words 'area' and the plural 'areas' at every opportunity, but they are doing that less frequently since I explained to them that that is what has caused the pandemic. The use of those words only encourages the old witch to hang around, prolonging the agony of her existence, and wasting precious time. The fact that some people are still using those words is what has caused the virus to mutate and produce a more infectious strain of itself.

I had to do this in order to take over the leadership of the human race, which I am in the process of doing. But as long as Dolly exists, she is still the leader, so I am exhorting everybody to shout at her, telling her to come back to life as a duck. Things won't improve for mankind until she has done that. It shouldn't take long now. I have finally turned the tables on her, with help from my friends, the Gods in Heaven. The fact that it has taken such a huge crisis to get the better of her is the fault of the people themselves, for idolising the Devil's accomplice. They should have known better than to embrace her decadent ways; they were all part of Satan's plan to destroy mankind by undermining our moral values. I wrote quite clearly in the Bible, "Man shall not go with man", and the same is obviously true for women. The meaning is clear to every adult. Dolly was, perhaps unwittingly, aiding and abetting the Devil himself by her vainglorious attempt to prove that she was more wonderful than God. And look what a balls-up she has made of running the world. She has been the leader of the world for the last sixty years or more, and she has led it to the brink of extinction. Her place in the Bible is known as the vainglorious Archangel Lucifer, but she is actually more of an Arch-demon.

It is too late now for Dolly to apologise and mend her ways. She has usurped my position as leader of the spirit world and stolen my throne in the Kingdom of the dead. I have to take it back because of who I am. I am the Lord God Almighty. I have successfully defended my position as King of the spirit world against all comers for three hundred thousand years, ever since I was Adam in the Garden of Eden, and I am not going to surrender my title to anybody; not now, nor ever. I am the best man for the job; the father of the human race and head of the family of mankind.

Tuesday 22nd December 2020. The fact that the virus has mutated into a more infectious strain is largely, but not uniquely, confined to the south east of England. It is no coincidence that that is where I come from. The rest of the world have closed their borders with Great Britain on this account. They do not want the infectious variant of the virus in their own countries. It looks like Britain is going to leave the European Union without a trade deal; so, it seems to me that Britain is going to be totally isolated without any trading partners. To top this, Boris Johnson, the Prime Minister, said on Sunday that Christmas is being cancelled this year. Most of Britain is in Tier 4, which is total lockdown; this means that all except essential workers are confined to their homes, and they are not allowed to visit other households, not even at Christmas. This situation won't improve for months; not until the majority of the population have been immunised.

I feel sorry for the people of Britain. The poor fools thought that they could sin against me, God, and get away with it. They drove me to murder, then they called me mad and locked me up for over forty-four years, over forty-three of which subjecting me to the torture of having libido-suppressing antipsychotic drugs forced on me when there is nothing wrong with me. Then they conspired to persecute me in order to turn me into a motherfucker, which I have always refused to be. But Heaven is MY Empire and now THE EMPIRE IS STRIKING BACK! The torrent of challenges confronting the people of the world, and in particular the British people, will only get worse until the late Mrs Dorothy Ayres is brought back to life as a duck. This is no longer an item of twee fashionable concern but, thanks to my friends, the Gods in Heaven, it has become the highly emotional issue that I wanted it to be all along.

The people know that I had to punish them for following my late mother, Mrs Dorothy (Dolly) Ayres, in order to get them to follow ME. I had no choice because of who I am. It is for their own good in the long run. Dolly is directly to blame for your misfortunes, folks. Get rid of her, NOW!

I am sending copies of the above entry and Sunday's entry to Lucy and also to Dr Twee Dampensquib.

Wednesday 23rd December 2020. I decided this evening to also send them to Queen Elizabeth II, Paul Rees, Justin Welby and Pope Francis.

Saturday 26th December 2020. I wrote the following letter to Lucy this morning: - Saturday Morning 26th December 2020
Lucy Lawless, The Golden GIRL Herself,

Dear Soulmate,
You do not behave like a woman who loves me. I do not doubt your love, Lucy, but I know that you are not yet a woman. It takes the sincere love of a good man to turn a girl into a woman; that is what I have consistently offered you for over twenty-one years now, Darling. When will you accept that I have proven my love for you in human terms and trust in my proof? When will you trust in your own love for me, as I do trust your love for me? When you are sure that our love is something we both can trust then you will find your adult courage. Then you will be what you really are – A WOMAN IN LOVE. Try looking up the lyrics to "Your eyes are the eyes of a woman in love". Don't be afraid of anyone or anything, Darling. Nothing and no one can tear us apart. These words come straight from my heart, Darling. We wouldn't love each other half AS MUCH IF OUR LOVE WAS EASY TO PROVE, BUT AFTER ALL THIS TIME I'M SURE WE HAVE MADE IT. When you are a real woman, nothing else will matter to you except your desire to prove it, to yourself and to me. I won't have to tell you what to do then; you will do what a woman in love does.
The end of our trials is in sight.
Take care of yourself, my Love, I have much more to say to you, but it

can wait until we talk, Bless you, my Queen,

    Yours with Love, Affection and Friendship,

    The King of Heaven,

    Emperor_Bob XX

    Cc. Dr Twee Dampensquib.

When it rains, it rains on the righteous as well as on the sinners, and when the sun shines, it shines on the evil people as well as the saints. So it is with the punishment from the Gods. I hope the majority of good people with whom I enjoy a lot of popularity will understand that the Gods visited the coronavirus pandemic upon the human race to punish my late mother's followers. Dolly's followers are still in power, although they are fewer in number than my followers. They have to be turned against their erstwhile leader in order to get rid of her, which we have got to do if I, God, am ever going to reign in Heaven again, let alone come to power on Earth. And I have got to come to power on Earth in order to save the world from the evils that beset the human race thanks to Dolly's misrule.

I do bring hope, though. The programme of rolling out the vaccines against COVID-19 is already underway and as far as we know, the vaccines also protect people from the new, mutant variations of the virus. Boris Johnson's government has succeeded in doing a trade deal with the European Union, so the situation for jobs and industry is not as bleak as I had feared. And moves are afoot to persuade all nations to cut carbon emissions by forty-five per cent by 2030 and the remaining fifty-five per cent by 2050, so there is hope that the Climate Change crisis can be solved, and I am hopeful that The Survival Party will play a leading role in this endeavour. My late mother's misery is increasing all the time, with help from the Gods in Heaven, so there is reason to hope that she will turn herself into a duck before too long; hopefully before Easter, by which time this country should be a safe place for me to resume my place in the community after all these years in the mad house.

Having mental sex with my late mother, Mrs Dorothy (Dolly) Ayres, is known colloquially as "opening the door". For decades it has been the graduation ritual for entry into manhood throughout the International Community. The men thought that opening the door didn't cost them anything except their innocence, but all this year THEY HAVE BEEN

PAYING THE PRICE FOR OPENING THE DOOR. And they thought they were getting free sex! The suffering they have had to endure by the coronavirus pandemic, not to mention the inclement weather – rainstorms and very STRONG winds, serves them damn well right for trying to make a motherfucker out of ME! And for driving me to homicide, locking me up for over forty-four years, calling me mad, and torturing me for over forty-three years with libido-suppressing antipsychotic drugs when there is nothing wrong with me and never has been.

REVENGE IS SWEET! As it says in the Bible, "'Vengeance is mine,' sayeth the Lord"! I am telling you men to GET RID OF THE OLD WITCH NOW, OR ELSE it will cost you even more dearly. Turn her into a duck. It suits me to have her turned into a fowl creature seeing as she has been a foul creature to me for all my life.

I sent copies of the above entry to Lucy Lawless, Dr Twee Dampensquib, Queen Elizabeth II, Paul Rees, Justin Welby and Pope Francis.

Monday 28th December 2020. I wrote the following letter to Lucy today: -
Monday 28th December 2020
    Lucy Lawless, The Golden GIRL Herself,

Dear Soulmate,
    For the vast majority of people, the meaning of their life is to earn enough money to look after themselves and their dependents. And to raise their children to become adults in the best way they know how. That used to be the meaning of my life when I was in my twenties, but I escaped from the daily grind by having the guts to go into business on my own and I made a success of it. By the time I was thirty I had twenty-four computer programmers working for me and I was making £thousands a week. (That was darn good money forty-seven years ago). By the time I was thirty-two I was looking after my business, buying my own house and raising my two sons single-handedly. I was waiting for the only girl I wanted to come back to me, but all I got was visits from my mother, and also from my stepmother, trying to seduce me. It was when I made it clear to both of them that I wasn't interested that my troubles started.
    My mother got her followers to make my life Hell until I killed my stepmother, in order to stop people at large from persecuting me. The rest

is history.

The meaning of my life has always been to protect the human race. First, I protected people from my stepmother, Iris, by killing her; meaning that people could then have my mother for their matriarch, which was what they wanted, AND WAS WHY THEY GOT ME TO KILL IRIS. Then I saved the human race from the Devil Himself, Edward Richard Pitchblack, by proving myself to be strong enough not to concede defeat to Him in our trials of mental strength over a period of thirty years, until He finally died, in despair of ever overpowering me. Then I still had to get Him off my back as He continued fighting me after He died, so I marshalled the spiritual armies that finally defeated Him and His hordes by turning Him into a Rottweiler dog which is what he is today.

I have decided that the meaning of my life now, is to play a leading role in saving the world from Climate Change. My method in doing this is by means of The Survival Party, with my updated Manifesto.

Twee Dampensquib has decided that the meaning of his life is to play a part in helping people to overcome mental illness. The fundamental belief of his profession is that this entails having mental sex with my late mother, Mrs Dorothy Ayres, otherwise known as "opening the door". I disagree with this fundamental assertion, and I disagree with the idea that antipsychotic drugs help people overcome mental illness. All the drugs do is to suppress a man's sex drive so that he can't have sex, mental or otherwise, with anyone. Which is a good way to treat perverts, but is an evil thing to do to a good man.

The meaning of my late mother's life has always been to justify her vanity by making a sexual conquest of the Lord God Almighty, myself. But she never did achieve that ambition when she was alive, and she never will now she is dead. She just isn't a good enough person to achieve her own ambition. She isn't woman enough to be the real Queen of the human race. I have received divine guidance, which I trust, that that is who YOU are, and the meaning of your life is to find that out for yourself. When you have found it out, you will find me waiting for you, Darling.

We will be able to have a sex life when I come off the drugs, which will be when my late mother comes back to life as a duck; until then I have hardly any sex drive at all, but we can still enjoy our love for each other, as people, and share our feelings telepathically, as we do. This will add to my late mother's misery, making it more likely that she clears off, out of the human race, having proved herself unworthy to stay in the race. Like I said before, she is a very bad loser.

Yours etcetera

Cc. Dr Twee Dampensquib

I then wrote the following letter to Lucy this evening: - Monday Evening 28th December 2020

Lucy Lawless, The Golden GIRL Herself,

Dear Soulmate,

As recently as yesterday, there was a feature on the BBC news channel about a boy who is critically ill. That is how my late mother likes to portray me – as a boy who is critically mentally ill. But no one with any grey matter between their ears takes any notice of the rantings of the old witch any more, except the psychiatric profession who follow a paranoid motherfucker called Sigmund Freud. All sensible people now know that I speak the truth when I say that Dolly is the immature one, not me. The evidence for this is that she has always had a girlish resentment of paternal authority: she resented the authority of her own father, and she resents the authority of God-the-father in the spirit world, thinking that she could do a better job than God of running the world. People gave her the chance to prove it sixty years ago, and she has been in charge of the world ever since. Judging by the state of the world today, she has failed, and failed miserably.

Instead of mental health being signified by having mental sex with Dolly, I suggest that mental health should now be signified by *finding* me, God, for in the world of the future we now have a patriarchy instead of a matriarchy, with myself instead of my late mother being the person in overall charge of the world. Maturity can be more fairly judged in future by having mental sex, "dancing", with one's own partner, instead of with the global village slut. Not that there aren't plenty of sluts around wanting to take over from Dolly, identified by such terms as "Synergy". But I, myself, wouldn't touch any of them with a barge pole. That kind of woman is my late father's choice, not mine. I prefer a woman who is faithful to me, not someone who dances with anyone and everyone. That makes me mentally healthy, choosy, not mentally ill.

If Twee Dampensquib sees my point of view, then he will take me off the paliperidone before the 6th January next year when I am due for my next jab. If that jab takes place, then he can guess the consequences when I come to power, which I surely will before long.

The end of our trials is in sight.

Yours etcetera

Cc. Dr Twee Dampensquib.

Thursday 31st December 2020. The situation is very bleak at the moment for the human race, especially the people of the UK. We have the coronavirus crisis and then there is the Climate Change crisis to contend with, and in the UK, we have the impending chaos caused by Brexit. This is all a direct consequence of the fact that the human race still follows my late mother, Mrs Dorothy (Dolly) Ayres, as is evidenced by the fact that people still talk about "opening the door" as evidence of mental health and still use the words "area" and "areas" on the television because these words sound a bit like my late mother's surname; as if these words somehow give them divine protection when the opposite is actually the truth. The truth is that the human race did not give ME, God, the credit I was due for saving their lives from Satan when I overpowered Edward Richard Pitchblack. From that point onwards they should have followed ME, not Dolly. That is why they are in the shit at the moment, and things will only get worse unless all Dolly's followers turn against their erstwhile leader AND KICK HER OUT OF THE HUMAN RACE WITHOUT FURTHER DELAY.

For example, the virus could mutate into a variation of itself upon which the vaccines do not work. They would then have to produce a new vaccine for the new variation of the virus. This would take a long time to produce and cost a huge increase in the death toll which already stands at almost a thousand a day in the UK. This could well happen unless all people DO AS I SAY FROM NOW ON. Accept the fact that I, Robert Brooks Strong, am the Lord God and OBEY MY WILL from NOW on. Try me further at your peril, good people.

Start by turning Dolly into a duck. This should be possible as ducks mate throughout the year. Then tell Twee Dampensquib to take me off his filthy drugs immediately, and give me my public apology for my approval before the Royal College of Psychiatrists publishes it. He knows what I want the public apology to say and he knows how much I am demanding from the Royal College of Psychiatrists in compensation, he can advise them of the figure. When I see evidence of widespread approval of the things in this journal extract, then the situation will improve for the human race especially the people of Great Britain. Accept the fact that I am the man in charge now and then things will improve for you.

Today is New Year's Eve. Out with the old year and in with the new, so it is fitting that I should say, "Out with the old leader and in with the new" today.

I sent copies of the above journal entry to Lucy and Dr Twee Dampensquib.

Friday 1st January 2021. I wrote the following letter to Lucy this evening: -
Friday Evening 1st January 2021
Lucy Lawless, The Golden GIRL Herself,

Dear Soulmate,
Just a line to thank you for sending me your loving vibes which I have felt very strongly today. They make everything in the world seem fine for me. I am so lucky to have won the love of the most wonderful girl in the world. One day you'll be the most wonderful woman in the world. All I need for perfect happiness is the pleasure of your company, but until that becomes possible, I can hope for a letter or an email from you to comfort me.

The people on the telly have been at pains to emphasise, today, that this day is the START OF A NEW ERA. They imply, of course, because of the fact that today, Great Britain has now left the European Union, but those in the know are aware of the fact that today is the start of MY era in earnest, having taken over from my late mother. There are still a few IDIOTS WHO DEFY MY WILL. I just say to those people, telepathically, "You're a glutton for punishment aren't you!" I have the confidence to say that, knowing that the Gods are on my side. Those who argue with me are arguing with the Gods who HAVE VISITED THE CORONAVIRUS PANDEMIC UPON THE WORLD CAUSING HUNDREDS OF THOUSANDS OF DEATHS. Argue with that if you will, you bastards. That includes the weather presenters who still use the words "area" and "areas", and Twee Dampensquib who still hasn't told me yet, that he has taken me off his filthy drugs.

Some people never learn, and some people never grow up. Twee seems to belong to the former and you seem to belong to the latter. Prove me wrong if you can, Twee and Lucy.

The end of our trials is in sight.

Yours etcetera

Cc. Dr Twee Dampensquib.

Sunday 3rd January 2021. I wrote the following letter to Lucy today: -
Sunday 3rd January 2021

Lucy Lawless, The Golden GIRL Herself,

Dear Soulmate,

I repeat, when you are a real woman, nothing else will matter to you except your desire to prove it; to yourself, to me and to the world. You will be in the frame of mind that Helen Reddy was in when she wrote the enclosed song, the lyrics of which I looked up for you.

When you are a woman, you will want to know WHO YOU ARE and what your place is in the hierarchy of all living things. Everyone's place is determined by the strength of their fighting spirit. I killed Iris on the 16th July 1976 to prove who I am. I had to do that or accept Iris as my Queen, which everyone else except me did. In doing so, I proved that I am the King. Several women have been strongly put forward to me since then as possible partners, namely Dorothy Ayres, Hannah Gordon, Jasmin Desbottes, Sally Williams and Victoria Navarro to name but the main contenders. But I have declined them all because none of them make me feel anywhere near as good as YOU do, Lucy, when you send me your loving feelings. In doing so, you have proven Aphrodite right when she made me aware, over twenty-one years ago, that you would be the only one for me. Aphrodite knew who you were from the moment of your birth, just as the Gods have known all my life who I am. It is spiritual knowledge.

I repeat that I am the King, and I am a man who knows his own mind. You are the only one I want for my partner, Darling. WHO DOES THAT MAKE YOU? When you know the answer to that question, it will save time if you let me know it by email.

The end of our trials is in sight.

Yours etcetera

Enclosure "I am woman" lyrics by Helen Reddy.

Monday 4th January 2021. I wrote the following letter to Lucy this morning:
- Monday Morning 4th January 2021

Lucy Lawless, The Golden GIRL Herself,

Dear Soulmate,

If we are ever going to get together then something has got to change. That something is yourself, Darling. Everyone is waiting for you to prove that you are a woman by fighting for me AS A WOMAN FIGHTS FOR HER MAN. In this circumstance that does not mean by aggression, but by the opposite. It does not come easily to two such proud people as you and me to eat humble pie, but that is what we have got to do. We have got to appeal to the soft side of my late mother's nature. We've got to tell the old witch that we know she is really a dear, sweet, kind old lady, and implore her to set me free and to let me go. We've got to tell her that we are sure she is really a good mother, in which case she will put MY happiness first, by releasing me to love you as we both want to do. We must make her realise that YOU are the only woman who makes me happy, and as far as I am concerned, YOU are the most wonderful woman in the world. We've got to implore these things of her in the name of LOVE and of our common humanity, and hope that she is still human enough to let me go.

I also suggest that YOU write to Dr Twee Dampensquib and implore him to take me off the antipsychotic medication in the name of our common humanity. He wants us to eat humble pie as well, and I think that with respect to both Dolly and Twee, these things have got to come from both of us.

As Xena told Gabrielle, "The dead can hear our thoughts." There are tears in my eyes as I write this letter. This has got to work; I've tried everything else. This must be what my late mother has been waiting for. It never occurred to me before that I had to ask her permission to get married. I always thought that adults can do as they please, but I was wrong. Family ties are more important than I realised. Now I know the meaning of the phrase, "Blood is thicker than water". Although I still say that that does not excuse incest, nor even attempted incest. Dolly has still got a lot to answer for.

The end of our trials is in sight.

Yours etcetera

Cc Dr Twee Dampensquib

I wrote in this journal on Thursday of last week what could happen if people still refuse to obey my will, THE WILL OF GOD. The followers of my late mother really are gluttons for punishment! We learned today that a new strain of the virus has evolved in South Africa. It is proving to be the most dominant strain that we know of, and the existing vaccines do not protect people from it. It will surely spread like wildfire around the world, including the UK. I told people that they are fighting the Gods in Heaven by refusing to obey my will, THE WILL OF GOD. I told them to turn the late Mrs Dorothy Ayres into a duck, but they wouldn't heed my warning; now they are getting ever deeper into the shit, as if things aren't bad enough with the existing strains of COVID. I also told them to tell Twee Dampensquib to take me off his filthy drugs before Wednesday, but I haven't heard anything from him so far. Some people never learn!

I am sending copies of this extract from this journal to Lucy, Dr Twee Dampensquib, Paul Rees, Justin Welby and Pope Francis.

Wednesday 6th January 2021. Two female psychiatric nurses came into my room this morning and injected me with 100 mil of paliperidone. When I told them that these drugs suppress my libido, one of them said that that may be a side effect of the medication but she was sure it was not what it was for. They actually believe that rubbish. It is obviously what the drug is for. It is my late mother's way of ensuring that if I don't have sex with *her* then I can't have sex with any other woman either. The drug totally suppresses my sex drive. I'd like to have a happy, healthy sex life with my partner, Lucy, but seeing as I can't have that, then I'd sooner have no sex at all than have sex with my late mother, Mrs Dorothy (Dolly) Ayres, even if every other man in the world has mental sex with her.

I don't intend to write to Dr Twee Dampensquib any more, nor to Lucy either. Twee is a psychiatrist and is consequently a contemptible acolyte of Dolly Ayres. Lucy is the most wonderful girl in the world, but that is just it; she will be fifty-three years old on the 29th March this year, but she is still an old girl. Until she is woman enough to communicate with me then I don 't think I'm helping her to become a woman by writing to her any more. I want a partner I can communicate with, not an overgrown adolescent that I have to educate.

Dolly's followers are still gluttons for punishment. They don't seem to realise how serious the existing punishment is. Hundreds of thousands of people have already died of COVID and thousands more people are dying from it every day. Everybody in the world; every man, woman and child is having their life made a misery by weeks and months of lockdown; millions of people all over the world are going bankrupt; every working person and every business person is getting ever deeper into debt, as is every nation, they are all getting their future generations into debt which they will have to repay.

Dolly's followers are to blame for all this suffering; they are the ones the Gods are punishing, for following a false God and idolising her, and for not following ME, the REAL God and for defying MY WILL, the will of God. Dolly is a dirty, incestuous, evil old witch. She is a monster of the worst kind and she has usurped my position as King of the Spirit World and also of the Material World. I, as God, have ordered her expulsion from the human race. I want her turned into a duck as soon as possible and until my order is obeyed, things will only get worse for the human race.

The new mutation of the COVID virus from South Africa will put paid to the hope that the human race has put in their vaccines. The vaccines don't work on the new mutant virus. Things will only get worse until all people DO AS I SAY; kick Dolly out of the human race, and OBEY MY WILL from now on.

Robert Brooks Strong. 6/1/2021.

Friday 8th January 2021. You don't need to be an erudite biblical scholar to know that I, God, visited one plague after another upon the people of Israel until they abandoned all their false Gods and followed me, the REAL God. The same thing is happening again, but on a global scale this time. At the moment we have the coronavirus pandemic, that will be followed by another pandemic of a more dominant strain of the coronavirus which is resistant to the existing vaccines. Once we have tamed the virus, the Climate Change crisis will be upon us in earnest, and that will be a crisis which dwarfs that of the coronavirus.

As I have said before, Climate Change has two causes, one is practical and the other is moral. To try to solve one without solving the other is like trying to dry yourself with a fresh towel whilst still standing under a running shower. Same-sex sexual relationships offend me, God, and what offends me antagonises the Gods in Heaven who influence the climate. This is the root of the moral cause of Climate Change.

If the coronavirus crisis and the Climate Change crisis aren't enough to dissuade Dolly's followers from following a false God, then we will find a new punishment to afflict the world, which will be even worse. I do not tolerate, nor allow the human race to follow false Gods. I, Robert Brooks Strong, am the Lord God Almighty and the King of the Gods in Heaven; the leader of the human race and the Head of the family of mankind; I have been ever since I was Adam in the Garden of Eden three hundred thousand years ago, and I will get together with Eve, Lucy Lawless, within my lifetime, whether my jealous, late mother likes it or not. My late mother, Mrs Dorothy (Dolly) Ayres (also known as "the door" and "the area"), is a false God who has usurped my position and she WILL be turned into a duck. If she cares about the human race or anyone in it, she will not waste any more time but turn herself into a duck without delay, to spare the people from more suffering and punishment. HER addiction to power is what is causing all the suffering and punishment.

Sunday 10th January 2021. The fact that same-sex sexual relationships have been legalised throughout the so-called "Free World" is the doing of my late mother, Mrs Dorothy (Dolly) Ayres. She has been the REAL power in the Free World for the last sixty years or more, prior to which same-sex sexual relationships were illegal and were not condoned by right-thinking people. SHE had them legalised in the name of "The Permissive Society", which many intellectuals in the Free World regarded as progressive. But the permissive society is not progressive at all; it is just an excuse for decadence. And a society which condones decadence is a society in decay, which is what the Free World is at the moment.

Dolly's attitude was influenced by the Bohemian, café society culture, which was fashionable among ageing adolescents between the two world wars of the last century, in which homosexuals were regarded as avant-garde and fashionable. Dolly never grew out of her notion of a Bohemian Utopia, which she attempted to impose upon the world.

The fact that she was MY mother made her a sexual magnet for the men of the world who made her the darling of their society, their heroine, irrespective of the fact that she never was a very wise person, nor a very moral person. Her main excuse for coming to power was her vanity; she thought that she was a more wonderful person than God, and the men of the world thought that they were getting free sex and easy sex by having mental sex with her, so they pandered to her vanity till it became a manifest paranoia. She ended up thinking that she actually IS God, not realising that she was treading on the toes of the man who REALLY IS God, her own son, myself. Those men are now paying for having mental sex with my late mother by the suffering, death, misery and financial debt of the coronavirus pandemic.

My late mother always has had a schoolgirl crush on me, which she never was woman enough to grow out of. When I became a man, she couldn't help herself but try to seduce me, and consequently has ruined my whole life seeing as she abused her power in her unsuccessful attempts to get me to become her lover. She has never even apologised for attempting to rape me, nor promised not to do it again: on the contrary, she thinks she has a divine right to demand sex from me seeing as all the other men in the world have mental sex with her, otherwise known as "opening the door", and to please her they conspire to make a motherfucker out of me.

The lesson to be drawn from all this is that if you are going to hero-worship anyone, make sure the object of your hero-status is a real adult, not an overgrown adolescent like Dorothy Ayres, nor Donald Trump, nor Boris Johnson, nor Adolph Hitler. Adulthood is not just a question of sexual maturity, nor even mental sex, "dancing", but it is also a question of having adult, socially responsible attitudes to life and not trying to impose a particular culture on a diverse world. And that does NOT excuse decadence disguised as diversity.

As long as the soul of the late Mrs Dorothy Ayres exists, humanity will never solve the problem of the moral cause of climate change, and the extinction of all life on Earth is therefore a certainty. She must be turned into an animal as quickly as possible. A duck seems to be her favourite option.

Saturday 16th January 2021. I gave Dolly's followers the order to turn their erstwhile leader into a duck, but they haven't obeyed me yet. In fact, they still use the words "area" and "areas" on the TV, especially the employees of the Meteorological Office. They are so stupid that they don't seem to realise that they are getting themselves ever deeper into the shit. Two more mutations of the coronavirus have been discovered in Brazil, and they are still doing research into the South African variant. All people coming into the UK by plane or ship or train have to be quarantined for two weeks unless they pass a COVID test after five days.

This is causing havoc in the airline industry. It is going broke and will need a massive government subsidy in order to survive. There is no end in sight to the lockdown, and the UK government have admitted that they are in a race against time to get the country back on its feet, by inoculating people faster than we are dying. So far, they seem to be losing: the light at the end of the tunnel is getting further away all the time. There are now over one thousand two hundred deaths per day in the UK, over four thousand deaths per day in the USA and over three thousand deaths per day in India. The total death toll from COVID now exceeds two million people. In the UK, the NHS is being overwhelmed; more people want hospitalising than there are hospital beds. Even the newscasters on the TV say that things will get worse before they get better. They won't start getting better until Dolly's soul is turned into a duck, they will only get worse until then.

There is a fight going on between Dolly and her followers versus me and mine. My followers include the Gods in Heaven and we are winning. Our enemies are idiots for thinking they can fight ME, God, and win.

Chapter 20

Stalemate, but to My Advantage

Events and Thoughts from Sunday 17th January 2021.

Sunday 17th January 2021. I haven't beaten Dolly yet, but she hasn't beaten me either, so it is, technically, stalemate. But, as time drags on, I have got life much happier than Dolly has. I have got the LOVE of the girl that I love and I have got the HOPE that things will improve for me. Dolly has no love and no hope; all she has got is the PAIN of unrequited love, and I know that that is the worst feeling in the world, and she will never have anything else until she turns herself into a duck. That is the only way by which she will ever be happy again.

Most of the people on the BBC news channel try to dishearten me by using the words "area" and "areas" for all they are worth, but they don't succeed in doing that because I have a very firm grip on reality, and I know where I stand and what the score is. So, although it is technically stalemate, I am actually winning, and there is no way by which I will not win; it is just a question of time.

Likewise, it is just a question of time before Lucy becomes a real woman. I have told her that she will not become a woman in my book until she realises the need to communicate with me and finds the courage to do so. I have therefore got victory in sight over both Dolly and Lucy. All I've got to do is bide my time and be patient, to win over both of the old girls.

Tuesday 19th January 2021. The loving feelings that I get from Lucy make me feel so great that I thought it would be churlish of me not to reward her with another letter, so I am sending her copies of today's journal entry and also Sunday's journal entry.

Thursday 21st January 2021. I wrote the following letter to Lucy and Twee Dampensquib today: - Thursday 21st January 2021

Empress Lucy Lawless, The Golden GIRL Herself,

Dear Soulmate,

You won't find out the meaning of your life until you succeed in proving that you are a real woman, and you won't prove that you are a real woman until you discover the meaning of your life.

If you think about it logically, that must imply that the meaning of your life IS to prove that you are a real woman. The same as it is for every other woman, and likewise for every man.

Becoming an adult is not just a question of sexual maturity, nor even having mental sex ("dancing"), but it is also a matter of developing socially responsible attitudes. That includes being a good judge of character, learning and applying communication skills, and learning and applying managerial skills. Not until these skills have been thoroughly tested, along with tests of your patience, courage, fortitude, tolerance, understanding, intelligence, wisdom and above all, LOVE, can you call yourself a real adult.

I used to think that homosexuals and lesbians were sub-humans, but your attitude to the LGBT community has made me change my mind. They are people, but the kindest way to regard their unnatural sexual proclivities is that they are symptoms of an incurable mental illness which requires antipsychotic medication to help them live celibate lives. They are amongst the people who never grow up.

The end of our trials is in sight.

Take care of yourself, my Love, I have much more to say to you, but it can wait until we talk, Bless you, my Queen,

Yours with Love, Affection and Friendship,

The King of Heaven,
Emperor Bob XX
Cc Dr Twee Dampensquib.

Saturday 23rd January 2021. I have this to say to the human race, and in particular the people of Great Britain; "DON'T SAY I DIDN'T WARN YOU!". All this week Great Britain and especially England has been subjected to a terrible rainstorm that the Meteorological Office have named "Storm Christoph". A month's rainfall has occurred in just two days, bringing terrible floods to vast swathes of the country. People have had their homes flooded and there has been nowhere for them to go. They cannot even visit other households because of the coronavirus lockdown restrictions. The weather is expected to get even worse next week.

On top of all this, the new strain of the coronavirus is now proving to be even more deadly than the previous strain as well as more contagious. It had been thought to be no worse, just more infectious, but now it is proving to be an even more vicious killer.

The followers of my late mother, Mrs Dorothy (Dolly) Ayres, are to blame for all these adverse conditions afflicting the human race, especially the people of Great Britain. Dolly and her followers thought they could take on the Gods and win. The poor fools, they can be identified by the way that they use the words "area" and "areas" at every opportunity because those words sound a bit like my late mother's surname. Things will only get worse for people until Dolly is brought back to life as a duck in her next life, and all the people of the world accept that I, Robert Brooks Strong, am the Lord God Almighty and obey my will henceforward.

I am the REAL leader of the human race and the head of the family of mankind, not my late mother; I have been ever since I was Adam in the Garden of Eden three hundred thousand years ago. Dolly is a usurper. She has usurped my position as the Emperor of the World and that is one of the main reasons why I am expelling her from the human race. Another reason is because she is an intolerable sex pest and she will obviously never change. She has ordered her followers to keep me a prisoner in a mental hospital for the last forty-four years because I refuse to have sex with her. We will all be a lot better off without her. So, get rid of her before it is too late. She has been the person in overall charge of the world for the last sixty years or more and is therefore the main person to blame for Climate Change, which will become irreversible in a few years' time unless we get rid of her in time for me to save the world from Global Warming and Climate Change.

I sent copies of the above entry to Lucy and also to Dr Twee Dampensquib.

Sunday 24th January 2021. I wrote the following letter to Lucy this evening:

- Sunday Evening 24th January 2021

    Empress Lucy Lawless, The Golden GIRL Herself,

Dear Soulmate,

    Things are moving rapidly now. I was right to blame, correctly, my late mother's followers for the ills afflicting the human race at the moment, in particular the people of Great Britain. The BBC have been trying to tell me that my thoughts are not reaching the masses of people. (I'll tell you how when we get together and talk). But I can tell from the cerebral activity, that I can sense telepathically, that millions of people are tuned in to my thoughts and Dolly's followers are just giving away the fact that they are shit scared of ME, now. And so they should be. They have persecuted me for all seventy-seven years of my life, but the boot is on the other foot now. My followers, realising that Dolly's followers are to blame for all the ills afflicting us, will now persecute Dolly's followers whom we greatly outnumber. As soon as they cotton on to this new reality, Dolly's followers will surely get rid of their erstwhile leader, if she doesn't duckify herself first.

    The ills afflicting us include the coronavirus pandemic, followed by subsequent pandemics that will happen when the mutant variants of the coronavirus become widespread; then, when we have tamed the virus, there will be massive unemployment, poverty and debt for most people as well as the huge national debt that will take generations to repay. And on top of all that there will be the Climate Change crisis to contend with. Dolly and her followers are directly to blame for all of these things. It will take me the rest of my lifetime to undo the damage that the old witch and her followers have caused.

    Thankfully, we'll soon have each other to lean on socially as well as spiritually and mentally. Once the door has been closed it won't take me long to clear my name and get my £x in compensation and above all, MY FREEDOM. Then I will register The Survival Party with the Electoral Register in the UK, and set about building up the executive, the management and the membership of The Party. I plan to employ a Campaign Manager in every Parliamentary constituency in Great Britain, who will liaise with the membership in his/her constituency, and between the Campaign Manager and the membership they will select a candidate to run for Parliament in that constituency at the next election. I plan to make

The Survival Party the dominant force in British politics within a very few years. I have already chosen who I want to run The Party's Head Office; my General Manager, Accounts Manager and IT Manager. My plans are exciting and you are welcome to join us if you want to.

The end of our trials is in sight.

Yours etcetera

Wednesday 27th January 2021. I wrote the following letter to my shrink, Twee Dampensquib, today. Note the list of people to whom I have copied the letter: - Wednesday Morning 27th January 2021

Dr Twee Dampensquib,
Medical Director,
Alcatraz Island Hospital.

Dear Twee,

The Gods in Heaven have sent the coronavirus pandemic to afflict the human race, especially the people of Great Britain, because people still refuse to obey MY WILL, THE WILL OF GOD. Over two million people have already died of the pandemic. You are aware that I want you to take me off all libido-suppressing antipsychotic medication, but you still refuse to do so. How does it feel, Twee, to know that you are largely to blame for the genocide of over two million people? And you, Lucy, you know that I want you to write to me but you still refuse to do so. How does it feel, Lucy, to know that you are also largely to blame for the genocide of over two million people?

Jesus Christ said, "If you love me, you will do as I ask".

My late mother, Mrs Dorothy (Dolly) Ayres, and her huge army of followers are directly to blame for all the ills afflicting the human race at the moment, especially the people of Great Britain: the inclement weather and the floods, the coronavirus pandemic with all its attendant ills such as the suffering and deaths, the misery of lockdown restrictions, the lack of schooling for our children, the unemployment, poverty and debt, as well as the national debt that will take generations to repay.

Those people can be identified by the fact that they give themselves away by using the words "area" and "areas" at every opportunity, as those words sound a bit like my late mother's surname. They might just as well say, "I'm to blame, persecute me!", as they are inviting the persecution by

MY followers, the army of the Lord. They have persecuted ME all my lifetime, but now it is payback time.

Yours sincerely,

Robert Strong.
Cc Lucy Lawless,
Paul Rees, Chief Executive of the Royal College of Psychiatrists,
Justin Welby, Archbishop of Canterbury,
Pope Francis,
Joe Biden, President of the USA
Boris Johnson, Prime Minister of the UK.

Saturday 30th January 2021. There is going to be a battle in the spirit world tonight between my late mother, Dorothy (Dolly) Ayres, and her army of followers, versus myself, Robert Brooks Strong, and my army of followers. The fact that it is mother versus son is irrelevant. A power struggle is a power struggle with neither side asking nor giving any quarter. A fight to the finish is a fight to the finish. I am convinced that my side will win because not only can I sense that we outnumber Dolly's forces, but we will fight harder because our cause is just. My followers are fighting to restore God the King, myself, to my rightful position of power in the world as the leader of the human race and the head of the family of mankind.

Our enemies are scared of us, and so they should be, because the person they follow is a usurper who has no right to hold power in the world. That is why they will lose the war, however the fight goes tonight, although I feel sure that we will win tonight.

The weather presenters have described this as a battle between the weather systems affecting the country and they have got a point; this is one of the main effects of the fight. Even if my side loses the battle tonight, I will still go on to win the war; I will just have to rebuild my army and fight them again. However the battle goes tonight, the war won't be over until Dolly is conceived as the embryo of a duckling.

I sense that Dolly is weary of fighting me and that she will throw in the towel at the first opportunity, but I am not taking that for granted. I won't have the power I need until I have taken it from her. I won't even say, "Thanks for the fight" until she is a duckling. Until then I won't have proved that MY WILL is stronger that hers, even though I know that that is the case.

Sunday 31st January 2021. Yesterday's anticipated fight was more of a dampsquib that a fireworks display. My army convinced me that we vastly outnumber Dolly's army because I could sense the cerebral activity from my followers and supporters and it was very encouraging for me. But I don't think the enemy showed up for the fight.

So, the stalemate goes on; but I have got Lucy's love and Lucy has got my love, and there is nothing that Dolly can do about that. Dolly has no love worth having. Even I, the Lord God, have no love for her, and won't have until she is a duckling. That serves her right for trying to rape me, on top of all her cruelty for the last seventy-seven years. She is an incestuous and decadent, degenerate old dead woman. All I can do about this situation is to hope that Dolly gets fed up with all the misery and clears off, out of the human race, before it is too late for the world to be saved from Global Warming and Climate Change. Until she clears off, her followers have the power to detain me in the mad house and suppress my libido with their filthy drugs, and they show every sign of continuing to do that indefinitely. But I remain far happier than Dolly is, thanks to my Darling Lucy and the Gods in Heaven.

I sent copies of yesterday's and today's journal entries in a letter to Lucy.

Friday 5th February 2021. The BBC news channel on the TV has degenerated into one big advertisement for the pro-poofery movement, which is my way of describing the LGBT community. They are using the medium of television to pervert and corrupt as many people as possible by insinuating that poofery is socially acceptable, and even desirable. I find this attitude to be thoroughly disgusting, so I don't watch the BBC news channel any more. I find that watching Channel 5 is a much more enjoyable experience.

I now have approximately twenty fish in each of the two tanks on this ward. It is impossible to count them accurately as they move so fast. We gave away about twenty fish including the original four adult fish. All the remaining fish are their descendants which we have bred.

I now play guitar about four times a week, including two sessions a week with The Humdingers. We play on other wards beside this one, and we now have a piece of music called "Telstar", which my friend David plays on my keyboard. The tune was originally a hit for a group called "The Tornados" back in the 1960s, played on the organ with guitar accompaniment. We still have the original four guitar tunes as well: "Apache", "Foot Tapper", "Nashville Boogie" and "Wonderful Land", three of which were hits for The Shadows.

I'm due for another injection of paliperidone tomorrow. I can't think of any way of getting off the drug. Except for the unthinkable, which would be to give in to my late mother's sexual demands. There is no way that could ever happen. That kind of behaviour is beneath me. It is true that I am a lady killer, but I could never be a motherfucker.

I am due for an injection of the anti-COVID vaccine before the 15th of this month. I will breathe a lot more easily when I have been inoculated, and I will then breathe even more easily when I have had my second shot, a few weeks later.

The weather here in the south of England remains miserable, as it has done for a long time now with a very few exceptional hours of sunshine. Almost all the time, the skies have been cloudy and overcast, and there has been much rain, some snow, and a general atmosphere of despondency, reflecting the mood of my late mother, Mrs Dorothy (Dolly) Ayres. She will never know anything in the least bit happy, until she relinquishes power by coming back to life as a duck.

I sent a copy of today's journal entry in a letter to Lucy.

I described recently my reasons for believing that the number 28 is inauspicious (unlucky), but it subsequently dawned on me that the number 29 is even more inauspicious. My late father lived at 29 Hollybush Road, Crawley, Sussex with his second family and me at the time when my late mother's machinations drove him to bankruptcy and he and his family and me had to do a moonlight flit to escape my father's creditors. My late first wife, Jasmin 1, lived at 29 Beechwood Avenue, Orpington, Kent, with her third husband and our son, Anthony, when she died of emphysema, caused by smoking too much.

I interpret these two coincidences on top of all the coincidences pertaining to the number 28 as signs from Heaven that irreversible Climate Change will occur in the year 2029, unless we achieve substantial cuts in worldwide carbon emissions by the end of the year 2028. Quite how substantial the cuts will need to be, remains to be seen; all I can say at this time is that we will all have to do our very best to cut carbon emissions as much as possible, and pray to Heaven that we escape catastrophe.

I have therefore, updated my Manifesto with a five-year plan to cut carbon emissions.

Friday 12th February 2021. I wrote the following letter to Lucy yesterday: - Thursday 11th February 2021

Empress Lucy Lawless, The Golden GIRL Herself,

Dear Soulmate,

I'm enclosing last Friday's journal entry for you. This is just a line to keep in touch.

I had my paliperidone injection on Saturday the 6th February. What a ridiculous way to treat a man of my age! I also had, yesterday, my anti-COVID inoculation. My right arm is beginning to feel like a pin cushion. My left arm still hurts from my injection on the 6th October 2020, when the girl hit the nerve in my arm with the needle. I have had painful pins and needles in my left arm and left hand ever since, so I don't have injections on the left any more.

My friend, David, who plays lead guitar for The Humdingers, as well as keyboards, hasn't been feeling well lately, so we haven't been practising nor performing for the last three weeks. The shrinks have been messing him around with his depot injections. He is on Bishopsgate ward and is therefore under Marionette Madre, poor chap. He is carrying a torch for his girlfriend as well, whom he hasn't seen for years, although he still loves her. Madre wants him to dance with Mrs Dorothy (Dolly) Ayres, like she does with all her "patients", but she is too deceitful, like all shrinks, to tell him so.

The weather in the South of England, lately, can't make up its mind what to do. Yesterday morning we had a couple of hours of sunshine, then the sky became overcast and we had a small flurry of snow, then we had some more sunshine in the afternoon, but it remained bitterly cold at -2⁰ C all day and it has been well below zero all night for weeks now. Today the sky has been overcast all day and it remains cold at -4⁰ C.

The mood of the people of Britain remains mostly despondent. Most of them are confused and don't know what to believe, nor whom to believe.

All they know is that times are hard, but they haven't got the sense to ask, "What have we done to deserve this?" The answers are all in my journals which have been published already. Channel 5 TV is like a breath of fresh air after watching little but my late mother's propaganda on the BBC. The target audience for channel 5 is mainly for young families, as there are many children's programmes on, which isn't a bad idea during lockdown to keep the kids happy. The afternoon movies are pretty good, and the channel, by and large, puts across my point of view on life.

The end of our trials is in sight.

Yours etcetera

Sunday 14th February 2021. I wrote the following letter to Lucy today: -
Sunday 14th February 2021

Empress Lucy Lawless, The Golden GIRL Herself,

Dear Soulmate,

My late mother, Mrs Dorothy (Dolly) Ayres, has ruined my whole life out of spite and jealousy because I have always refused her incestuous sexual demands of me. Hell hath no fury like a woman scorned! But I have always believed, and still do believe, that incest is beneath the dignity of REAL human beings.

If Dolly has as much as one grain of conscience left in her soul, she would make amends to me for seventy-seven years of abuse and cruelty by relinquishing power and coming back to life as an animal, presumably a duck. Now that I am approaching the final years of my life, she could at least give me a few years of freedom after having been her prisoner all my life. She could relinquish power by handing it over to someone such as myself who knows how to handle it, which is more than she ever did, judging by the state of the world today.

We satisfied each other sexually yesterday afternoon in spite of the paliperidone. Thank you, Darling. I could tell it was good for you, too, by the loving feelings that you gave me yesterday evening. Twee Dampensquib still insists on the needless cruelty of abusing me with his filthy drug. He won't say why, and I can only guess that he is obeying Dolly's wishes to see that if I don't have sex with her then I can't have sex with anyone else either. But our love still shines through in spite of all this abuse and decadence.

One thing is one hundred per cent certain – Dolly will NEVER get what she wants from me, so she can forget it. I will always be a human being, from one lifetime to the next, as I know that you will be, too, Darling. We love our children, the human race, too much not to protect them, and we know how much they need our protection from the forces of evil – forces which Dolly has embraced, even though she pretends otherwise. She is a wolf in sheep's clothing. Her decadent ways and incestuous desires have let the side down, but I will not do so. If Dolly loved me as a REAL human mother should, then she would put MY happiness before her own sexual gratification. The fact that she doesn't proves that she is not worthy of the position of power that the human race has invested in her.

The end of our trials is in sight.

Yours etcetera

Cc. Dr Twee Dampensquib.

Monday 15th February 2021. I wrote the following letter to Lucy this evening: - Monday Evening 15th February 2021

Empress Lucy Lawless, The Golden GIRL Herself,

Dear Soulmate,

I had the best orgasm of my life with you this morning, and I could feel you coming with me. I'm sure you had a similar experience. I'm only now, seven hours later, just beginning to come down from the high that you gave me. We have both got good reason to feel proud of ourselves. When it comes to love making, which is the most important part of any relationship, you are the most wonderful woman in the world by far. You are certainly all the woman I want and the only woman I want. I LOVE YOU with everything I've got and everything that I am. And I'm happy beyond measure that you feel the same way about me.

The Daily Mirror carried a front-page headline today, "THE ROAD TO FREEDOM" which I think was influenced by yesterday's letter to you from me. I sense that Dolly is at tipping point and will go soon, but we will have to continue to be patient, and wait and see what happens. Maybe the old witch has some vestige of a conscience left, in which case yesterday's letter may well have done the trick.

When I was a boy, I learned a song at school called, "The Camptown

Races". The lyrics go like this: -

"De Camptown darkies sing dis song. Do dah, Do dah,
Wi' de Camptown racetrack five miles long. Do dah, Do dah, Day.
G'wine to run all night, G'wine to run all day,
Well I bet my money on de bobtail nag, somebody bet on de bay".

That song was about my conflict with Edward Richard Pitchblack, the Devil Himself. I was the bobtail nag and He was the bay in the song. A lot of people put a lot of money on Pitchblack to get the better of me, but they all lost. That was what the PPI scandal was all about. The banks had to pay out £billions to ordinary people who had been overcharged with Personal Protection Insurance on bank loans and hire purchase agreements, which were underwritten by the banks, because that was the ruling of the supreme court when I overpowered Pitchblack and disposed of his soul. One of us had to win and the loser is forever a loser.

Law degrees are known as LLP or LLB, in honour of us two combatants. YOU are the "LL" in question. And your love is the prize awarded to the winner. I couldn't be happier. The winner takes it all.

The end of our trials is in sight.

Yours etcetera

Wednesday 17th February 2021. I wrote the following letter to Lucy this morning: - Wednesday Morning 17th February 2021

Empress Lucy Lawless, The Golden GIRL Herself,

Dear Soulmate,

I have been waiting for years for my late mother to relinquish power by duckifying herself, but I am not waiting any longer before starting to get my own way in the world. I now have enough of a personal following of my own to get my own way, whatever she gets up to. I insist that I am the leader of the human race and the head of the family of mankind, not my late mother. I killed once already to prove it.

I have singled out seven individuals from my late mother's following, for persecution by my army of followers. They are among the kingpins of her army of followers and I am making examples of them. When you have the sense to write to me and ask me who they are then I will write back and tell you, but I will tell you now that Twee Dampensquib is one of them. The Chinese have a proverb – Confucius, he says, "Man who treads on the toes

331

of a giant must expect to have his arse kicked mightily". Twee should have thought of that before he tried to force his filthy libido-suppressing drugs on me. He has been treading on my toes for years, but now I have enough influence to make his life a living Hell and that is just what I am doing. This will continue until he starts obeying me, starting by taking me off the drugs.

I have chosen you, Darling, to be the subject of friendly persuasion by my army. Many modern films and TV shows have the lead female encouraged by her friends to write to the lead male who is waiting to hear from her. I don't need to tell you who they are actually talking about.

I've said enough for now. I'm now expecting to be told what I want to hear.

The end of our trials is in sight.

Yours etcetera

Cc Dr Twee Dampensquib.

Monday 22ⁿᵈ February 2021. I wrote the following letter to Lucy this morning: - Monday Morning 22ⁿᵈ February 2021

Empress Lucy Lawless, The Golden GIRL Herself,

Dear Soulmate,

The end of the world will happen from irreversible Climate Change in eight years' time unless Dolly goes and goes NOW. I am sure that incest is beneath the dignity of REAL men and women and I am sure that I am a REAL MAN. So, I could not bring myself to have sex with my late mother even if I fancied her, which I don't, much to her chagrin; not even if the fate of the world depended upon it, which it looks like it does. The old witch is still playing "chicken" with me, but it is a game which she has got to lose, and she WILL lose because it is MY WILL, the will of God, that she does so. And MY WILL is the strongest force in the Universe, stronger than Dolly's will as I am now proving and will continue to prove at all costs. This is my PROOF that I AM GOD. I have to prove it to Twee Dampensquib in order to get off the filthy libido-suppressing drugs that the bastard insists on forcing me to take. Then I will be able to make love to you properly, Darling.

Things have got to change and change very soon or it will be too late to prevent the end of the world from happening in 2029. We have got to get worldwide carbon emissions down by forty-nine per cent before the end of 2028, and at the moment it doesn't look like we, the human race, will reach that target. Great Britain and the rest of the world NEED my leadership in order to prevent this catastrophe.

The end of our trials is in sight.

Yours etcetera

Cc Dr Twee Dampensquib.

Friday 26th February 2021. I wrote the following letter to Lucy this morning: - Friday Morning 26th February 2021

Empress Lucy Lawless, The Golden GIRL Herself,

Dear Soulmate,

My army is going from strength to strength. We have gone from being an underground movement to an accepted part of British society with our own TV channel, Channel 5, as well as having all the UK tabloid press on our side. My leadership is accepted as having been proven by my army who now have a clear plan of action that I have given them. We are fighting for a cause – that of the survival OF THE HUMAN RACE AS WELL AS ALL OTHER OF NATURE'S CREATURES. (There go the Gods again with my Caps Lock button). To achieve this, we have got to restore God, myself, to my position of power in the world, and get rid of the usurper, the late Mrs Dorothy (Dolly) Ayres.

My plan to persecute the seven kingpins of Dolly's army is working well. I am hoping to convert Twee Dampensquib to our side, but until we do so I am having to hurt him because his insistence upon medicating me with his filthy libido-suppressing drugs indicates that he is, perhaps unwittingly, still a kingpin of Dolly's army. Dolly is the one behind the use of these drugs, to see that people who don't have sex with her can't have sex with anyone else either. The old witch is still a nymphomaniac fifteen years after her death, but she is close to tipping point now that she can't protect her soldiers from me. I repeat that I am making examples of the kingpins of her army. I think she will duckify herself very soon.

I can't make any moves to further the plans for The Survival Party for the next four months because of the coronavirus lockdown restrictions. It won't be until 21st June this year that every adult in Britain has been

333

inoculated and the restrictions will then be just about entirely lifted. So, until then I will continue to increase my covert influence through the media and by the telepathic waves of cerebral activity that I can sense, to gain the ascendancy over my late mother's influence; then there will be no stopping me. I am preparing to get my public apology from the Royal College of Psychiatrists for forty-five years of unjust detainment in mental hospitals, for forty-four years of which I have been tortured with injections of filthy libido-suppressing drugs when there has never been anything wrong with my mental health. So, I am now demanding £x in compensation. If I don't get it, without quibble, then I shall continue to fight the psychiatric profession in both the spiritual and the material worlds until I win. I am planning to get my apology, my compensation and my freedom at the end of June this year.

As soon as I am free and have money in the bank, I shall start my legal fight to clear my name by a retrial of my "crime" and getting a verdict of self-defence against undue social pressure. I shall also then take out premises in central London for the headquarters of The Survival Party, register the Party with the UK Electoral Commission and start to develop the membership of the Party by advertising my Manifesto free to those interested in joining my Party.

Your plans are also working well. By not communicating with me, you are playing hard to get and making me want you more and more. Everything is falling into place thanks to guidance from the Gods in Heaven.

The end of our trials is in sight.

Yours etcetera

Cc Dr Twee Dampensquib.

And I wrote this letter to Lucy this afternoon: - Friday Afternoon 26th February 2021

Empress Lucy Lawless, The Golden GIRL Herself,

Dear Soulmate,

We made love again this morning. You gave me another most beautiful orgasm, and I could feel that I did the same for you. Well done, Darling, and thank you. Our love life, and my level of happiness, just keep on getting better and better all the time, in spite of the paliperidone and in spite of my late mother's machinations; even if we can only come together about once a fortnight. Dolly would be gnashing her teeth with jealousy if she had any teeth to gnash. And I am very happy to be rubbing her nose in her own jealousy before putting her out. That's how to train a dog, and it serves her right – the spiteful, domineering, bullying bitch. That'll teach her not to assume that she has the right or the power to have a sex life with me! That's your privilege; because the Gods in Heaven say so and so do I, as their King – for you make the most wonderful Queen.

When Dolly finally gets that message, I think that'll be enough to make her clear off, out of the human race, and I say, "Good riddance to bad rubbish".

The end of our trials is in sight.

Yours etcetera

Cc Dr Twee Dampensquib.

Sunday 28th February 2021. I wrote the following letter to Lucy today: - Sunday 28th February 2021
    Empress Lucy Lawless, The Golden GIRL Herself,

Dear Soulmate,
    I read on the internet that you have developed an interest in politics. I also read that you are now worth thirty million USD. (I wish they'd say US$ if that's what they mean!). I'll get straight to the point. I have a vacancy for a Party Treasurer now that I have sacked Flyboy Alltalk. It occurred to me that you could do a lot worse with your time and your money than come to England and help me run The Survival Party. There are ninety-two counties in Great Britain, encompassing 64.11 million people, which is a much bigger pool of souls for you to look after than the 4.85 million souls who live in New Zealand, which already has an excellent political leader in Jucinda Arderne. You could afford to employ a Campaign Manager in every county in Great Britain, who would have the responsibility of putting forward a Parliamentary Candidate in every Parliamentary constituency within his/her county at the next election. The Campaign Managers would have the job of organising elections by the Party members of Prospective Parliamentary Candidates in every constituency.
    I have been unable to get to the printers to have the latest version of

my Manifesto duplicated professionally because of the fact that we are all in lockdown over here, so I have run you off a loose-leaf copy of the latest Manifesto for you to consider. And I have included a page of my suggested advert for distribution of the Manifesto to any member of the public who is interested.

I think this is the right move for you, professionally and socially, and it is something that will play an important role for you in shaping the future and the very survival of the planet.

The end of our trials is in sight.

Yours etcetera

Enclosed: copy of the March 2021 Manifesto.

Chapter 21

Times of Trial, and Decision

Events and Thoughts from Monday 1st March 2021

Monday 1st March 2021. I wrote the following letter to Lucy in the small hours of this morning: - Monday Morning 1st March 2021

Empress Lucy Lawless, Queen of the Gods,

Dear Soulmate,

Dolly has now become the natural enemy of all living things, including the human race. We must make plans to save the world, irrespective of what she and her followers get up to. I now have a huge following of people who know my thoughts and obey my wishes; I call them my army. For the time being, Alcatraz Island hospital is my base; it is my castle, my fort and my palace.

Too often, the word "decadence" is associated with opulence and material greed, which is something I am not and never will be guilty of. I use the word, not only in the above meaning, but also as a decline in the moral fibre of human beings and a lack of a sense of worth and a sense of purpose in life, resulting in a "don't care" attitude and corresponding bad behaviour.

There will be an International Climate Change conference being held in Glasgow, Scotland, this November. Whatever the next eight months holds for me, I want you to be at that conference, representing The Survival Party. This will be our chance to signal the fact that WE have arrived, and to make the presence of The Survival Party felt on the International stage. Ideally, I want all the delegates at that conference to get a copy of our Manifesto, so no one can say that they do not know my thoughts.

We must make plans to get me out of Alcatraz Island and into 10 Downing Street as quickly as possible. I am fully confident that the British people will vote me into power and that I will win at a general election if I get out of hospital and get The Survival Party started as soon as possible, although I can't make a move until July because of the coronavirus lockdown restrictions. Dr Twee Dampensquib's cooperation will obviously be invaluable.

The fight is on, in earnest, Take care of yourself, my Love, I have much more to say to you, but it can wait until we talk, Bless you, my Queen,
    Yours with Love, Affection and Friendship,

    The King of the Gods,
    Emperor_Bob XX
    Cc Dr Twee Dampensquib

Tuesday 2nd March 2021. I wrote the following letter to Lucy this evening:
- Tuesday Evening 2nd March 2021
    Empress Lucy Lawless, Queen of the Gods,

Dear Soulmate,
    I repeat that I believe the end of the world will happen from irreversible Climate Change in 2029 unless we, the human race, cut our worldwide carbon emissions by forty-nine per cent by the end of 2028. At the moment it does not look as though we will achieve that target. If I get my public apology, my freedom and my £x in compensation within the next four months, then I think I can develop The Survival Party into a Party which could swing the balance in favour of giving the human race a fighting chance of survival. I will only get those things if my late mother, Mrs Dorothy (Dolly) Ayres, comes back to life as an animal, presumably a duck, in the very near future.
    As far as I am concerned, a world which bullies me into having sex with my mother against my will, is not a world which is worth saving. I will not, therefore, give in to my late mother's sexual demands of me at any cost to the world. The fate of the world is up to Dolly's will. If she wishes the world to survive, then she knows what she must do, before it is too late. If she doesn't wish the world to survive then the world is doomed anyway. She is the leader – it is up to her what happens.
    If the world is doomed, then Dolly's followers will only have

themselves to blame, for putting into power a woman without the moral fibre to uphold the most sacred taboo of the human race, the taboo against incest. As well as the taboos against sodomy and lesbian sex and adultery, which she has also blatantly flouted.

Let us hope and pray that the words in the following song, which I wrote in 1967, were just a warning and not a self-fulfilling prophesy: -

"I sat alone and sank my weary body, into oceans of despair.

I missed the boat that all the others ride on, 'cos no one wants me there.

"Too late", I cried, to the moon I cried. "Too late", I cried to the moon.

"Too late", I cried, to the moon I cried. "Too late", I cried to the moon."

The fight is on, in earnest,

Yours etcetera

Cc Dr Twee Dampensquib

Wednesday 3rd March 2021. I wrote the following letter to Lucy this morning: - Wednesday Morning 3rd March 2021

Empress Lucy Lawless, Queen of the Gods,

Dear Soulmate,

We made love again last night and I could feel you coming with me. That made me so very happy and proud that I can do that for you despite our present circumstances with the antipsychotic drugs and everything. I love you so very much, Lucy, and I can sense that you feel the same way about me, even though you are not yet woman enough to tell me so. I don't know what you are afraid of. I will never let you down, nor give away your secret if you ask me not to. But you really should treat me like a person, and it would be so nice if you tell me that you love me.

I looked up the lyrics to "Secret Love" and copied them here for you. You are not the first person to have had a secret lover, and I very much doubt that you will be the last. You will find an enormous sense of relief when you declare your feelings to the world. Every woman will understand and so will every real man. Trust me not to disappoint you.

I'll stake my life and my very soul that our feelings are true love, and that our true love will conquer all. I'm sure that all my plans will become reality very soon. I'll get my freedom, my public apology, clear my name and get my £x in compensation and be the leader of the best Political Party in Great Britain and the world. I'll make you proud of me, Darling, just you wait and see.

The whole world, not just us, depends upon Dolly duckifying herself. If she doesn't do so, and soon, it will be all over for everybody before long.

The fight is on, in earnest,

Yours etcetera

Cc Dr Twee Dampensquib

Friday 5th March 2021. I wrote the following letter to Lucy this morning: -

Friday Morning 5th March 2021

Empress Lucy Lawless, Queen of the Gods,

Dear Soulmate,

There are only two ways by which the present situation can develop. Either my late mother, Mrs Dorothy (Dolly) Ayres, comes back to life as an animal, presumably a duck, in the immediate future or she continues to prolong the agony of her existence in which case the world will come to an end from irreversible Climate Change in eight years' time.

In the case of the latter event happening, Dolly's followers will be to blame for the way they have treated ME for the last fifty-one years. In the case of the former event happening, Dolly's followers will have to become MY followers and on MY terms.

My terms are as follows: -

1). I demand a full public apology from the Royal College of Psychiatrists, along the lines that I have already stated in my previous correspondence, for forty-five years of unjust detainment, for forty-four years of which I have been tortured with injections of antipsychotic drugs when there has never been anything wrong with my mental health. I want this in the immediate future.

2). I demand £x compensation from the Royal College of Psychiatrists, to be paid by the 21st June this year.

3). I demand a retrial of the "crime" I committed on the 16th July 1976, and a verdict returned of "Justifiable homicide by reason of self-defence against undue social pressure" by the 21st June 2022.

4). I demand compensation to be paid by the British Government on behalf of British society of £y for bullying me into killing my stepmother,

Mrs Iris Brooks, on the 16th July 1976 to be paid by the 21st June 2022.

5). I demand an immediate reply from all the people receiving a copy of this letter, stating that the above four terms are agreed. If my terms are not met, without quibble, I will have no mercy on the souls responsible.

Yours etcetera

Cc Dr Twee Dampensquib, Medical Director, Alcatraz Island Hospital.
Paul Rees, Chief Executive, the Royal College of Psychiatrists.
Boris Johnson, Prime Minister.
Rishi Sunak, Chancellor of the Exchequer.

Saturday 6th March 2021. Two psychiatric nurses came into my bedroom today, and one of them, a young feller, injected me with 100 mil of paliperidone. These people seem to be so thoroughly indoctrinated that they actually believe that they are doing some good by pumping that muck into my arm. They certainly don't pay any attention to my point of view, and I am the man who has to suffer from the poison.

Sunday 7th March 2021. It looks like Dolly is still prolonging the agony of her existence, and I cannot help thinking that maybe another day or two won't make that much difference to my plans under the present circumstances. I've got to get my plans for The Survival Party underway on the 21st June this year, when the lockdown ends. This means that I've got to get my public apology, my compensation and my freedom by then; which means that Dolly has got until the end of April, this year, to duckify herself or the worst will happen: it will take all of May and the first three weeks of June to get everything organised.

If Dolly doesn't duckify herself by the end of April, it will mean that irreversible Climate Change will be inevitable in 2029 with catastrophic consequences for all life on Earth. It will be the end of the world, and Mrs Dorothy (Dolly) Ayres will be solely responsible. Not to mention the idiots who put *her* into power.

So, Dolly has got until the end of next month to get the Hell out of the human race, or it will be the end, for all of us. The people made *her* into God. Pray to *her* for salvation. I am the REAL God, but I cannot get on with my job of saving the world whilst *she* continues to exist. So, she has got until the end of April at the latest, to get out, or it really will be too late.

If I can get going before the end of June this year, that will give me two and a half years to get into power, and then five years to put my five-year plan into operation to cut carbon emissions by forty-nine per cent by the end of 2028. That is cutting it fine, but it should just about be possible.

I'm now going to blow my own trumpet for a bit, and I make no apologies for doing this. There never was a great leader who was not full of hubris.

It was ME, not my late mother, Mrs Dorothy (Dolly) Ayres, who killed the tyrant matriarch I had for a stepmother, Mrs Iris Brooks. It was ME, not my late mother, who overpowered Edward Richard Pitchblack, the Devil Himself, causing him to die in 2009. And it was ME, not my late mother, that marshalled the spiritual armies who finally defeated Satan and His hordes in August 2014, by turning Him into a Rottweiler dog. These achievements are my justification for claiming that I, not my late mother, nor anyone else, am the leader of the human race and the head of the family of mankind.

I have been in all my lives, ever since I was Adam in the Garden of Eden, three hundred thousand years' ago. And Lucy Lawless is my soulmate and partner, who was then Eve, not my late mother. I know this because I have received divine guidance from the Goddess of Love, Aphrodite, that this is the case, and Lucy herself has borne this out and proven it to me.

I sent copies of the above entry to Lucy and to Twee Dampensquib and Paul Rees.

Tuesday 9th March 2021. I sent the following letter to Lucy today: - Tuesday Morning 9th March 2021

Empress Lucy Lawless, Queen of the Gods,

Dear Soulmate,

I repeat that I have received signs from Heaven that Climate Change will become irreversible in 2029 unless we, the human race, cut our worldwide carbon emissions by forty-nine per cent by the end of 2028. This will have catastrophic consequences for all life on Earth, but I have a plan to avert this catastrophe. I cannot get on with my plan, however, whilst the spirit of my late mother, Mrs Dorothy (Dolly) Ayres, continues to exist, so I have given her until the end of next month to say her final goodbyes and then clear off, out of the human race. If she leaves it beyond the end of April it will be too late, even for me, God, to save the world and we will all be doomed.

This could not be more serious.

Yours etcetera

Cc Dr Twee Dampensquib.
Paul Rees, Chief Executive, The Royal College of Psychiatrists.
Boris Johnson, Prime Minister.

Thursday 11th March 2021. I wrote the following letter to Lucy today: -
Thursday Afternoon 11th March 2021

Empress Lucy Lawless, Queen of the Gods,

Dear Soulmate,

I repeat my schedule for the foreseeable future as follows: -

1. The Immediate Future. Say "Goodbye" to my late mother as she enters her next life. And come off all neuroleptic and antipsychotic drugs.

2. Until 21st June this year. Organise the following with Dr Twee Dampensquib: -

A. My public apology. To be submitted for my approval, then given to the Royal College of Psychiatrists for publication.

B. Arrange with the Ministry of Justice for my absolute discharge on the 21st June.

C. Arrange with the Royal College of Psychiatrists for my compensation of £x to be paid by the 21st June. This being £y for forty-five years of unjust detainment plus £z for forty-four years of torture by injections of antipsychotic drugs when there has never been anything wrong with my mental health.

3. As soon as I am free.

A. Find myself a flat in the Chelsea District and move in.

B. Take out office accommodation in the Westminster District for the Head Office of The Survival Party; employ my General Manager, Accounts Manager and IT Manager; register The Party with the Electoral Commission of the UK and open a bank account in the name of The Party.

C. Engage a solicitor and start proceedings for my retrial.

D. Put the staff to work advertising the Manifesto and building up the membership of The Party.

4. Until 21st June next year.

A. Continue building up the membership of The Party, and employing Campaign Managers, one in every county in Great Britain.

B. Arrange with the Government my £w compensation for bullying me into killing my stepmother, Mrs Iris Brooks, on the 16th July 1976.

C. Secure a verdict of self-defence at the retrial.

5. Until the end of 2023. Organise with the Campaign Managers for a Parliamentary Candidate in every constituency in Great Britain to stand at the next election, and push for that to take place by the end of 2023.

6. Until the end of 2028. Pursue the five-year plan to cut carbon emissions as per the Manifesto. Hopefully, we will avert the catastrophe of Climate Change becoming irreversible in 2029.

7. Accommodate Lucy into my plans, whenever she is ready to normalise our relationship by communicating with me.

Yours etcetera

Cc Dr Twee Dampensquib.

Paul Rees, Chief Executive, The Royal College of Psychiatrists.

Wednesday 17th March 2021. I wrote the following letter to Lucy today: -

Wednesday Morning 17th March 2021

Empress Lucy Lawless, Queen of the Gods,

Dear Soulmate,

You are associated with the number 5. Your rival for the job of the Queen of society, Hannah Gordon, is associated with the number 3. Your victory over her has now been signified by the fact that the bookies are now paying out on the first 5 places in the Cheltenham Gold Cup instead of 3. She was my late father's choice of Queen, not mine. She is identified by the use of the word "synergy". As far as I am concerned, she is just one of those things that Heaven has sent to try me. It is a trial which I have passed, and so have you.

As King, it is a part of my job to decide what people are, just as it was my mother's job before me. People have been eating your spirit by eating 5 portions of fruit and veg' per day. The reason your life is murder is because society is feeding on your spirit. Everybody knows that I have decided that you are still a girl, not a woman, until you realise the need to communicate with me and find the courage to do so. That is why your life is murder at the moment.

If you have had enough of people feeding on your spirit, then declare to the world that you are a woman in love with me and not afraid to show it. That is what everyone is waiting for, not just me, but every other adult in the world. You have proven your adulthood sexually, but not yet socially. I am a person, Lucy, and that gives me the POWER to make you treat me like one, so please send me an email or a letter to let me know how you feel about me. I am a living person with a living person's needs, not just a spirit, so please treat me like one, for your own sake.

Yours etcetera

Friday 19th March 2021. I wrote the following letter to Lucy today, note the addressee line: - Friday Morning 19th March 2021

Empress Lucy Lawless, the Dancing GIRL Herself,

Dear Soulmate,

Your life is murder at the moment because everybody in the world is treating you like a girl, not yet a woman. I repeat that to be an adult you need to learn and apply communication skills. This is the case BECAUSE I SAY SO, and I AM THE KING.

If you want to know what to say to me when you contact me, try saying, "Thank you" for the lovely Queen Lucy album that I created for you; including the title track which was a labour of love. And I obviously feel that you are worth it. I still do.

Yours etcetera

Cc Dr Twee Dampensquib.

Sunday 21st March 2021. I wrote the following email to my brother, Bill, in the small hours of this morning: -

Dear Bill,

Dolly's followers, who are almost all of the adults in the International Community, are determined to follow Dolly to the end of the world, and it looks as though that is exactly what is going to happen from irreversible climate change in eight years' time unless Dolly comes back to life as an animal by the end of next month. If she leaves it beyond the end of April, it will be too late even for me, God, to save the world. All I can do is to tell everyone the score, and tell them to pray to Dolly to clear off, out of the human race, before it is too late. The people deified Dolly, so pray to her for salvation. She has got just forty days to go or the world will be doomed.

I'm sorry this message isn't more cheerful, but I've got to tell it like it is.

All the best to you,

Bob

I sent identical copies of this email to my cousin, Shaun, in America and to my niece, Rachel, in Italy. I hope it will influence Dolly if we all pray to her to clear off.

I sent a copy of this journal entry to Lucy and also to Dr Twee Dampensquib.

Wednesday 24th March 2021. I wrote the following letter to my son, Christopher, today: - Wednesday 24th March 2021

Mr Christopher Brooks, c/o Troy Evans.

Dear Chris,

You stood up to your father, and gave me a piece of your mind. It took a man to do that and I couldn't be more proud of you for proving yourself. I'm sure that one day you'll be just as proud of Troy.

I defended you by making Jim Shyster so shit scared of ME, that neither he nor anybody else would dare to kill you. It was your Nan, my mother, who jeopardised your life in an attempt to blackmail me into having sex with her. But it didn't work. Jim Shyster is the man who James Bond (licensed to kill) is an allegory for; he is the real James Bond, but nobody is going to bond with him, because of ME. I know you will find this hard to believe, but it is the REAL truth.

I hope you get back with Jessica, because she really loves you and would make you a good wife. All the blokes at Ashworth hospital were jealous of you for making Jessica yours. She is a woman you could be proud of.

I love you as well.

Take care of yourself, son, and don't catch the dreaded virus.

Yours, with love,

Dad.

Cc Dr Twee Dampensquib.

Lucy Lawless.

I also wrote the following letter to Lucy today: - Wednesday 24th March 2021

Empress Lucy Lawless, the Dancing GIRL Herself,

Dear Soulmate,

I thought you'd like to see the enclosed copy of today's letter to my son, Christopher.

I hope you're not too angry with me for making a stand on the issue of you communicating with me, but that's what you've been challenging me to MAKE you do for ages.

Yours etcetera

Friday 26th March 2021. I wrote the following letter to Lucy today: - Friday 26th March 2021

Empress Lucy Lawless, the Dancing GIRL Herself,

Dear Soulmate,

I thought you'd like this picture of The Humdingers. I'm the man on the left in the red, gold & black shirt. The man in the middle, leaning forward, is John; he plays drums on an electronic drum kit, and the chap on the right with the long hair is my mate, David, who plays lead guitar and keyboards.

We've made love a few times recently and it has always been absolutely wonderful. Thank you, Darling. No other woman or girl can match your Regal Countenance. You have a look that says, "I know I'm the best" and you prove it to me every time. If that were not the case, you wouldn't have won MY love, which you surely have done.

Yours etcetera

Monday 29th March 2021. I wrote the following letter to Lucy this morning:
- Monday Morning 29th March 2021

Empress Lucy Lawless, the Dancing GIRL Herself,

Dear Soulmate,

You are still not behaving like a woman who loves me. I don't know what you are afraid of, but I do know that the solution to all fears is to have the courage of an adult human being. I do not doubt your love for me, so you force me to conclude that you are still a girl and not yet a woman. This is obvious to every adult person who knows you, which is why they are making your life murder at the moment – to MAKE you search your soul until you find your adult courage.

You won't find the meaning of your life until you pass this test, so go on, girl, write to me and tell me that you love me. I looked up the lyrics to "Woman in love" and also "A woman in love" and copied them here for you. When you find the meaning of your life, that will be what you become – A REAL WOMAN.

Good luck to you, girl, you're almost there.

Yours etcetera

Tuesday 6TH April 2021. I wrote the following letter to my brother, Bill, today. Note the list of people I am copying it to: -
Tuesday 6th April 2021

Mr. Bill Brooks,

Dear Bill,

I believe that Climate Change will become irreversible, with catastrophic consequences for all life on earth, in 2029 unless we, the human race, cut our carbon emissions by forty-nine per cent by the end of 2028. At the moment it does not look as though we will achieve this target. If I am able to enter the political arena this year, my influence may be enough to swing the balance in favour of giving the human race a fighting chance of survival. I have given myself a timetable of events to action in order to achieve this, but they depend upon our late mother, Dolly, coming back to life this month.

Dolly insists that I become her lover, but I refuse to do this. I insist that Dolly comes back to life as an animal, presumably a duck, but she refuses to do this. This battle of wills has turned into a game of "chicken" with the fate of the world at stake. One of us has to give in and it will not be me. I am Lucy's lover, not Dolly's. Lucy and I are both determined that it is going to stay that way, and we believe that our true love will conquer all adversity.

So, Lucy and I are exhorting all our many friends and supporters and followers to shout at the old witch, telling her to clear off, out of the human race, THIS MONTH, before it is too late, even for me to save the world.

All the best, brother,

Bob
Cc Rachel in Italy.
Shaun in America.
Lucy in New Zealand.
Dr Twee Dampensquib, Medical Director, Alcatraz Island Hospital.
Paul Rees, Chief Executive, The Royal College of Psychiatrists.

Thursday 8th April 2021. I wrote the following letter to Lucy this morning:
- Thursday 8th April 2021
　　Empress Lucy Lawless, the Dancing GIRL Herself,

Dear Soulmate,

It occurred to me that maybe you don't communicate with me because you are frightened of me, for being God. I will tell you two secrets: -

1.　All worship is hero-worship.
2.　All heroes are just people, men and women.

Now that I've given you that information, I think it is wisest to continue to keep it secret. But it should be enough for you not to be frightened of me. Treat me right and I'll be the most loving and loyal friend you could hope for; and I'm sure that's how you feel in all your relationships. So, all that is left for me to say is what our relationship is. Are we not a man and a woman who are lovers? If you agree that is what we are then please have the common humanity to write to me and tell me so. Stop teasing me by playing hard to get. That is no way to treat a lover.

Or are you frightened of committing yourself to a new relationship, having had two failed ones in the past? There's no shame to admit that you made mistakes before, but you should know me well enough by now to trust me, and to trust yourself that we have both found true love at last. Ask

Aphrodite, the Goddess of Love, and she'll tell you that I'm the best man you'll ever find. She fancies me herself, but she knows her place and she is wise enough not to tread on your toes.

Yours etcetera

Cc Dr Twee Dampensquib.

Enclosures: Song lyrics to: -
I'm your man,
Stand by your man,
When you tell me that you love me.

Sunday 11th April 2021. I wrote the following letter to my shrink this morning: - Sunday Morning 11th April 2021

Dr Twee Dampensquib,
Medical Director,
Alcatraz Island Hospital.

Dear Twee,

I have maintained for a long time that it is not me that is mentally ill, but it is society itself that is mentally ill. The free world is an empire of democracies and my late mother, Mrs Dorothy (Dolly) Ayres, has been the Emperor for over sixty years now. Elizabeth has been the Queen who has status but no power, whilst Dolly has had power but no status. This schizophrenic society was created by a group of thinkers after the Second World War to prevent another Hitler from ever coming to power. This suited both Elizabeth and Dolly. Dolly did not want fame or fortune. What she wanted was a sexual relationship with the best man she could find, who turned out to be her own son, myself.

Yours sincerely,

Robert Strong.
Cc Lucy Lawless,
Paul Rees, Chief Executive of the Royal College of Psychiatrists,
Justin Welby, Archbishop of Canterbury,
Pope Francis,
Joe Biden, President of the USA

Boris Johnson, Prime Minister of the UK.

Chapter 22

Close to Victory

Events and Thoughts from Sunday 11th April 2021.

Thursday 15th April 2021. I wrote the following letter to my shrink in the early hours of this morning: -

Thursday Morning 15th April 2021

Dr Twee Dampensquib,

Medical Director,

Alcatraz Island Hospital.

Dear Twee,

Further to Sunday's letter, when I spoke to you on Tuesday, I asked you if you would now be taking me off the antipsychotic medication and you replied that you were thinking about it but that there was a lot to think about. In order to help you think about it, let me clarify the situation for you.

My late mother, Mrs Dorothy (Dolly) Ayres, has been the sexual and therefore the REAL leader of the human race for over seventy years now. By keeping a low profile in life, and doggedly pursuing her sexual desire for me, she has appealed to people's sense of humour and therefore their humanity. This has maintained her leadership role and helped keep the peace of the world insofar as every adult knew who the REAL boss REALLY was, and this bone of contention is what causes the wars. That has been the good effect of her leadership, but the bad effect is that this has caused her to put her own sexual desire ahead of the very survival of the people. She has led the world to the brink of extinction from irreversible Climate Change and she now seems determined to push it over the edge by prolonging the agony of her existence.

In order to protect the world, I have had to lead an insurrection against my late mother's authority by becoming the sexual leader, and therefore the

REAL leader myself. It should be obvious to you by now that I now command a vast swathe of the adult population of this country and the International Community; in fact, ALL sensible people who do not want the world to come to an end. I am now the man in charge, Twee, whether anybody else likes it or not. If you do not comply with my wishes, as stated in Sunday's letter and my previous correspondence, then you will become the man who will be to blame for the end of the world happening in eight years' time. Think about that! The world NEEDS me to get my libido freed, and this can only happen by you taking me off these infernal drugs.

Yours sincerely,

Robert Strong.
Cc Lucy Lawless,
Paul Rees, Chief Executive of the Royal College of Psychiatrists,
Justin Welby, Archbishop of Canterbury,
Pope Francis,
Joe Biden, President of the USA
Boris Johnson, Prime Minister of the UK.

Saturday 17th April 2021. I wrote the following letter to Lucy this morning:
- Saturday Morning 17th April 2021
     Empress Lucy Lawless, the Dancing GIRL Herself,

Dear Soulmate,
     Further to Thursday's letter, addressed to Dr Twee Dampensquib, I can now tell from the absolutely colossal volume of cerebral activity that I can sense telepathically, that people are flocking to my side in their droves. They do not want the world to come to an end, so I have now led a successful insurrection against the authority of my late mother. The whole human race has made me their leader. I am sure that Dolly will depart soon, but that does not matter any more; I have replaced her already in the hearts and minds of all the people. I am sure that Twee Dampensquib will now comply with my wishes, as stated in my letter of last Sunday, namely: -
     1. To come off all drugs immediately.
     2. To receive a full apology for my approval before giving it to the Royal College of Psychiatrists for publication.
     3. To receive an absolute and unconditional discharge from hospital

as soon as the coronavirus lockdown restrictions are lifted, which now looks like the end of July this year.

4. To receive my compensation from the Royal College of Psychiatrists of £x, to be paid on the date of my discharge.

I am also sure that I will get my retrial, with a verdict of self-defence, in the immediate future. And payment of a further huge compensation demand from the British government. This should be enough money to build and sustain the development of The Survival Party. I have had feedback from people that the views expressed in my latest Manifesto meet with the approval of the majority of people in Great Britain; so I am confident that The Survival Party will get into power, hopefully by the end of 2023. I am having my latest Manifesto professionally duplicated, and I will send copies of it to yourself and the people getting copies of this letter.

I have been having weekly psychology sessions with a very nice man called Dr Elias since the beginning of March this year. We discuss my life story and my views on Religion and Politics. The man agrees with me substantially on almost everything.

Yours etcetera

Cc Dr Twee Dampensquib,
Paul Rees, Chief Executive of the Royal College of Psychiatrists.

Sunday 18th April 2021. I wrote the following letter to Lucy this evening: -
Sunday Evening 18th April 2021
Empress Lucy Lawless, the Dancing GIRL Herself,

Dear Soulmate,

I don't know who Twee Dampensquib follows in life; I don't think it is Dolly, nor me; maybe it's Sigmund Freud seeing as he is a psychiatrist, or maybe one of the Hindu Gods seeing as he is from India, but whoever it is, that God had better follow ME from now on unless he wants the whole world to become uninhabitable from irreversible Climate Change in eight years' time. I have told Twee that I AM THE BIG MAN HIMSELF, and I have now proven it. I am the King of all the Gods of all religions, including psychiatry, and including Hinduism. I am the man who was once called Adam three hundred thousand years ago in the Garden of Eden; the male progenitor of the human race. And you, my love, were of course Eve,

Adam's wife and eternal soulmate.

Today I've been proof-reading previous chapters of my latest book, prior to publication, and I knew last August that the day would come when the imminence of irreversible Climate Change would force everybody to join my side in this civil war against my late mother. I just prayed that the tide of public opinion would change in my favour in time for me to prevent Climate Change from becoming irreversible. I can now say with complete confidence that my prayers have been answered. I repeat that I am now the man in charge of the free world. This vote of confidence from the Gods in Heaven confirms to me that my plan for tackling Climate Change, as outlined in my Manifesto, is the best plan that has been put forward, and that I am the best man to carry it through, as the Prime Minister and leader of Great Britain.

I still don't really know what your reason is for not communicating with me. I can only put it down to the fact that you are still being a silly girl in some ways, and all I can do is to pray that you will grow out of it. I hope this prayer is also answered soon.

Yours etcetera

Cc Dr Twee Dampensquib.

Friday 23rd April 2021. One of the main things that people want from God is an explanation of the meaning of life. Everyone wants to know the answers to the questions, "Why am I here?" and "What is life all about?". The simple answer is that "Life is what you make it". It is up to each individual to give him or herself a reason for living and then to live your life according to your own lights. But in doing so, you fulfil a higher purpose, which is to be tested by the Gods in Heaven. In his conceit, mankind thinks that his science can explain everything, and so it has become unfashionable to talk about the will of the Gods, or even to acknowledge their existence. Which is not very wise because the will of the Gods explains a lot that science can never explain but nonetheless affects every one of us every day. Life on earth is a process of undergoing tests, whoever you are, and the main ones are tests of your moral fibre, and that means both your social concerns for those less fortunate than yourself and also your sexual morals. These are all tests of your conscience, and the better you do in these tests, the happier you are in Heaven in the afterlife.

Part of the trial of your moral fibre lies in your obedience to the will of God as expressed in all of the Holy writings of all religions. One of the main expressions of MY will is clearly written in the Bible, "Man shall not go with man", and the same obviously applies to women. It has been Satan's purpose to undermine the moral fabric of society by making it socially acceptable to condone the decadent filth of homosexuality. After Satan's demise, His will has been continued by his accomplice, Mrs Dorothy (Dolly) Ayres, and this is the moral cause of both the Climate Change crisis and the coronavirus pandemic. These are both caused by the will of the Gods in Heaven which Dolly has defied and encouraged all her followers to defy.

The Gods have a STRONG influence on the climate, and therefore the weather in all places on earth. For example, the weather in Australia. The Australians are gluttons for punishment like most people. The day after they voted to allow same-sex marriages was the day that the drought hit New South Wales; but they didn't heed the warning and continued with same-sex marriages; so, the Gods sent them the bush fires, but they still didn't heed the warning, so they were sent the floods to make them aware of the anger of the Gods. They still haven't learned, and the so-called religious leaders either don't know the obvious truth, or they haven't got the guts to tell it.

Same-sex relationships are now so prevalent in the world that the Gods had to send a worldwide pandemic to warn people of their folly. That is the reason for the coronavirus outbreak which has so far killed over three million people. It is the same reason as the punishment of the cities of Sodom and Gomorrah in Biblical times but on a global scale this time. Satan caused all this, and his accomplice, Dolly, whose real identity is the vainglorious arch-demon, Lucifer. That is why I, God, have sentenced her to permanent exile from the human race. We will all be better off without her.

Climate Change has two causes, one is practical and the other is moral. To rectify one cause without rectifying the other is like trying to dry yourself with a fresh towel whilst still standing under a running shower. The towel just gets as wet as you are. Many world leaders are now trying to rectify the practical causes of Climate Change, although their plans are for too little, too late, but they will not succeed unless they rectify the moral cause as well. The Manifesto for The Survival Party addresses both causes of Climate Change.

I sent a copy of the above extract with the following letter to Lucy with a copy to Twee Dampensquib: -

I am also sending copies of the above journal extract and copies of the Manifesto to Joe Biden, Justin Welby and Pope Francis, my brother, Bill, my niece, Rachel, my cousin, Shaun, and Troy's mother, Paula.

Friday 23rd April 2021

Empress Lucy Lawless, the Dancing GIRL Herself,

Dear Soulmate,

I've been looking at your website on the internet, and on Wednesday I noticed a mention of Westwell, which I take as a nod of the head in my direction, but the reference was removed when I looked again today.

I noticed from your interviews that your conversation still deals with twee, shallow topics. Are you going to carry on being a singer until the world becomes uninhabitable in eight years' time, knowing that you could have helped prevent it if you had gone into politics? Or are you going to join me in the deep end of life?

I'm sure Dolly will depart soon if she hasn't done so already. I told her that if she has anything else to say then actions speak louder than words. She must duckify herself this month. In any event I am waiting to hear from Twee Dampensquib that he is taking me off the drugs, preparing my public apology, arranging my discharge and arranging my compensation with the Royal College of Psychiatrists. I'm on the road to freedom and I'll see you there.

I thought you'd like to see today's journal entry.

Yours etcetera

Cc Dr Twee Dampensquib.

Monday 26th April 2021. The longest chapter in the Book of Revelations in the Bible is called, "The End of All Things". I am as brave as any man or woman but this prospect fills my heart and my very soul with stark naked FEAR; as it would with any man or woman who is as keenly aware of the reality of the situation as I am. As far as I can foresee, the only hope that the world has got is for the entire human race to shout at the late Mrs

Dorothy (Dolly) Ayres to GO and to GO NOW, before it is too late. Tell her to GET ON WITH IT as the Archbishop of Canterbury did at Prince Philip's funeral recently.

She is aware that I have given her until the end of this month to get out, but we are nearly there now and she shows no sign of going imminently. She seems determined to go down with the world when Climate Change becomes irreversible, and she is dragging every other living thing in the world down with her if she can't have the man she wants – which she can't. And she can't BECAUSE I SAY SO, and I AM GOD, NOT HER. I am the only man with a workable plan to avert this catastrophe, but she keeps me a prisoner in a mental hospital because I refuse to have sex with her. I have to do this because of who and what I am. I cannot become a motherfucker because that is not what A REAL MAN is. MEN obey the taboo against incest and I cannot bring myself to break that taboo. I would sooner die like a man than live like a subhuman being.

I copied the above entry in a letter to Lucy with the following footnote: - All I can do now is to pray that the hopes of the world cut some ice with Dolly.

I had my second Astra Zeneca jab today. At least I won't die of COVID which is a painful way to go, although we will all die in anguish if Climate Change becomes irreversible, because that will mean that the whole world will become uninhabitable. Dolly has got just four more days to give me a fighting chance of preventing this.

Even if the end of the world does happen, Lucy Darling, my spirit and yours will remain bonded. Not even cosmic forces can separate our spirits, my Love. We will always love each other because of who we are – Time and Nature. No force anywhere can change that.

I also sent a copy of the letter to Twee Dampensquib.

Tuesday 27th April 2021. I wrote the following few lines to Lucy today: - Tuesday 27th April 2021

Empress Lucy Lawless, the Dancing GIRL Herself,

Dear Soulmate,

It's up to Dolly what happens now. Either she brings about the end of the world by prolonging the agony of her existence, or she ushers in the arrival of God's Kingdom on Earth by turning herself into a duck. It's her decision. The human race made a God out of her by deifying her. We will see in the next three and a half days if they did the right thing.

Yours etcetera

Cc Dr Twee Dampensquib.

Thursday 29th April 2021. It is necessary for the late Dolly Ayres to come back to life as a duck, but she hasn't got the guts to do what needs to be done. The consequence of this is that the world is going to come to an end from irreversible Climate Change in 2029. Dolly has got just two more days and one night to GET ON WITH IT if the worst is to be avoided, but it doesn't look like that is going to happen. Dolly is my own mother, but she doesn't love me. She just wants me for sexual gratification, but she is out of luck because I won't stoop to that, and anyway I have never been so desperate that I'd have sex with my own mother. She has an immense following of misguided people who obey her every wish, and she wishes to keep me as a prisoner in a mental hospital, so I cannot do anything to help the world out of the mess that she has got it into.

Lucy Lawless is the woman whom the Gods have chosen for me, but she hasn't even got the guts to write me a letter. I have been writing to her for over twenty-one years, but she has never once communicated with me at all. She won't even talk to me, and she won't say why not. If I didn't know better, I'd say she is mentally ill, but I don't believe in mental illness, that is just another way of saying "immaturity".

Twee Dampensquib is my legal guardian and my psychiatric consultant. He has insisted for many years on medicating me with drugs that suppress my sex drive, as well as having a whole host of other bad and adverse effects on me. He won't say why he does this cruelty to me, and he says that I suffer from a delusional disorder, which is nonsense. He just hasn't got the brains nor the guts to take me off his stupid filthy drugs.

I am surrounded by grown people who act like children. They haven't got the brains nor the guts to act like REAL ADULTS. If Dolly, Lucy and Twee are the best that the human race has to offer, then the human race won't survive and it won't deserve to.

Come on, you people! Make me proud of you! Do what men and women have got to do! And when I tell you what to do, say, "Yes Sir".

I sent a copy of the above journal extract in a letter to Lucy with a copy to Twee Dampensquib.

Saturday 1st May 2021. I wrote the following letter to Dr Twee Dampensquib today: - Saturday 1st May 2021

    Dr Twee Dampensquib,

    Medical Director,

    Alcatraz Island Hospital.

Dear Twee,

My late mother has still not yet departed so I am still leading an insurgency against her authority. My fellow insurgents and I are fighting to save the world from irreversible Climate Change which we believe will be inevitable in 2029 unless I come to power in this country in the near future. And by "this country" I mean not only Great Britain but also the entire adult world. Make your mind up, Twee, do you have the balls to join this insurgency under my leadership? Are you with us or against us? Your decision is a pivotal one in the entire history of the whole human race. Twee.

If you are with us then I expect you to comply with my wishes, as follows: -

1. You take me off all antipsychotic drugs immediately.

2. You prepare my public apology along the lines I have already told you and submit it to me for my approval before giving it to the Royal College of Psychiatrists for publication.

3. You arrange with the Royal College of Psychiatrists for the payment of my compensation of £x to be paid by the day I leave hospital.

4. You arrange with the Ministry of Justice for my absolute and unconditional discharge from hospital as soon as the coronavirus lockdown restrictions are lifted.

If you are against us then you are taking your life into your own hands, Twee. We are fighting to save the world from a mad old dead woman who is determined to destroy it if she can't have the man she wants, which she can't, and we have to be ruthless against those who stand in our way. Don't say I didn't warn you.

I am due for another injection of paliperidone on Thursday 6th May. If that injection takes place, then I will take it that you are not with us and are therefore against us.

I repeat that we are fighting for the survival of all life on earth, by the policies outlined in the Manifesto of The Survival Party.

Yours sincerely,

Robert Strong.
Cc Lucy Lawless.
Paul Rees, Chief Executive of the Royal College of Psychiatrists.
Joe Biden, President of the USA.

I also sent copies of this letter to Justin Welby, and my brother, Bill, my niece, Rachel, my cousin, Shaun, and Troy's mother, Paula.

I had a shopping trip yesterday, and I collected my copies of the Manifesto which I had professionally duplicated, as well as some compliment slips.

Today I posted ten copies of the Manifesto to my circulation list, together with some journal extracts which I thought would make interesting reading for people.

Wednesday 5th May 2021. I wrote the following letter to Twee Dampensquib in the small hours of this morning: - Wednesday Morning 5th May 2021

Dr Twee Dampensquib,
Medical Director,
Alcatraz Island Hospital.

Dear Twee,

I repeat that it was ME, not my late mother, the arch-demon Lucifer, who killed the tyrannical matriarch that I had for a stepmother, Mrs Iris Brooks. It was ME, not my late mother who overpowered Edward Richard Pitchblack, the Devil Himself, causing Him to die in 2009. And it was ME, not my late mother who led the spiritual armies that finally defeated Satan and His hordes by turning Him into a Rottweiler dog in August 2014. These achievements are my justification for claiming that I, not my late mother nor anyone else, am the leader of the human race and the head of the family of mankind. I have been ever since I was Adam in the Garden of Eden three hundred thousand years ago.

It has been MY WILL and my wisdom that has guided and guarded the human race all through the ages, so the weight of history is on my side in this civil war between me and my late mother. There is too much at stake here to let her win. Unless I win, there is a STRONG probability that the world will come to an end from irreversible climate change without my influence in the near future.

YOU have the power to usher MY Kingdom, the Kingdom of God, into the world by joining the insurgency against her authority, TODAY, before my injection tomorrow. I will close by reminding you of the motto of the Royal College of Psychiatrists, "LET WISDOM PREVAIL".

Yours sincerely,

Robert Strong.
Cc Lucy Lawless.
Paul Rees, Chief Executive of the Royal College of Psychiatrists.
Joe Biden, President of the USA.

Thursday 6th May 2021. I wrote the following letter to Lucy this afternoon:
Thursday 6th May 2021
Empress Lucy Lawless, the Dancing GIRL Herself,

Dear Soulmate,

I was injected again this afternoon with paliperidone.

Twee Dampensquib lacked the courage to join my insurgency against the authority of the mad old dead woman that I have for a mother, even though that means making an enemy out of me, which proves that he is also lacking in wisdom; both of which are attributes of a good leader. So, Twee has failed both of my tests, and seeing as I am a good leader which Twee is not, I will have to allow him more time to change his unreasonable and intransigent attitude to medicating and detaining me.

But he will have to change it soon because I have been on Caslegate Ward for nearly three years already, and unless the status quo changes soon, climate change will become irreversible in another eight years with catastrophic consequences for all life on earth and Twee Dampensquib will be to blame, for depriving this country and the world of my political leadership which it is obviously crying out for.

I am hoping that my psychologist, Dr Elias, will have words with Twee on my behalf, because I know that Elias agrees with me. We will have to see what the future holds.

Yours etcetera

Cc Dr Twee Dampensquib.
Paul Rees, Chief Executive, the Royal College of Psychiatrists.

Saturday 8th May 2021. I have a CPA meeting on Monday, which is their silly way of saying a case conference, so I am preparing the following statement which I intend to read out at the meeting and give everyone there a written copy of, as well as a copy of my Manifesto: -

No amount of psychobabble from Twee Dampensquib and Marionette Madre can obscure the simple truth that I am being detained in hospital and tortured with antipsychotic drugs, as I have been for the last forty-five years, because I refuse to have sex with my late mother, Mrs Dorothy (Dolly) Ayres. I only have sex with any woman, dead or alive, mentally or physically, if I want to make her happy. I do not wish to make Dolly happy, and I do not love her; in fact I despise her. Her jealousy of everyone I have ever loved, including my sons, Anthony and Christopher, my late father, Frank, and my ex-girlfriend, Jasmin, caused her to drive a wedge between me and them which I cannot forgive her for. Her feelings for me are not those of maternal love but of incestuous sexual desire. If she loved me, she would want me to be happy, which I am with Lucy Lawless, whom I regard as my real Queen, not Dolly, much to her chagrin.

Dolly has a huge following of misguided people who obey her every wish, and she wishes to ruin my life by detaining me in a mental hospital, and tormenting me with antipsychotic drugs when there is nothing wrong with my mental health and I am not in the least psychotic. I never have been. It was Dolly's wish, that all her followers obeyed, that drove me to committing my index offence forty-five years ago. I never wanted to kill anybody, but I have to live in the same society as all those people who did want me to. I will not, however, be bullied into having sex against my will with my late mother. So, it looks as though the status quo will continue.

As far as I know, I am the only man with political ambitions who has a Manifesto with policies to end Climate Change before it becomes irreversible in eight years' time with catastrophic consequences for all life on earth. If the worst happens, as looks likely without my political influence, then Twee Dampensquib will be to blame for depriving Great

Britain and the world of my political leadership that it obviously desperately needs.

I sent a copy of the above journal extract in a letter to Lucy.

Ringo Starr wrote a song in the 1960s which The Beatles sang, called "We all live in a yellow submarine". Dolly is the yellow submarine that everyone lives in: "yellow" for cowardice and "submarine" because she lives anonymously beneath the surface of society. I do not intend to be a yellow submarine. At the risk of tempting fate, I will say that, to continue the nautical metaphor, I am The Titanic Mk 2. But I have little fear of being brought down because my nemesis, Satan, is both dead AND gone; I have already brought Him down for ever.

Unless the whole world is to be brought down by irreversible Climate Change, one of two things has to happen in the very near future: either Dolly throws in the towel and comes back to life as an animal, or Twee Dampensquib joins the insurgency against her authority under my leadership. Realistically, I have got to get into political power by the end of 2023 at the latest, to put my five-year plan into operation. It will be near-impossible to do this unless Dolly throws in the towel. As the leader of an insurgency, too many people will put too many obstacles in my way. I know people. They will be reluctant to see me as the winner unless I get rid of Dolly first. REAL power is sexual, it is not democratic. Twee Dampensquib has already taught me that lesson.

So, we are back to square one. It is all up to Dolly. If she wants the world to survive, then she will have to throw in the towel and come back to life as an animal in the very near future; how near in the future is up to Dolly to decide – I think it is already too late, but I would like to be proven wrong. If she doesn't do that, then it will prove that the human race made a very unwise decision when they deified Dolly, because THAT MISTAKE WILL HAVE CAUSED THE END OF THE WORLD. (That was the Gods again, playing with my Caps Lock button. I decided to let the capital letters stand).

I can tell from today's weather here in the South of England that Dolly is getting ever closer to tipping point. It has been very cold and miserable and very rainy all day, which I am sure is a reflection of Dolly's mood. I don't think it will be long, now, before she throws the towel in, and duckifies herself. If she has anything left to say, then I will repeat that actions speak louder than words. She should GO and GO NOW. All I have to say is GET ON WITH IT. If the world is to be saved, it will be a darn close-run thing.

I will send copies of the above journal extract to Lucy and to Twee Dampensquib and also to the people at Monday's meeting. Let's hope that Dolly becomes aware of it.

Sunday 9th May 2021. I think that what Twee and Lucy and everyone else is saying to me, by their behaviour, is that they will do as I ask when and only when I prove myself to be the winner in this conflict with my late mother, by vanquishing her soul. This WILL happen when the prospect of irreversible Climate Change becomes so dangerously imminent that Dolly can no longer bear it. That tipping point has already been reached, in view of the fact that Climate Change is like a huge juggernaut – you have to apply the brakes early in order for it to stop in time. Otherwise, it crashes with terrifying and catastrophic consequences. In this metaphor, the brakes are policies to cut carbon emissions by prohibiting the burning of fossil fuels as per my Manifesto. Check mate, mother.

Tuesday 11th May 2021. I had my CPA meeting yesterday and I read out aloud both Saturday's and Sunday's journal entries. Nobody had any points to raise to argue with me, but Twee Dampensquib simply repeated the point that he is in charge of me and he intends to continue medicating me with antipsychotic drugs. He won't say why and he won't be drawn on the subject.

This is not very wise of him, because when I have vanquished Dolly's soul, which I surely will before long, then I will have enough influence to make him regret taking that attitude with ME. And I surely will make an example of him to deter other people from taking such a high-handed attitude with ME in future. Perhaps he thinks that I would not have the courage to do so, in which case I will surely prove him wrong.

When I have vanquished Dolly's soul, my power and influence will be boundless. I will be able to get from Twee Dampensquib all the things I want from him, that I have recently written about. I will also be able to have my way concerning a retrial and get a truthful verdict of self-defence plus a really big compensation settlement – enough to finance the future of The Survival Party.

I sent a copy of the above journal entry in a letter to Lucy with a copy to Twee Dampensquib.

Chapter 23

On the Road to Victory

Events and Thoughts from Wednesday 12th May 2021.

Wednesday 12th May 2021. I wrote the following letter to Lucy this morning with a copy to Twee Dampensquib. I enclosed copies of the song lyrics to, "The Vicar of Bray" and also, "Praise my Soul, the King of Heaven", to both Lucy and Twee: -

Wednesday Morning 12th May 2021

Empress Lucy Lawless, the Dancing GIRL Herself,

Dear Soulmate,

Twee Dampensquib suffers from a "Vicar of Bray" complex. This is a syndrome, the symptoms of which are a determination to prove that he is the King of his own little Kingdom. He insists on medicating me with antipsychotic drugs, not because I am psychotic, which I am not, but to prove that he is the boss by asserting his will over mine. He is a psychiatrist, and therefore, by definition, one of Dolly's followers. When I have vanquished Dolly's soul he will sing, "Praise my soul the King of Heaven" instead of, "The Vicar of Bray".

Take care of yourself, my Love,

I have much more to say to you, but it can wait until we talk, Bless you, my Queen,

Yours with Love, Affection and Friendship,

The King of the Gods,
Emperor_B0B XX
Cc Twee Dampensquib

Thursday 13th May 2021. My late mother looked in on me for another chat this afternoon, and I told her that she is a victim of circumstances of her own making: namely by legalising same-sex sexual relationships. It is the condoning of these relationships that is the moral cause of Climate Change, because, as I have already explained, they offend me, God, and therefore they offend the Gods in Heaven as I am their King, and the Gods have a STRONG influence on the climate. So, she is now hoisted on her own petard. When she legalised same-sex sexual relationships in 1967 it was her way of throwing down the gauntlet to me, God. She was saying, "If you don't like it, what can YOU do about it, God?" Now she knows. I can turn YOU into a duck, Dorothy. I've already said, "Check mate", so now I'm saying for the last time, "Goodbye duck"!

I sent copies of today's entry to both Lucy and Twee Dampensquib.

Monday 17th May 2021. It's almost over now. Dolly is losing and there is nothing she can do about it except throw thunderstorms with torrential rain, lightning and hailstones all over the UK. She has been doing this for all this month. We have had our April showers in May this year. It is going to get worse as this week progresses, culminating in heavy rainfall and gale force winds on Thursday and Friday. (According to the Meteorological Office).

These are the throes of Dolly's demise – what, in a mortal, would be called their death throes. She doesn't like what is happening but this is all she can do about it. I think she'll be the embryo of a duckling by this time next week. She made an enemy of ME, the Lord God Almighty, and this proves that that is the most stupid thing that any person could do. This is how her era, the era of Lucifer, a more dangerous person than the Devil Himself, ends.

My era, the era of the Kingdom of God, will start to dawn the instant her soul leaves the human race. No one knows how long my era will last for. When I die, I shall rule as God the Father from my place in the Spirit World until I come back again to live my next life. No one knows what my name will then be, nor how many years or centuries will elapse before that happens. It depends upon who is around at the time. We won't be seeing any more of Lucifer nor her sidekick, Satan, by any other names, for the foreseeable future. One thing is for sure; in my next life, I will have these journals to remind me of what I went through in this life. I'm sure my journals will last for millennia. That's **IF** the world survives the Climate Change crisis.

I don't know if I will have enough time to save the world from irreversible Climate Change. I will, of course, do my best, but I fear that Dolly has already left it too late. The world will be lucky if we survive the Climate Change crisis. **IF** we do, then I'm sure that Lucy will still be my soulmate in my next life. She is The Great Woman behind The Great Man that I am. She leads the world in Loving Me.

I am sending a copy of today's entry in a letter to Lucy, with a copy to Twee Dampensquib.

Sunday 23rd May 2021. I wrote the following letter to Lucy this morning: - Sunday 23rd May 2021
Empress Lucy Lawless, the Dancing GIRL Herself,

Dear Soulmate,
Dolly is still prolonging the agony of her existence and she will continue to do so until it becomes unbearable for her. That will be when the imminence of irreversible climate change becomes too dangerous for the world. The clowns that Dolly has put into political power all over the world are doing their best, but their best is not good enough to prevent Climate Change from becoming irreversible in 2029. They are all doing too little, too late, on the practical causes of Climate Change and nothing at all on the moral cause. When it gets too hot for Dolly to bear, she will come back to life as a duck and that will be when I will come to power.

Unless my compensation demand of £x is met without quibble by the day I leave hospital, I will disband the Royal College of Psychiatrists when I come to power. Their present social function will be met by the Social Guidance Institute, who will do a much more enlightened and humane job of handling miscreants than the shrinks do at present. The members of the Royal College of Psychiatrists will be relegated to the social function of being the custodians of incorrigible sexual perverts.

The motto of the Royal College is, "Let Wisdom Prevail", but the shrinks have taught me that wisdom does not prevail – POWER DOES. If you speak wisdom to power, power wins the argument every time. It is the same with the legal system, Justice does not prevail – POWER PREVAILS. And when Dolly is a duck, I shall be the man with all the power. I have a long memory and a thirst for revenge, so beware Twee Dampensquib, Marionette Madre and Morris Vinestock (my shrink from Broadmoor). It is only an idiot who defies the will of the Lord God Almighty, as Dolly is discovering. Think about that, Twee, two weeks from today when my next injection of paliperidone is due. A lot of shrinks will end up as the cleaners of public lavatories, and I shall laugh at them from my rooms in 10 Downing Street and Chequers.

And, when I come to power, you, Lucy, will regret your attitude of overtly ignoring me. It's no fun having a lover who won't even write to you.

Yours etcetera

Cc Twee Dampensquib
Paul Rees, Chief Executive, the Royal College of Psychiatrists.
Joe Biden, President of the USA.

Saturday 29th May 2021. I sensed yesterday that Dolly agreed with me that MY influence on the political scene will make all the difference between survival and catastrophe in 2029, and that she had decided to duckify herself today, as the only hope of survival that the world has got. As people said to me when I was fighting Satan, "The world has got two hopes – Bob Hope and No Hope".

This afternoon and this evening I sensed a colossal volume of cerebral activity from all the telepathic people of the world, making me think that Dolly has been duckifying herself. I expect I'll get confirmation of this over the next couple of days, so I won't put this journal extract in a letter to Lucy and Twee until Tuesday as there won't be any post until then anyway.

If I am right about Dolly, then I am now the Emperor of the Free World and recognised as being the Lord God Almighty – whether Dr Twee Dampensquib likes it or not. I am the boss, now, so he'll have to do as I say from now on. I don't think I need to restate my demands of him.

My psychologist, Dr Elias, left the hospital at the end of last week. Before he left, he told me that he hopes that all my wishes will come true. His appointment was only temporary, and I should be getting a new psychologist soon, who will be a permanent appointment. Not that that will matter a jot anyway if I am right about Dolly.

Sunday 30th May 2021. I felt the cerebral activity very strongly all night, last night. So much so that I didn't get a wink of sleep all night. It wasn't just the physical sensation of the cerebral activity, but the anticipation of a life without that accursed woman that kept me from sleeping. It is now Sunday morning, and I've had a shower and a shave; applied my testosterone gel, and had my breakfast and my morning pills, and I can still feel the cerebral activity. I can feel it so strongly that it convinced me that Dolly has finally gone, until I heard the weather presenter on the TV use the word "areas", sounding so confident that Mrs Ayres is still around. I had first-hand experience of Dolly on Friday, but none this morning, so I have concluded that Dolly is still trying to duckify herself, without success so far. The weather is supposed to improve today but the sky has been overcast so far all morning, telling me that Dolly is still around. I expect she'll go today as the ducks are still mating. They mate throughout the year according to the internet.

It is now Sunday afternoon and the weather here has perked up considerably, but I can tell that Dolly has not yet disappeared by the fact that the weather presenters are still using the word "areas" in their weather forecasts. The weather is expected to stay sunny during tomorrow and Tuesday, but thundery downpours are predicted for Wednesday and Thursday. It is Dolly who causes the thunder; she stole it from me many years ago when I was just a boy. This implies that Dolly is still fighting against being turned into a duck, when I thought, she had agreed to go that way. So, it is obvious that the old witch is in two minds – she doesn't know what to do. She must consider the fate of all living things in the world, including herself. Unless I get into power soon, it will be the end for all living things, and that means that Dolly must go, and go soon. I still think she has already left it too late, but I hope to be proved wrong on that count.

I am due for another injection of paliperidone on Sunday 6th June which upsets me, not least because it now looks like that injection will go ahead, and that will waste another month before I get my sex life back to normal. Which will frustrate all my followers as well as Lucy and myself.

Eight days ago, there was an unmistakeable SIGN FROM THE GODS when a volcano erupted right next to the city of GOMA in the Democratic Republic of Congo. Dolly would be wise to heed such signs. It was a clear sign that MA must GO. Hundreds of thousands of people evacuated the city of GOMA, just carrying with them what possessions they could carry. There is still molten lava underneath the surface of GOMA, and there are fears of another eruption in the immediate future.

Monday 31st May 2021. I've finally worked out the real reason why Lucy has never once communicated with me in all the twenty-one years I've been writing to her. It is her way of proving to herself that SHE is the boss. It is the same as the reason why Twee Dampensquib insists on medicating me with his filthy drugs when he knows damn well there is nothing wrong with me. It is his way of proving to himself that HE is the boss.

I don't mind other people thinking that they are the boss or trying to prove it to themselves. I know that that is who I am. I proved it to myself and to the world on the 16th July 1976 when I killed my stepmother, Iris. She was the person who the whole of society accepted was the real leader of the human race, and I took that title from her. I proved it again when I overpowered Edward Richard Pitchblack, the Devil Himself, and disposed of His soul. Now I am challenged again, this time to dispose of the soul of my late mother, who is Satan's boss, the Arch-demon Lucifer, otherwise known as the late Mrs Dorothy (the door) Ayres. Her soul will inhabit the body of a duckling in the near future. This will be the final challenge before I am accepted by the whole of society as the leader.

It is a sign of immaturity in a person to think that they are the boss when they do not know their real place in the world. A person's place is determined by the strength of their spirit. People are whoever they prove themselves to be. I just hope and pray that I dispose of Lucifer's soul in time to lead the human race in the battle against Climate Change before it becomes irreversible in 2029.

I am now going to send copies of Saturday's, Sunday's and today's journal entries to Lucy Lawless, Dr Twee Dampensquib, Paul Rees the Chief Executive of the Royal College of Psychiatrists and to Joe Biden, the President of the United States of America.

Thursday 3rd June 2021. When it comes to Climate Change, most world leaders are floundering, not knowing for sure what to do. The most sensible ones are following the lead of Antonio Guterres, the Secretary General of the United Nations, who said that to stop Global Warming from exceeding the 1.5^0 C limit, beyond which Climate Change will become irreversible, with catastrophic consequences for all life on earth, all the nations of the world must cut their carbon emissions by forty-five per cent by 2030 and the remaining fifty-five per cent by 2050.

I say that this is too little, too late because it does not take into account the ever-increasing destruction of the world's rainforests in the Amazon, Indonesia, Malaysia and Siberia. I am sure that the scientists who came up with those figures chose 2030 and 2050 as the most convenient round numbers, not necessarily the most accurate numbers. I say that we all must cut carbon emissions by forty-nine per cent before 2029, which means by the end of 2028, and then the remaining fifty-one per cent by 2049.

So, as I say, even the most sensible of world leaders have set target dates of too little, too late, and they don't even look like achieving those targets. And, I would like to know what targets China has set for cutting carbon emissions. They are still building coal-fired power stations over there. Xi JinPing talks about a zero-emissions target date of 2060, but at this rate 2060 will not exist, the world will come to an end from irreversible Climate Change in eight years' time if my figures are correct. Even if they are not, it is better to aim for these target figures just in case they are.

If I get into political office by the end of 2023, that will give me a chance to put my five-year plan into operation to cut carbon emissions. That gives me two and a half years from now, to build my Party, The Survival Party from nothing into an election-winning Party in Great Britain. Given my kudos and my popularity and my organising ability and my compensation money, that is not impossible. In any event, my arrival on the political scene with my Manifesto could well make all the difference between survival and catastrophe in 2029.

But my late mother is still continuing with clinging to her hope that I will change my mind and embark upon a sexual relationship with her. I repeat that I will never have a sexual relationship with my late mother. The end of the world is a more preferable option as far as I am concerned, and I am proving it. Not least because my love-making is committed to Lucy Lawless, my Queen, and my love is King as I am also proving.

I can tell that these thoughts of mine are putting my late mother in a wistful mood. She knows, now, that she has no choice but to join a pair of copulating ducks and come back to life as one of their offspring. The only other option is for her to prolong the agony of her existence until it is too late, even for me, to save the world from irreversible Climate Change, and that will mean the end for all living things, including herself. A duck is a more preferable option for her. I said to her that she will be happy as a duck. A duck can walk on the land, swim in the water and fly through the air, which is more than a person can do. She has probably forgotten what happiness is like – she has been so miserable for so long, suffering from unrequited love. This is her only escape.

Friday 4th June 2021. This is a letter to my late mother: -

Dear Mother,

It is all up to you what happens now. You can usher into the world the arrival of my Kingdom, the Kingdom of God, by turning yourself into a duck, or you can continue to prolong the agony of your existence and thereby bring about what, to quote the Book of Revelations is, "The End of All Things". These are your only two options. Whichever one you choose this is the last and most wistful "goodbye" ever. Your action will speak louder than my words. **IF** we all survive, then I will always look upon ducks differently from now on. I will always remember this little ditty: -

Be kind to your web-footed friend.

For a duck may be somebody's mother.

Be kind to the denizens of the swamp.

For it's dismal, dark and damp.

You may think that this is the end.

WELL, IT IS!

I will now send copies of yesterday's and today's journal entries to Lucy Lawless, Dr Twee Dampensquib, Paul Rees and Joe Biden.

Sunday 6th June 2021. I have one more final letter to write to my late mother, Mrs Dorothy (the door) Ayres, as follows: -

Dear Mother,

You must either learn to take "NO" for an answer, the same as everybody else has to at some point in their lives from someone, or else you must prolong your agony and bring about "the end of all things" from irreversible Climate Change, which I might be able to prevent if I was free, in which case you will deny future generations of people the right to have a life and discover the facts of life for themselves. I don't believe you are that selfish, but even if you are, YOU now have no choice but to say, "Goodbye cruel world", and get on with it.

I will now send copies of this journal entry to Lucy Lawless, Dt Twee Dampensquib, Paul Rees and Joe Biden.

Thursday 17th June 2021, I haven't written an entry in this journal for eleven days because I have been waiting patiently for my late mother to realise the need to turn herself into an animal, presumably a duck, and to get on with it. The human race hasn't got the intelligence, nor the wisdom, nor the courage to kick out this disastrous leader, so unless she goes willingly, and goes soon, they will follow her all the way to extinction.

My reasoning hasn't changed since I wrote in this journal two weeks' ago today. All I can add is that the world has two hopes – Bob Hope and No Hope, and I am the Bob in question. The world needs a STRONG leader to combat Climate Change; someone who has the political will to enact laws to prohibit the burning of fossil fuels, and thereby reduce carbon emissions by forty-nine per cent before the end of 2028. My five-year plan in the Manifesto of The Survival Party will do just that.

But unless Dolly goes and goes soon, all my plans will transpire to be no more than castles in the air. All I can do is to continue waiting with the rest of the human race for the end to come from irreversible Climate Change, and make the most of what time I have left.

Not that my time is spent enjoyably, the evil drugs that this idiot shrink insists on poisoning me with see to that. Their effects are horrendous, and not just the suppression of my sex drive. My sense of balance is being destroyed. My hands shake uncontrollably at times, and my weight is far too high in spite of a rigorous diet. My energy levels are way too low and I don't have the mental strength to exercise my body as I ought to and would like to do. I am kept in a permanent state of artificially induced tiredness and lethargy. *I have been treated this way by the psychiatric profession for the last forty-four years although there has never been anything wrong with me.* My revenge, when it comes, will be appropriate. I will start by hitting the bastards in the pocket. I want enough compensation money to finance the building of The Survival Party.

I will put the above entry in a letter to Lucy, with copies to Twee Dampensquib, Paul Rees and Joe Biden.

Friday 18th June 2021. I forgot to add, yesterday, to the list of the effects of the drugs I am on, the fact they make my skin itch, all over my body; including the insides of my nostrils which is a very embarrassing place to have a scratch. This is yet another reason for me to curse these shrinks and their accursed, evil drugs.

Saturday 19th June 2021. I included yesterday's entry with the following letter to Lucy: Saturday 19th June 2021
    Empress Lucy Lawless, the Queen of the Gods,

Dear Soulmate,
    It occurred to me today to write the following to you: -
    Most married people stay together for the sake of their children and for the sake of appearances. All real women and real men give their orgasms to the real King and Queen, which is who WE are, Darling. That is not to say that couples who have been together for years and years do not have genuine affection for each other, but people of that age usually have learned their place and are content to let the glamour boys and girls chase the elusive butterfly of love, knowing that the youngsters will have to find out the truth for themselves. The truth, Lucy, is that you and I have a monopoly on love because of who we are – the mother and father of the human race. Dolly is the mother-in-law and is now becoming the most unpopular person in the world, having been the darling of society in her day. But her day is over, now, and I cannot foresee any future for her in the human race at all. Her only option is to turn herself into an animal, presumably a duck, and to get on with it. There is no place in the world of humans for someone who hates the Lord God, as she obviously does. Her jealousy of my popularity is her own undoing.
    I still say that you could and should communicate with me and the fact that you don't is a sign of immaturity. You have nothing to lose and everything to gain by communicating with me. I won't do or say anything to disturb the double life that you have chosen to live – ostensibly happily married to Rob Tapert but really being MY lover. I'd sooner be me than your husband. It must be horrible to have a hypocritical wife with an

unfaithful heart. Your LOVE and the fidelity that goes with it is something that any man, if he is a man, would kill for. I proved that on the 16th July 1976. I just knew that I did not want Iris to be my Queen, so I had no choice but to kill her or deny my own identity to myself, which I could not do. That is the same reason why I could not have sex with Dolly, she is not my Queen. I trusted the hope that I would one day find a woman who would be worthy of my love, even before I knew your name, and before I believed in the Gods. But they believed in me and guided me to you and I thank them for that with every fibre of my being.

Yours etcetera

Cc Twee Dampensquib
Enclosures: song lyrics to
The Captain of her heart,
Lucy in the sky with diamonds,
When?

Monday 21st June 2021. It's true what people say, "Cometh the hour, cometh the man". This means that when the hour of need arises, so does the man to save the situation. I am the only man with the leadership and the policies needed to save the world from irreversible Climate Change, bur my late mother, Mrs Dorothy (the door) Ayres, who is the sexual, and therefore the REAL leader of the world, keeps me a prisoner in a mental hospital because I refuse to have mental sex with her ghost. Unless Dorothy comes back to life as an animal, presumably a duck, in the immediate future, Climate Change will become irreversible in eight years' time without my political influence to save the situation. If that happens it will mean that the whole world will become uninhabitable and it will be the end of all life on earth. I would sooner that happens than be bullied into having sex against my will with my late mother, when she can save the situation by duckifying herself; which is what WILL happen, BECAUSE I SAY SO, and I am now the person in charge of affairs, not my late mother. I am the King of the Gods and Lucy Lawless is my Queen. I will not betray my Queen for anything. The will of the Gods is stronger than the will of Mrs Dorothy Ayres, as I am now proving. This is the final word on the subject.

I sent the above journal entry in a letter to Lucy with a copy to Twee

Dampensquib.

I sent the following letter to Lucy this afternoon: - Monday Afternoon 21st June 2021

Empress Lucy Lawless, the Queen of the Gods,

Dear Soulmate,

I am enclosing a copy of the lyrics to a song called, "You can't be true to two", which I thought are appropriate in the present situation. These lyrics were what prompted my late mother to leave my late father for my late stepfather back in the 1950s, and I'm hoping they will have a similar effect on you, now. I'm not jealous of Rob Tapert, but I must admit I don't like you maintaining your husband-and-wife relationship with him. I've surely said and done enough by now for you to make up your mind who you want. Please don't keep me waiting any longer before you even communicate with me.

Yours etcetera

Friday 25th June 2021. I have one final thought to put to my late mother: -

Dear Mother,

Only you can put an end to the nightmares that we are both going through. Turn yourself into a duck, Mother. That is the only way by which you will ever get over me. You will forget all about me when your fight for life becomes your only concern. And it is the only way by which I shall ever be free from you; free to be with the woman I love, and free to pursue my career and, hopefully, free to save the world from irreversible Climate Change. If you think about it, you will know that I am right, so goodbye and get on with it.

Bob

I shall put today's journal entry in a letter to Lucy with copies to Twee Dampensquib, Paul Rees and Joe Biden.

Wednesday 30th June 2021. I wrote the following letter to Lucy today: - Wednesday 30th June 2021

Empress Lucy Lawless, the Queen of the Gods,

Dear Soulmate,

Just a line to keep in touch with you. The West Coast of the USA and Canada is currently experiencing a catastrophic heatwave caused by Climate Change. People there are dying from the heatwave by the dozens. I fear that my prediction of the end of the world from irreversible Climate Change in eight years' time is already starting to come true. This is just the thin end of the wedge. There is nothing I can do about it whilst my late mother, Mrs Dorothy (the door) Ayres, is still prolonging the agony of her existence. She is prolonging her own nightmare as well as that of every other living thing on the planet, especially that of people with foresight. I will never be her lover whatever happens, so she is just wasting everybody's time by playing such a dangerous game.

We came together most beautifully on Sunday afternoon (UK Time). Thank you, Darling, for bobulucydating me. It was the best orgasm of my life and I could feel that it was for you as well. Unfortunately, the paliperidone prevents me from being able to do it more often, but things will improve once the old witch disappears. All our millions of followers will be glad as well, when that happens.

Yours etcetera

Cc Dr Twee Dampensquib.
Paul Rees, Chief Executive, the Royal College of Psychiatrists.
Joe Biden, President of the USA.

Friday 2nd July 2021. Further to Wednesday's entry in this journal, I have been saying for years now that the main problem confronting the human race is its disastrous leader, my late mother, Mrs Dorothy (the door) Ayres. SHE has been the sexual, and therefore the REAL leader of the world for the last seventy years or so, and she has led the world to the brink of extinction from irreversible Climate Change. She is now pushing the world over the edge by prolonging the agony of her existence. What is happening at the moment in the USA and Canada is just the start of it. I hope that current events will give the human race the sense of urgency needed to survive.

I am the STRONG leader that the world needs at the moment – the man with the political will to enact laws prohibiting the burning of fossil fuels, thereby cutting carbon emissions by forty-nine per cent by the end of 2028.

All the present world leaders have set a target date of 2030, but this is two years too late. The world will end in 2029 unless the human race does as I say. What is happening in America and Canada at the moment is just the start of it. The world must kick out its present leader, my late mother, and put ME in power without delay if it wants to survive.

My late mother keeps me a prisoner in a mental hospital because I refuse to have sex with her ghost when the REAL criminal lunatics are the followers of my late mother. They are not just committing suicide; they are dragging the rest of the world down with them. I want all my followers to make life Hell for the enemies of the human race – they can be identified by the way they use the words "area" and its plural "areas" all the time because those words sound a bit like my late mother's surname. Those who use those words on television are the biggest criminal lunatics in the world because they are encouraging the old witch to hang around wasting precious time.

Dorothy must join a pair of copulating ducks and come back to life as one of their offspring and the rest of the human race must encourage her to do this. The instant her soul leaves the human race will be the moment when I come to power. Unless this happens very soon it will be too late for me to save the world from irreversible Climate Change, which is the main thing that I came into this world to do.

I am sending today's entry in a letter to Lucy, with copies to Twee Dampensquib, Paul Rees and Joe Biden.

Saturday 3rd July 2021. I wrote the following letter to Lucy this morning: - Saturday 3rd July 2021

Empress Lucy Lawless, the Queen of the Gods,

Dear Soulmate,

We came together again yesterday afternoon at 4.15 p.m. (UK Time), and so did all our millions of followers; men and women all over the world. The notion of "dancing with Bob and Lucy" has replaced the notion of "opening the door" as proof of adulthood throughout the International Community. You and I have become the sexual, and therefore the REAL leaders of the human race. We haven't yet managed to get rid of the old witch, your mother-in-law, but we have totally undermined her power and authority.

All other courting couples talk to each other and have social intercourse leading up to sexual intercourse, but because of circumstances not of our making, we have had to do things the other way round! All others have physical sex leading up to mental sex, "dancing", but with us, our sex life is purely mental and spiritual but nonetheless REAL! We are recognised throughout the adult world as the shining example of what TRUE LOVE is. Bless you, my Queen, and thank you again for bobulucydating me. We and all our billions of followers have many happy orgasms ahead of us. The old era in the history of the world has ended and the new era has dawned.

Now we have to concern ourselves with the problems confronting the human race. The vaccines that people have invented are overcoming the problem of the coronavirus pandemic, but the Climate Change crisis is a serious problem. I still think that the best solution lies in my Manifesto of The Survival Party. In order to apply this solution, I must get out of hospital as quickly as possible, register the Party with the Electoral Commission of the UK, open a bank account in the name of the Party and start my programme of recruiting membership of the party by advertising the Manifesto free to all interested people. I must also get a public apology from the Royal College of Psychiatrists and clear my name by having a retrial of my "crime", committed forty-five years ago this month, replacing the verdict to one of "self-defence against undue social pressure".

Yours etcetera

Cc Dr Twee Dampensquib.
Paul Rees, Chief Executive, the Royal College of Psychiatrists.
Joe Biden, President of the USA.

Sunday 4th July 2021. Society, today, in the free world, is still dominated by the followers of the late Mrs Dorothy (the door) Ayres, my late mother. These people are the most dangerous criminal lunatics that the world has ever known, because they are not only committing suicide, they are dragging all other living things on the planet down with them. From the mud slides of Japan to the floods in the UK to the wildfires and the heatwave in Canada there is ample evidence that Global Warming is overtaking the way of life of the human race and we are doing too little, too late, to stop it. MY PREDICTION THAT THE WORLD WILL COME TO AN END IN EIGHT YEARS' TIME FROM IRREVERSIBLE CLIMATE

CHANGE IS COMING TRUE. We are fighting a battle against Climate Change, and we, the human race, are losing at the moment. Our only way to win is to get rid of this disastrous leader, Mrs Dorothy (the door) Ayres.

We have known for years that we are destroying the environment by our way of life, but people are still driving vehicles with internal combustion engines, flying in jet planes and burning coal in power stations. The leader of society, Mrs Dorothy Ayres, must take responsibility for this madness and go before it is too late for me to do anything about it.

People have rejected the wisdom of God, myself, in favour of following the warped mind of my late mother, who is obsessed with incestuous sexual desire, and keeps me a prisoner in a mental hospital because I refuse to have sex with her ghost, when I AM THE MAN WITH THE FORESIGHT TO REALISE THAT THE HUMAN RACE IS COMMITTING SUICIDE BY LEADING AN UNSUSTAINABLE WAY OF LIFE.

The only solution to this problem is for us to make the late, mad, old, dead woman join a pair of copulating ducks and come back to life as one of their offspring. I can then take charge of the situation and stop this madness, although I fear it may already be too late to stop my prediction from coming true. We must close the door immediately and bring about the end of her era.

I am sending a copy of this journal entry in a letter to Lucy, with copies to Twee Dampensquib, Paul Rees and Joe Biden.

I wrote the following letter to Lucy this afternoon: - Sunday Afternoon 4th July 2021

Empress Lucy Lawless, the Queen of the Gods,

Dear Soulmate,

I repeat the salient points of my argument as follows: The whole of society in the whole of the free world is still dominated by the followers of my late mother, Mrs Dorothy Ayres, also known as "the door". The human race is losing in the war against Climate Change which will become irreversible in 2029 unless we all cut our carbon emissions by forty-nine per cent by the end of 2028. The present target date of 2030 is too late because it does not take into account the ever-increasing destruction of the world's rainforests in the Amazon, Indonesia, Malaysia, Siberia and the

Arctic Circle.

The leader of the human race, the late Mrs Dorothy Ayres, must take responsibility for this impending disaster and go, NOW, before it is too late. If she won't go willingly, then the human race must make her go, NOW, or face catastrophe in eight years' time.

I am the STRONG leader that the world needs in the war against Climate Change; the man with the political will to enact laws prohibiting the burning of fossil fuels, thereby cutting carbon emissions by forty-nine per cent by the end of 2028. But I cannot start doing this until I am a free man. My late mother keeps me a prisoner in a mental hospital because I refuse to have sex with her ghost. Her warped mind is obsessed with incestuous sexual desire.

She must take responsibility for the fact that we are losing the war against Climate Change and go. She must join a pair of copulating ducks and come back to life as one of their offspring. If she won't do this willingly we must **MAKE** her do it, immediately, or face the end of the world in eight short years' time. I can't promise to avert the impending disaster; I fear that my late mother may have already left it too late, but I AM the best hope that the human race has got.

Yours etcetera

Cc Dr Twee Dampensquib.
Paul Rees, Chief Executive, the Royal College of Psychiatrists.
Joe Biden, President of the USA.

Monday 5th July 2021. I sent copies of yesterday afternoon's letter to Lucy, together with copies of the Manifesto and compliment slips to Xi Jinping, Vladimir Putin, Sir Ed Davey (leader of the Liberal Democratic Party), Boris Johnson, Nicola Sturgeon (leader of the Scottish National Party), Sir Kier Starmer (leader of the Labour Party) and Antonio Guterres (Secretary General of the United Nations).

Tuesday 6th July 2021. I wrote the following letter this morning: - Tuesday 6th July 2021.

Cc Boris Johnson,
Sir Kier Starmer,
Sir Ed Davey,

Nicola Sturgeon,
Caroline Lucas,
Paul Rees,
Justin Welby.
Dr Twee Dampensquib

Dear Leaders,

The human race has rejected the wisdom of God, myself, in order to follow the warped mind of my late mother, Mrs Dorothy (the door) Ayres, who is none other than the vainglorious Arch-demon Lucifer, the Devil's accomplice. They will pay for this mistake with their lives when Armageddon happens, which it will, from irreversible Climate Change in the year 2029. The end of the decade, 2030, will be too late. This WILL happen UNLESS the human race can persuade the late Mrs Ayres to take responsibility for the fact that the human race is losing the war against Global Warming and Climate Change and turn herself into a duck in the immediate future; leaving ME to take over the role of the leader of the human race.

I am the man with the political will and the policies and the courage to cut carbon emissions, hopefully in time to avert disaster if she hasn't already left it too late for me to take over.

It's up to you now. You are being tested. If you can persuade the old witch to clear off then you will save the world. If you can't then the worst will inevitably happen.

Yours faithfully,

The King of the Gods,
Robert Strong.
Also copies to: -
Joe Biden
Antonio Guterres
Pope Francis,
Vladimir Putin,
Xi Jinping
President Erdogan,
Kim Jong Un

I shall send a copy of the above letter to Lucy as soon as I go to the shops on Thursday and buy some stamps.

The cretins injected me with paliperidone again this morning. Hopefully my letter of this morning will do the trick of getting rid of my late mother and then I won't have to take the filthy drugs any more.

Chapter 24

Tipping Point?

Events and Thoughts from Wednesday 7th July 2021

Wednesday 7th July 2021. I wrote to Lucy this morning, copying Monday's and Tuesday's journal entries and I added the following footnote: -

WEDNESDAY

I'm sorry I haven't been able to dance much, lately. The paliperidone has been getting the better of my sex drive. I don't think my late mother can hang on for much longer. The weather here in the south of England has been atrocious for a long time now. It is very gloomy, just like the spirit of the old witch. I don't think she can take much more of this before she gives in and duckifies herself. Let's hope she does so.

Thursday 8th July 2021. It was about seventy-six years ago, during the Second World War, that D-Day occurred. This was, as far as I can tell, the first universal acclamation of the spiritual leadership of my late mother, Dorothy. She has always kept a low profile in life, avoiding fame and fortune. Her main desire was for a sexual relationship with the best man she could find, which eventually transpired to be myself. I have broken many taboos in my life, but never the taboo against incest; mainly because I never was sexually attracted to my mother, much to her chagrin. She died in 2006, but that did not stop her from trying to seduce me, like she had done so many times when she was alive. She even tries to rape me by imposing herself upon my consciousness when I have been enjoying mental sex with my partner, Lucy, but my powers of concentration are strong enough not to be distracted and I always give my orgasm to Lucy, not my late mother, Dorothy. Dorothy's behaviour is annoying in the extreme, but I never let her steal my orgasm although she tries her hardest to do so.

In today's society Dorothy's influence is still prevalent. The powers-that-be are still her followers, especially in the legal and the psychiatric professions, so there is no hope for me to ever get my freedom, except by giving in to my late mother's sexual demands, which I refuse to do, and always will. Lucy Lawless is the Queen of MY heart and I will never betray my Queen by having sex with any other woman, not even mentally. So, my only hope is if I can persuade Dorothy to come back to life, preferably as an animal.

In today's world, there is plenty of evidence that the human race is losing the war against Global Warming and Climate Change, from the mud slides in Japan to the famine in Madagascar, to the volcano at GOMA in the Democratic Republic of Congo, to the floods in the UK and Australia, to the heatwave and wildfires in British Columbia, Canada, and Oregon and California in the USA. These are just a few examples of the conflict between the human race and Mother Nature, which the human race is losing. Dorothy presides over this state of affairs, and it is ample evidence that she is letting the world down, especially the human race which still follows her. She must take responsibility for letting the world down by her inadequate leadership and go, before it is too late, which it may be already. The above examples of how the human race is losing are evidence that my prediction that Armageddon will occur from irreversible Climate Change in eight years' time is already coming true. Bit by bit, the world is already becoming uninhabitable, and this process will get faster and faster as the next eight years go by.

The only solution to this problem is for the human race to cut their carbon emissions by forty-nine per cent by the end of 2028 or irreversible Climate Change will occur in 2029. The present target date of 2030 is too late because it does not take into account the ever-increasing destruction of the world's rainforests in the Amazon, Indonesia, Malaysia, Siberia and the Arctic Circle. If we do succeed in this target, we must then cut the remaining fifty-one per cent of carbon emissions by 2049. To meet these targets, the human race needs a STRONG political leader to take charge of the war against global carbon emissions, and I maintain that I am the best man for this job. The world needs my leadership, political as well as spiritual. It needs a man with the political will and the policies and the courage to put them into practise. Without my leadership, the world is doomed to Armageddon in eight years' time. Neither Joe Biden nor Antonio Guterres nor Xi Jinping nor Vladimir Putin has got what it takes to make a success of this job.

I want to get on with it and submit myself to the British public for election to the job of Prime Minister, which is the highest office that a person of common birth can aspire to in this country. But first I need to get out of hospital and clear my name, which won't be hard for me once my late mother has disappeared although it is impossible while she still exists. This is why I have been trying so hard to get rid of her spirit which still haunts me, pestering me for sex and thwarting my ambitions by keeping me locked up in a mental hospital.

Saturday 10th July 2021. I copied Thursday's entry in this journal into a letter to Lucy with the following copy list: -

    Cc Boris Johnson
    Sir Kier Starmer
    Sir Ed Davey
    Nicola Sturgeon
    Caroline Lucas
    Paul Rees
    Justin Welby
    Dr Twee Dampensquib
    Joe Biden
    Antonio Guterres
    Pope Francis
    Vladimir Putin
    Xi Jinping
    President Erdogan
    Kim Jong Un

I couldn't get to the shops last week to buy stamps, so I had to rely on the little shop here in the hospital, which didn't have any first-class stamps, so I had to make do with second class stamps which take longer for the letters to arrive.

Tuesday 13th July 2021. I didn't have enough stamps for everyone on my copy list last week, and yesterday the little shop in the hospital didn't have any stamps at all. The last six entries on the above copy list will have to wait until I go to the main shop tomorrow, before I can buy some 1st class stamps and post them. Their letters have been sitting on my desk since last Thursday.

Wednesday 14th July 2021. I wrote the following letter today to my selection of world leaders: - Wednesday 14th July 2021.

Cc Lucy Lawless
Boris Johnson
Sir Kier Starmer
Sir Ed Davey
Nicola Sturgeon
Caroline Lucas
Paul Rees
Justin Welby
Dr Twee Dampensquib
Joe Biden
Antonio Guterres
Pope Francis
Vladimir Putin
Xi Jinping
President Erdogan
Kim Jong Un

Dear Leaders of the human race,

The Gods inflicted the coronavirus pandemic, which has already killed over three million people and caused immense suffering and financial problems, upon the human race for four main reasons: -

1. As a demonstration of our power.

2. As a punishment for following the warped mind of the false God, my late mother, Mrs Dorothy (the door) Ayres.

3. As a warning, not to treat ME the way you do, but to give ME, not my late mother, the respect due to God.

4. To ground most of the world's jet aircraft because the environment cannot sustain the volume of air traffic that prevailed before the coronavirus pandemic.

The impending Climate Change crisis is going to dwarf the crisis of the coronavirus pandemic, and cost far more lives and far more money. We, as a species, will be lucky if we survive the Climate Change crisis, many species won't.

Armageddon, caused by irreversible Climate Change, will bring about the extinction of all life on earth, and it WILL happen in the year 2029 unless we close the door on the old era and welcome in the new era, without further delay. To achieve this, we must **make** the spirit of the late Mrs Dorothy (the door) Ayres join a pair of copulating ducks and come back to life as one of their offspring. This is what is meant by the phrase, "closing the door", and it is necessary for our survival to do it immediately.

Mrs Dorothy Ayres has been the sexual, and therefore the REAL leader of the world for the last seventy years, (this is what is meant by the phrase "opening the door"), and she has led it to the brink of extinction from irreversible Climate Change. She is now pushing it over the edge by prolonging the agony of her continuing existence. Closing the door is the only way by which she will ever get over her unrequited sexual desire for me, and it is the only way by which I will ever be free from her; free to be with the woman I love, free to pursue my career and, hopefully, free to save the world from extinction. Last week I set you a test which you have yet to pass. If you don't pass it soon it will be too late. Dorothy has had her day and got the world into an appalling mess. It is time she quit and let me have mine because she has left me a lot of mistakes to correct and problems to sort out. The sooner I have the chance to get on with it, the better. I can't start whilst I am a prisoner in a mental hospital.

Yours faithfully,

The King of the Gods,
Robert Strong.
I sent Lucy a copy of this letter, together with a letter and the lyrics to, "Physical", and "Getting to know you", which I thought were meaningful in the present circumstances.

Friday 16th July 2021. I wrote the following letter this morning: - Friday 16th July 2021.
Cc Lucy Lawless
Boris Johnson
Sir Kier Starmer
Sir Ed Davey

Nicola Sturgeon
Caroline Lucas
Paul Rees
Justin Welby
Dr Twee Dampensquib
Joe Biden
Antonio Guterres
Pope Francis
Vladimir Putin
Xi Jinping
President Erdogan
Kim Jong Un

Dear Leaders of the human race,

The recent catastrophic floods in western Germany, Belgium, the Netherlands and northern France, as well as the recent catastrophic heatwave on the western side of the north American continent are just two, recent examples of the effects of Climate Change. This is a direct consequence of the bad management and inadequate leadership of the late Mrs Dorothy (the door) Ayres, my late mother.

Climate Change is largely caused by people driving vehicles with internal combustion engines, and it would cut carbon emissions if we switched to electric vehicles. But people won't buy electric vehicles whilst there is such a shortage of electric points at which they can charge their batteries. If I was Prime Minister, I would have every lamp post in every city, town and village in the country converted so it could also act as an electricity charging point. I would make all vehicle manufacturers build vehicles with a fourth pin on their electric plug, on which would be encrypted the registration number of the vehicle, which could be read by the metre supplying the electricity, so that the electricity company would know who to charge for their electricity. I am sure that the British Standards Institute could design the appropriate plugs and metres. I would have done this years ago, so that we would not be in such dire straits at the moment.

But sadly, I am not the Prime Minister. I am held a prisoner in a mental hospital, where I am tortured with the horrendous effects of antipsychotic drugs, by the followers of my late mother because I refuse to have sex with the old witch, like they all do. She has got almost every adult in the

International Community to conspire to make a motherfucker out of me. But they are all out of luck because Lucy Lawless is my Queen not Mrs Dorothy Ayres, whose spirit belongs to a bygone era.

The spirit of the late Mrs Dorothy Ayres must join a pair of copulating ducks and come back to life as one of their offspring. If she won't do this willingly, we must **make** her do it. It must be done in the immediate future or the extinction of all life on earth will be a certainty in eight years' time.

Yours faithfully,

The King of the Gods,
Robert Strong.

Sunday 18th July 2021. I wrote the following letter today to my list of world leaders: - Sunday 18th July 2021.

Cc Lucy Lawless
Boris Johnson
Sir Kier Starmer
Sir Ed Davey
Nicola Sturgeon
Caroline Lucas
Paul Rees
Justin Welby
Dr Twee Dampensquib
Joe Biden
Antonio Guterres
Pope Francis
Vladimir Putin
Xi Jinping
President Erdogan
Kim Jong Un

Dear Leaders of the human race,

Further to my recent letters, I remind you that the human race is losing the war against Global Warming and Climate Change. This is largely because our leader, my mother, the late Mrs Dorothy (the door) Ayres, keeps ME a prisoner in a mental hospital because I refuse to have sex with her. (Having mental sex with Dorothy, otherwise known as "opening the door" has been the graduation ritual for entry into manhood in the whole of the international community for the last seventy years. I chose a different route to prove myself, but almost all other men chose to open the door). I am kept a prisoner when I am the only man with wisdom and the foresight and the political will and the policies and the courage to cut carbon emissions in time to avert the disaster of irreversible Climate Change.

The only solution to this problem is for us to turn the spirit of the late Mrs Dorothy Ayres into the body of an animal, presumably a duck. We must close the door on HER era and welcome into the world MY era, the era of the Kingdom of God.

There are things that you people can do about this. You can shout, mentally, at the old witch. Tell her to turn herself into a duck, and encourage all your supporters to tell her the same. Tell her to GO and GO NOW, before it is too late. Tell her to "GET ON WITH IT", which is what all her followers said to me forty-five years ago when they were desperately bullying me into killing the tyrannical matriarch that I had for a stepmother, Mrs Iris Brooks.

You can also use your influence to get me out of Alcatraz Island Hospital and into 10 Downing Street as quickly as possible. I'm sure the Great British public will vote for me, as I am by far the most popular man in this country, and deservedly so after what I have done and what I have been through. If you want to know the whole story, then you can read my autobiographies. They are very enlightening and can be accessed from my website. The address is: -

http://www.robert-brooks-strong.olympiapublishers.com/
Yours faithfully,

The King of the Gods,
Robert Strong.

Tuesday 20th July 2021. I wrote the following letter this morning. I'm hoping that I can withdraw some cash from the ward safe and buy some stamps from the little shop in the hospital; otherwise, I will have to wait before I can post these letters.

Tuesday 20th July 2021.
Cc Lucy Lawless

Boris Johnson

Sir Kier Starmer

Sir Ed Davey

Nicola Sturgeon

Caroline Lucas

Paul Rees

Justin Welby

Dr Twee Dampensquib

Joe Biden

Antonio Guterres

Pope Francis

Vladimir Putin

Xi Jinping

President Erdogan

Kim Jong Un

Dear Leaders of the human race,

The Devil came down to Earth as a human being. His name was Edward Richard Pitchblack, but that does not matter now. If you read my autobiographies, you will see that I spent over thirty years in mental combat with Him. I eventually overpowered Him and destroyed His power for ever. With help from the Brotherhood of Mankind and our friends in the insect world, the ants, I turned Him into a Rottweiler dog in August 2014, which is what he is now and what he will remain as for as long as there are dogs on this planet, if we, the human race, are careful. My late mother, Mrs Dorothy (the door) Ayres (the Arch-Demon Lucifer), wasn't just His accomplice, she wasn't just in cahoots with Him, she was His Boss. She got Him to do her bidding for her when, in April 1970, she got Him to take spiritual possession of my girlfriend, which destroyed what was a loving relationship. She always destroyed my happiness because of her jealousy of everyone I ever loved, because of her insane, incestuous, obsessive sexual desire for me. And now she wants me to become her lover. I would prefer for Armageddon to happen than become my mother's lover.

I want her to give in to my will and turn herself into a duck. She wants me to give in to her will and become her lover. She has turned this battle of wills into a game of "chicken" with the fate of the world at stake from irreversible Climate Change. SHE WILL HAVE TO GIVE IN, BECAUSE

MY WILL IS THE WILL OF GOD, AND IT IS THE STRONGEST FORCE IN THE UNIVERSE.

I have received Divine Guidance from the Goddess of Love, Aphrodite herself, that Lucy Lawless is the right woman for me, and my experience of mental and spiritual love-making with Lucy has proven this to be the truth. Lucy is my Queen and I will not betray her. My late mother has no chance at all with me: she will have to learn to take NO for an answer, just like everyone else has to from someone at some time in their life.

I rely on you people to support me in my endeavour to get rid of this usurper. She is not the real God, I am. She has taken advantage of my youth and inexperience to usurp my Godhood from me by claiming to be God herself. And look what a mess she has made of the authority that the human race invested in her. She has led the world to the brink of extinction from irreversible Climate Change, and now she is pushing it over the edge by prolonging the agony of her continued existence. For all our sakes, get rid of her while there is still time. There isn't much time left. Make her join a pair of copulating ducks and come back to life as one of their offspring.

Yours faithfully,

The King of the Gods,
Robert Strong.

Wednesday 21st July 2021. I was in luck yesterday. I managed to withdraw some cash from the ward safe, and the little shop in the hospital had some 1st class stamps, so I was able to get all my letters off to post yesterday. Thank Heaven.

I wrote the following letter to Lucy today: -

Wednesday 21st July 2021

Empress Lucy Lawless, the Queen of the Gods,

Dear Soulmate,

I thought you might like the enclosed picture of the man who is still waiting for you. It is an enlargement of a snap that was taken for the hospital records a couple of years ago. It turned up yesterday when the staff were sorting out some old paperwork.

I have the feeling that my recent letters to world leaders are doing the trick of getting rid of the old witch that I have for a mother. The pressure I am applying is working.

Recent floods in southern Germany and Austria as well as the catastrophic floods in China are all adding pressure on the old witch to go, before it is too late to avoid Climate Change becoming irreversible. My prediction that without my political influence the world will come to an end in eight years' time is already coming true. So, those who are keeping me from power haven't got long to change their attitude or they, too, will die when the world comes to an end.

Take care of yourself, my Love,

I have much more to say to you, but it can wait until we talk, Bless you, my Queen,

Yours with Love, Affection and Friendship,

The King of the Gods,
Emperor_B0B. XX.
Cc Dr Twee Dampensquib
Paul Rees, Chief Executive, the Royal College of Psychiatrists.
Joe Biden, President of the USA.

Thursday 22nd July 2021. I wrote the following letter this morning, but I won't be able to post it to the world leaders on my copy list until tomorrow afternoon at the earliest as I don't have any stamps until I can get to a post office, which I'm hoping to do tomorrow afternoon when I go to the West Yorkshire Hospital for an eye test.

Thursday 22nd July 2021.
Cc Lucy Lawless
Boris Johnson
Sir Kier Starmer
Sir Ed Davey
Nicola Sturgeon
Caroline Lucas
Paul Rees
Justin Welby
Dr Twee Dampensquib
Joe Biden
Antonio Guterres

Pope Francis
Vladimir Putin
Xi Jinping
President Erdogan
Kim Jong Un

Dear Leaders of the human race,

Recent climatic disasters such as the floods in China, as well as the floods in southern Germany and Austria, as well as the continuing heatwave and wildfires on the western side of the North American continent, all add weight to my prediction that without my political influence, the end of the world will happen in eight years' time. This prediction is now coming true.

If you think about it, this is the inevitable consequence of treating ME, God, the way I have been treated by the British psychiatric profession for the last forty-five years. Their motto is, "Let Wisdom Prevail", but wisdom has not been prevailing, power has. The power of the warped mind of my late mother, Mrs Dorothy (the door) Ayres, and the influence of her misguided followers has prevailed. Her policy of condoning sinful same-sex sexual relationships and making them socially acceptable also shares the blame for the coming Apocalypse. This policy is nothing but moral decadence disguised as diversity, and is bringing about MY judgement – the judgement of God upon the sinful human race.

But all is not yet lost. We still have a little time left, **IF** it is used wisely by those who can keep a cool head in a crisis. Our best hope is if I can get into power as the British Prime Minister by the end of 2023, then I can put my five-year plan, as described in The Manifesto of The Survival Party, into operation, to cut carbon emissions by forty-nine per cent by the end of 2028, averting the Apocalypse in 2029. The Manifesto deals with the moral as well as the practical causes of Climate Change, which no other political leader is addressing. This gives me two years and five months from now to get out of hospital, clear my name and get my compensation, and build up The Survival Party to the stage whereby we can field a candidate in every Parliamentary Constituency in Great Britain at the next General Election, which I hope will be at the end of 2023.

Boris Johnson is only so popular *because of his name.* It is a combination of my name, "BOB", and the maiden-name of the matriarch I killed, "IRIS JOHNSON". It is ME who is really the popular one with the

397

Great British people.
    Yours faithfully,

    The King of the Gods,
    Robert Strong.

Thursday 29th July 2021. I wrote the following letter today to my list of world leaders:
    Thursday 29th July 2021.
    Cc Lucy Lawless
    Boris Johnson
    Sir Kier Starmer
    Sir Ed Davey
    Nicola Sturgeon
    Caroline Lucas
    Paul Rees
    Justin Welby
    Dr Twee Dampensquib
    Joe Biden
    Antonio Guterres
    Pope Francis
    Vladimir Putin
    Xi Jinping
    President Erdogan
    Kim Jong Un

Dear Leaders of the human race,
    It is not really surprising that the human race is losing the war against Global Warming and Climate Change when you consider who we have got for a leader; a mad, old, dead woman with no morals at all called Mrs Dorothy Ayres. A woman who never did have anything to offer to society except free mental sex and a warped mind. All she asked in exchange for sex was an obligation from her followers to bully and coerce her own son, myself, into having an incestuous sexual relationship with the old witch.
    Unfortunately, her followers have not had the mental strength, nor the moral courage to get rid of this disastrous leader and put into power a man, such as myself, with the foresight to predict the impending Climate Change

crisis and the proven courage to take steps to remedy the situation. These followers of my late mother are to be found in the leading positions of the British legal profession and the British psychiatric profession, and these are the people who control my life, unfortunately for all of us.

Her followers are now discovering that mental sex with Dorothy, otherwise known as, "opening the door", wasn't as free as they had thought. There was a hidden cost in that they proved incapable of fulfilling their obligation to their heroine to coerce me into having sex with her. She led everyone to believe that I was just a boy because I wouldn't have sex with her, but they were all wrong. I AM A REAL MAN, and in my book a real man is not a motherfucker; I believe that there are good reasons for the taboo against incest, and I stick to my beliefs.

So, if you are thinking, "What can I do about all this?" the answer is, "Keep up the pressure on the old witch. We are winning!" The thundery downpours of torrential rain that the UK has been recently subjected to confirm this. Keep on mentally shouting at her to turn herself into a duck. Tell her to "GO" and "GO NOW", whilst there is still a little time, and keep on telling her to "GET ON WITH IT".

Yours faithfully,

The King of the Gods,
Robert Strong.

Friday 30th July 2021. I wrote the following letter to my list of world leaders this morning: - Friday 30th July 2021.

Cc Lucy Lawless
Boris Johnson
Sir Kier Starmer
Sir Ed Davey
Nicola Sturgeon
Caroline Lucas
Paul Rees
Justin Welby
Dr Twee Dampensquib
Joe Biden
Antonio Guterres
Pope Francis

Vladimir Putin
Xi Jinping
President Erdogan
Kim Jong Un

Dear Leaders of the human race,

There is a civil war going on at the moment in the spirit world, between myself and my late mother, Mrs Dorothy Ayres. It is a battle for the hearts and minds of all the men and women who comprise the human race. I ask you, therefore, to consider what each of us has to offer the world. SHE offers apparently free mental sex, and a way of life based upon the apparent freedoms of the permissive society such as the condoning of same-sex sexual relationships as being socially acceptable and the acceptance of incest as an acceptable relationship between mothers and sons even if it is against the will of the son in question. I offer a proven way of life based upon sustainability, morality, common sense and decency. MY way is based upon "dancing" with Bob and Lucy as an alternative to "opening the door" as proof of adulthood, and has been proven by the example of my previous life when I sacrificed my son, Jesus Christ, to save the world. I predicted years ago that HER way will lead to the annihilation of the human race, and now Global Warming and Climate Change are proving me right. Armageddon is almost upon us. I stand by my prediction that the Apocalypse will occur in 2029 unless we get rid of the spirit of my late mother in the immediate future.

It has been MY will and MY wisdom that has guarded and guided the human race throughout all my lives, ever since I was Adam in the Garden of Eden three hundred thousand years' ago. My late mother has always been jealous of me and jealous of my soulmate, Lucy, who was Eve all those years ago. She always thought that she was a more glorious being than me, which is why she has always defied the will of God and encouraged all her followers to do the same. Now look where that attitude has got us. We are on the brink of the extinction of all life on Earth thanks to seventy years of HER being in charge of the world! We don't have much time left to get rid of her, so turn her into a duck before it is too late. I've told you how. Shout at her, mentally, to turn herself into a duck; tell her to GO and GO NOW, and tell her to GET ON WITH IT.

Yours faithfully,

The King of the Gods,
Robert Strong.

Saturday 31st July 2021. My late mother's spirit paid me another visit in the small hours of this morning and embarked upon a head-to-head battle of wills with me at two a.m. She tried to persuade me to give in to her will in order to end the forty-five years of torture that her followers have been putting me through, by becoming her lover. In my semi-conscious state, I was, at first, tempted to go along with this, but I immediately thought of my Queen, Lucy, and my friends, the Gods in Heaven, and I knew I could never let them down. We have a bond of love and understanding which is stronger than the forces of life and death. I very soon became fully conscious and my immediate thought was that my late mother must obey MY will, not the other way round. She must turn herself in to a duck whether she wants to or not. I felt her give in to my determination and I knew, then, that I had passed my final test as King of the Gods. I then felt worthy of the faith that the Gods had invested in me. I had passed my own ultimate test and overpowered the Devil's boss herself, the vainglorious Arch-demon Lucifer. The very fact that she had tried this on with me at this time confirms that my strategy of appealing to the leaders of the human race to put pressure on the old witch has been working. I am now convinced that she will do as she has been told, turn herself into a duck, and GET ON WITH IT. Her tipping point has finally passed and, as I write this, she is falling.

I share my victory with the Gods, especially those outstanding people we call, "THE MAGNIFICENT SEVEN", and at this point in this book I shall name the seven people who I consider have earned the right to be included in this exclusive band of people. They are, in no particular order: Chairman Mao Tse Tung, The Prophet Muhammad, the boy who was Jesus Christ in his last life (I am keeping his identity a secret), Myself (the King of the Gods), My Soulmate, Lucy Lawless (the Queen of the Gods), Aphrodite (The Goddess of Love) and Mrs Iris Brooks (the woman I killed, My Stepmother). As far as I can tell, we are the seven people upon whom the human race depends for its survival from the forces of evil that, by definition, would destroy us if they could. There are, of course, many other worthy people, but these seven have proven to me that we are true heroes and are deserving of hero-worship. That is why I say, WE ARE THE REAL

MAGNIFICENT SEVEN.

It is now Saturday afternoon and there has hardly been a mention of the word "AREAS" on the BBC news channel all day; not even on the weather forecast, which tells me that the old witch is going even if she hasn't actually gone yet. I'll know for sure that she has gone when the weather presenters use the words "REGION" and "REGIONS" instead of "AREA" and "AREAS". That will tell me that, not only has Mrs Ayres departed, but that my influence is beginning to dominate the media like hers used to do.

Sunday 1st August 2021. We had torrential rain and thunderstorms in the south of England yesterday which tells me that the old witch is still putting up a fight, but the gloomy weather today tells me that she knows her hope of avoiding duckification is very forlorn. I don't think she has long to go now, especially as my most recent letters to world leaders are encouraging them to keep up the pressure on the old witch.

Monday 2nd August 2021. I wrote the following letter this morning to my list of world leaders: - Monday 2nd August 2021.

Cc Lucy Lawless
Boris Johnson
Sir Kier Starmer
Sir Ed Davey
Nicola Sturgeon
Caroline Lucas
Paul Rees
Justin Welby
Dr Twee Dampensquib
Joe Biden
Antonio Guterres
Pope Francis
Vladimir Putin
Xi Jinping
President Erdogan
Kim Jong Un

Dear Leaders of the human race,

The only way forward is for all of us to redouble our efforts to get rid of the old witch that I have for a mother, the late Mrs Dorothy Ayres, in the immediate future. We have got to make her turn herself into a duck without further delay. This is the only way by which she will ever overcome her unrequited feelings of sexual desire for me, and it is the only way I will ever get the freedom that we all need for me to have in order for me to do my work. It is also the only way by which the human race stands a chance of averting the impending catastrophe of irreversible Climate Change. We must all shout at her to end her own nightmare as well as that of every other thinking person by joining a pair of copulating ducks and coming back to life as one of their offspring. She knows it is what she got to do. Tell her that there isn't any more time left. She must do it NOW.

I have got to be at the forthcoming international Climate Change conference in Glasgow in early November this year. I want to address the assembly on behalf of The Survival Party. That gives me just three months from now to get out of hospital, clear my name with a public apology for forty-five years of abuse and collect the first instalment of my compensation money from the Royal College of Psychiatrists; then I need to start building up The Survival Party and putting it on the political map in time for the forthcoming conference.

This is all possible if, and only if, we all shout at the old witch to "GET ON WITH IT", and encourage everyone that we all influence to do the same.

Yours faithfully,

The King of the Gods,
Robert Strong.

Wednesday 4th August 2021. I sent copies of Saturday's and Sunday's journal entries to my list of world leaders this morning.

Chapter 25

Keeping up the Pressure

Events and Thoughts from Friday 6th August 2021.

Friday 6th August 2021. Two girls came into my room this afternoon and injected me with 100 mil of paliperidone. I have already told you, dear reader, about the effects of this revolting chemical compound. It is the price I have to pay for rejecting the sexual advances of my late mother. Hell hath no fury like a woman who's been scorned! She richly deserves to pay my price for treating me in this inhuman way. I will make her forfeit her own very humanity by making her come back to life as a duck, against her will. It is no less than what she deserves. She is not only ensuring that I remain sexually frustrated, but also my soulmate, Lucy, has to suffer this, because of what these inhuman monsters who follow my late mother are doing to me; not to mention all our millions of followers who want to dance with Lucy and me.

I will get my revenge on my late mother's followers by hitting them in the pocket when I have got rid of the old witch. I will sting them for enough compensation money to pay for the creation of the most powerful political Party in Great Britain; The Survival Party. When I have bled the Royal College of Psychiatrists dry, I will do the same thing to the British Government on behalf of all the professional bodies in Great Britain whose members constitute my late mother's followers; especially the legal profession. I haven't forgiven them, yet, for the kangaroo court that "tried" my case at the Old Bailey in January 1977 and sent me to Broadmoor, when they knew damn well that I had only done what they, themselves, had bullied me into doing.

Saturday 7th August 2021. I heard on the evening news on TV that Dundee United have thrashed Glasgow Rangers at football today. This result ended a run of seventeen months without defeat for the Glasgow team. This tells me that "D" is being "done" by a "united" force of people, and is very encouraging news for me, as it confirms that my strategy of writing to my list of world leaders is working and that my message is getting through to the right people. The fact that Dundee United beat a Glasgow team augers well for the COP26 conference in November which is being held in Glasgow. At this rate my plan to be at that conference could well become reality. If this happens, I may well get the chance to address the assembly on behalf of The Survival Party, which, as I wrote previously, is what I want to do.

If I meet with any resistance to my plans to raise enough compensation money to fund the creation of my new political Party, The Survival Party, then I shall have no mercy on the souls who stand between me and my objective. I can foresee several people coming back as rats in their next lives.

Monday 9th August 2021, I wrote the following letter to Lucy this morning:
- Monday 9th August 2021
    Empress Lucy Lawless, the Queen of the Gods,

Dear Pet,
    I hope you don't mind me calling you that, but it is what you are forcing me to do by refusing to communicate with me. I've got my psychiatrist's hat on this morning, and I've been thinking about your behaviour, especially your unique refusal to communicate at all with me. If I didn't know better, I'd accuse you of having a mental illness, but I don't believe in the mental illness model. To accuse someone else of having a mental illness, as psychiatrists do, only gives away their lack of understanding of human nature.

    I think you may have been a cat in a previous life because you certainly have a feline characteristic in that you have an independent spirit and a mind of your own and you only do what you want to do. But that's all right with me, Dear. If you enjoy curling up on my lap and purring (figuratively speaking) I still love you anyway, even though your behaviour is like that of a dumb animal. Just like a pet, you make me know you love me too, without speaking a word.

    I think your behaviour stems from an enormous and overwhelming desire to be loved and accepted and appreciated for what you are, and is partly due to your childhood as a girl amongst so many brothers. Your tendency to be a "tomboy" and to outdo the boys at being tough, which earned you celebrity as Xena, the Warrior Princess, stems from your childhood. But this belies your nature as a woman with a loving heart, a warm personality, and enormous strength of mind.

You still retain the name "Lawless" although it is a long time since you split up from your first husband, Garth Lawless, and this gives a clue to your nature. Your streak of apparently childish petulance and disregard for the norms of society does not win you friends, and does indeed hurt some people who love you, such as myself. You hurt my feelings by not even saying "Thank You" for the lovely Queen Lucy CD Album I created and produced for you, including the title track which was a labour of love; and many people who have heard the album admire that track. You have also never thanked me for all the lovely poetry I have written for you, and that also hurts me. How can I love you as a friend when you behave like that? That is no way to treat a friend, let alone a lover. Which is why I call you "pet"; that is the only way you will let me love you. A human friend is someone who responds in kind when you communicate with them.

Take care of yourself, my Love, and keep on purring,

I have much more to say to you, but it can wait until we talk,

Bless you, my Queen,

Yours with Love, Affection and Friendship,

The King of the Gods,

Emperor_B0B. XX.

Cc Dr Twee Dampensquib

I sent copies of Friday's and Saturday's journal entries in a letter to Lucy, with copies to Dr Twee Dampensquib and Paul Rees.

Saturday 14TH August 2021. I wrote the following letter to my list of world leaders this morning: - Saturday 14th August 2021.

Cc Lucy Lawless

Boris Johnson

Sir Kier Starmer

Sir Ed Davey

Nicola Sturgeon
Caroline Lucas
Paul Rees
Justin Welby
Dr Twee Dampensquib
Joe Biden
Antonio Guterres
Pope Francis
Vladimir Putin
Xi Jinping
President Erdogan
Kim Jong Un

Dear Leaders of the human race,

This is just a line to say, "Well done for trying to get rid of the old witch, Lucifer, otherwise known as the late Mrs Dorothy (the door) Ayres. But keep up the pressure on her, and don't think her demise is a foregone conclusion. She will fight us to the end". Don't be afraid to use the phrase "Close the door upon her era" when addressing your followers and supporters. It is vital that we do this.

By espousing the permissive society, she has persuaded the human race to live a life of hedonism and sinfulness, not that they needed much persuasion, but the fact that they have used up their stock of moral fortitude is the moral cause of Climate Change. She persuaded people that it was OK to defy the will of God, and they made the foolish mistake of going along with that. Now look where that has got the world. All the countries round the Mediterranean Sea are now on fire as well as the western side of the North American continent. China and Northern Europe as well as western India are experiencing their worst floods ever. The human race gave her the powers of a God and she has proven to be a failure in the job, so we will now have to take those powers away from her before it is too late to prevent Climate Change from becoming irreversible, and the only way to do that is by turning her soul into the body of a duck, even though she doesn't want this to happen.

Now that the human race has realised their foolish mistake, we must make her depart from us immediately. I want her gone in time for me to get discharged from hospital, clear my name with a public apology and collect the first instalment of my £x in compensation from the Royal College of Psychiatrists, register The Survival Party of Great Britain with the Electoral Commission of the UK, and get to the COP26 in Glasgow by the 31st October. I have emailed Alok Sharma, the President of the COP26 and informed him of all this, so all we need is for the old witch to clear off and we will stand a chance.

I see that Dundee United thrashed Glasgow Rangers at football last Saturday, which is a good omen. "D" is being "done" by a "united" group of people; that is a direct effect of my letters to you people. We are having success. Keep up the pressure on the old witch, Lucifer, and we will stand a chance of survival, otherwise we won't. I see that they even named the Spanish heatwave "Lucifer", so my warnings ARE being heeded, thank Heaven.

Yours faithfully,

The King of the Gods,
Robert Strong.

Sunday 15th August 2021. I wrote the following letter to Lucy this afternoon: - Sunday Afternoon 15th August 2021
Empress Lucy Lawless, the Queen of the Gods,

Dear Pet and Soulmate,

Thank you for bobulucydating me yesterday. We still came together in spite of the paliperidone. I don't think I'll be taking it for much longer and I'll tell you why!

Antonio Guterres, the Secretary General of the United Nations, has issued a CODE RED for humanity because of Climate Change. (This is what I've been saying for years). The western side of the North American continent, Nevada, California, Oregon, Vancouver Island and the rest of British Columbia is all on fire; as are the countries surrounding the Mediterranean Sea, starting with Turkey and working anticlockwise, Greece, Italy, Sicily, Spain, Portugal and now Algeria and Tunisia; they are all on fire as well. Countries not on fire are experiencing torrential rainfall causing floods, such as Japan, China, northern Turkey, Germany, Belgium, the Netherlands, Austria, Switzerland and parts of the UK. They are all suffering from Climate Change. This is not in the future; it is already happening NOW.

I've had a song going through my head all day, today, with the lyric, "I don't want to set the world on fire". I can sense that this is the tune going through the head of my late mother, Dolly. She doesn't want to set the world on fire, and she doesn't want to come back to life as a duck, either, but those are her only two options. She has got to decide her own least worst option. I feel sure she'll decide to come back as a duck, but the longer she leaves it before making her decision the more countries will suffer the adverse effects of Climate Change. The game of "chicken" is irrelevant. The decision is hers and hers alone. She is the leader of the human race as long as her spirit exists in human form, so it is up to her to decide the fate of the world. I am YOUR lover, not hers, and there's nothing that Dolly or anyone else can do about that fact.

I feel sure that the situation with respect to the devastation caused by Climate Change will improve from the moment that she becomes the embryo of a duckling. The Gods have a huge influence on the climate and they will be only too happy to please me from the instant that I come to power, which will be the moment that Dolly disappears. I'll let you know, of course, when that happens.

Yours etcetera

Cc Dr Twee Dampensquib

Thursday 19th August 2021. I wrote the following letter to Lucy this afternoon. Note the copy list: - Thursday Afternoon 19th August 2021

Empress Lucy Lawless, the Queen of the Gods,

Dear Pet and Soulmate,

You ARE Mother Nature, and you are winning in the war between us and my late mother, Dolly, with her colossal army of misguided followers. I am also winning in this war with MY followers, The Taliban (who follow the ways of Allah, my Muslim name) winning against Dolly's followers, the Western establishment. Dolly IS Lucifer Herself, the leader of the Devil's army and Satan's Boss. She is the person that the Western establishment still follow, and that is why they are all up shit creek without a paddle when it comes to Climate Change. I am their only hope of survival and I can't help them until Dolly becomes a duck.

Without ME, the COP26, starting on the 31st October, won't make any significant difference to Global Warming and Climate Change. Since I wrote to you on Sunday, southern France has also caught fire and Haiti has also joined the list of countries experiencing floods. For someone who doesn't want to destroy the world, Dolly is making a good job of doing just that, by prolonging the agony of her existence. I repeat that SHE is the leader of the world; what happens to the world is HER responsibility.

Everyone in the world who can see beyond the end of their nose is wondering if Dolly has got what it takes to sacrifice herself in order to save the world. If she hasn't then we have all had our chips. If she has, then she had better GET ON WITH IT without further delay.

Yours etcetera

Cc Dr Twee Dampensquib,
Paul Rees, Chief Executive, The Royal College of Psychiatrists,
Joe Biden, President of the United States,
Vladimir Putin, President of Russia,
Xi Jinping, President of China.

Saturday 21st August 2921. I wrote the following letter to Lucy this morning: - Saturday Morning 21st August 2021
Empress Lucy Lawless, the Queen of the Gods,

Dear Pet and Soulmate,

Firstly, I want to say, "Thank you" for bobulucydating me again. We came together again last night (UK time) most beautifully, as always. This confirms my conviction that you and I are right for each other. Your ghost and my ghost are eternal dancing partners. My late mother's ghost doesn't stand a chance with me. Our bond is stronger than the forces of life and death. If one or both of us were to die, Heaven forbid, then we would still be lovers.

Secondly, I want to say that I feel sorry for my late mother, Dolly. For making me her lover one day. She could and should have heeded the words of Alan Price in the song O Lucky Man, "…without that dream you are nothing, nothing, nothing. You have to find out for yourself that dream is dead". I have been asking, "Why does Dolly still persist in hanging about? Why won't she take NO for an answer?" The answer is that it is beyond her ability to forget her dream, which has been her lifetime's ambition. She cannot accept that her whole life has been in vain. But it hasn't been in vain. She was MY mother, and she can be proud of the fact that she played a large part in making me the man I am today.

If I was her, I would take the ATTITUDE THAT IT IS BETTER TO KNOW THAT YOU ARE BECOMING A DUCK THAN NOT KNOWING WHAT YOU ARE! I would sooner become a duck than go through that torment again. That was what I went through from October 1971, when Jasmin 2 left me until July 1976 when I killed Iris, and thereby proved to myself that I AM A MAN. That was when I discovered that you are NOT a man *until you know you are*; until then I had no idea whatever I might be. Dolly and her friend, Satan, put me through all that. I had to accept that my dream was dead and I had to take NO for an answer, even though I would sooner have died. Now it is my time to put Dolly through it.

Unless Dolly thinks the unthinkable and duckifies herself in the immediate future then the whole world is doomed. I have no confidence in the whole gamut of the world's politicians of today to solve the practical problems of Climate Change, and they aren't even trying to rectify the moral cause of the problem. Without MY leadership, both political and spiritual, they are all floundering, and the COP26 summit won't come up with any workable answers to the problems of Climate Change. I can't lead them whilst I am still being treated like a criminal lunatic by Dolly's followers, for doing, forty-five years ago, what they, themselves, bullied me into doing. The solutions to all the problems of Climate Change, including the moral issues, are to be found in my Manifesto of The Survival Party of Great Britain, but it needs me in person to put the policies into practise. The only way is for Dolly to come back to life as a duck without delay. Since I wrote to you on Thursday, Israel and also Lebanon have become subjected to wildfires causing loss of life. Dolly has got a lot to answer for whatever happens. Her best answer is, "QUACK". As long as her spirit continues to exist in human form, SHE is the leader of the human race and what happens to all of us is up to her. *IF* she really loves us, she will say, "Goodbye", and go. If she doesn't, we have no chance at all.

I want to discuss the future with you, including the issue of the world's leadership in the future, and there is much I want you to know that it is not wise for me to put in writing at the moment. It is not fair of you to make me shoulder the burden of these matters on my own. Even I need discussion with important people on such weighty matters, and you are the most important person in my plans, together with my grandson and heir, Troy Daniel Evans.

Yours etcetera

Cc Dr Twee Dampensquib,
Paul Rees, Chief Executive, The Royal College of Psychiatrists,
Joe Biden, President of the United States,
Vladimir Putin, President of Russia,
Xi Jinping, President of China.

Sunday 22nd August 2021. I wrote the following letter this morning to my list of world leaders: - Sunday 22nd August 2021

Cc Lucy Lawless
Boris Johnson
Sir Kier Starmer
Sir Ed Davey
Nicola Sturgeon
Caroline Lucas
Paul Rees
Justin Welby
Dr Twee Dampensquib
Joe Biden
Antonio Guterres
Pope Francis
Vladimir Putin
Xi Jinping
President Erdogan
Kim Jong Un

Dear Leaders of the human race,

The fact that the Taliban have taken over in Afghanistan is no accident, nor coincidence. THE BETTER MEN WON! This is a natural consequence of the fact that their leader, myself, Allah, is a better person than the leader of the Western establishment, my late mother, Lucifer. All the anti-Taliban propaganda from the Western media and politicians is just sour grapes from a bad loser!

The lesson to be drawn from this is that if the West want to win in future conflicts, then they had better get rid of their disastrous leader, Lucifer, otherwise known as the late Mrs Dorothy Ayres, my mother, and put me, God, into a position of power. The only way to achieve this is to turn her soul into the body of a duck. The human race will be better off without her.

The Afghan conflict was a physical manifestation of the civil war between myself and my late mother in the spirit world. When my late mother, Dolly, known colloquially as "the door", has been duckified, we will all live in a world free from conflict. But first we must close the door on her era; then we will all live in the era of the Kingdom of God and be happier for it. If we close the door in time, we will survive the Climate Change crisis. Otherwise, we won't. Time is of the essence and we have no time to lose.

Yours faithfully,

The King of the Gods,
Robert Strong.

Tuesday 24th August 2021. I wrote the following letter to Lucy this morning, with a copy to all my list of world leaders: - Tuesday Morning 24th August 2021

Empress Lucy Lawless, the Queen of the Gods,

Dear Pet and Soulmate,

I have one final message for my late mother, as follows: - **LUCIFER'S DENOUEMENT**

Dear Mother,

I, God, am a more glorious being than you, Lucifer. The victory of my people in Afghanistan, The Taliban, proves it, for now and for all time. That is what you have waited three hundred thousand years to find out, and now you know. You have lost me to a better woman in Lucy Lawless, who is Mother Nature Herself and my eternal soulmate. These facts are the last straw that has now broken the spine of your resistance to my will, and you now have no choice but to obey me when I say, "Find yourself a pair of copulating ducks and come back to life as one of their offspring. GET ON WITH IT; TODAY."

Your life was not in vain. You will be remembered forever as the woman who paved the way for the dawning of the glorious Kingdom of God upon the Earth.

Thanks for the fight; one of us had to lose, and that one is you. Good luck in your next life, in the world of ducks. This is the final CHECK MATE.

Goodbye duck,

Bob

Afghanistan is now in good hands, which is more than I can say for the Western world, until I become the Prime Minister of Great Britain. I wish to be known as "The OWL" because the owl is, famously, a wise-looking old bird, and the letters form the acronym of "Official World Leader".

Yours etcetera

Cc Lucy Lawless

Boris Johnson

Sir Kier Starmer

Sir Ed Davey

Nicola Sturgeon

Caroline Lucas

Paul Rees

Justin Welby

Dr Twee Dampensquib

Joe Biden

Antonio Guterres

Pope Francis

Vladimir Putin

Xi Jinping

President Erdogan

Kim Jong Un

MJB4 Chapter 26

Misère Au Vert

Sunday 19th September 2021. I wrote the following letter to Lucy this morning, with a copy list to my World Leaders: - Sunday 19th September 2021

Empress Lucy Lawless, the Queen of the Gods,

Dear Soulmate,

Further to yesterday's letter, I have decided that the time has now come to put my cards on the table and reveal my plan to save the world. For those who play cards, I am playing a hand of misère au vert. Firstly, I repeat that I am the King of the Gods, and one of the main reasons I am here in this world, at this time, is to save the world from the impending catastrophe of irreversible Climate Change. My plan is as follows: -

As soon as my late mother, Mrs Dorothy (Dolly) Ayres (otherwise known as "the door"), becomes a duck, I will get enough money in compensation to build my Party, The Survival Party of Great Britain, up to the stage whereby we can field a candidate in every Parliamentary Constituency in Great Britain at the next General Election, which I think will be at the end of 2023. Then, depending, of course, upon the will of the Great British people, I plan to lead The Survival Party to victory with myself as the new Prime Minister. I feel sure that the Great British people will vote for a man with a plan rather than the Brexit Poster-Boy, Boris Johnson, who is obviously out of his depth as the leader of this great country. I can then put my five-year plan, as outlined in my Manifesto of The Survival Party of Great Britain, into operation, to start cutting carbon emissions in time to prevent Climate Change from becoming irreversible in 2029.

Great Britain will lead the world by example, in the field of cutting carbon emissions, and, as King of the Gods, I shall make the United Nations feel obliged to follow the British example.

All my plans are now laid. The world is now waiting for Dolly to turn herself into a duck. That is all that is needed for me to start my real work in this world.

Take care of yourself, my Love, and keep on purring, I have much more to say to you, but it can wait until we talk, Bless you, my Queen,

Yours with Love, Affection and Friendship,

The King of the Gods,
Emperor_B0B. XX.
Cc Boris Johnson,
Sir Kier Starmer
Sir Ed Davey
Nicola Sturgeon
Caroline Lucas
Paul Rees
Justin Welby
Dr Twee Dampensquib
Joe Biden
Antonio Guterres
Pope Francis
Vladimir Putin
Xi Jinping
President Erdogan
Kim Jong Un

Monday 20th September 2021. I wrote the following letter to my solicitor today, and I also wrote the subsequent letter to Lucy this evening: - Monday 20th September 2021

Jane Rabbit,
Solicitor.

Dear Jane,

After speaking to you this morning, it is now obvious that applying for another Tribunal would be a waste of my time and yours. Please, therefore, cancel my instructions to prepare for another Tribunal. I enclose copies of a couple of letters I wrote on Saturday and Sunday, for your information. They will enlighten you if you try to understand them.

Yours sincerely,

Robert Strong.

Monday Evening 20th September 2021

Empress Lucy Lawless, the Queen of the Gods,

Dear Soulmate,

When we danced this morning (UK time), I could sense the intensity of your need for me to caress your beautiful breasts as I made love to you. Don't worry, Darling, you have got me where you want me, just as I have got you where I want you. Let's face it, Darling, we need each other, and we have both got who we need, even though you are too scared of my late mother's influence to communicate with me. I guess you have got too much to lose by doing so. You are lucky. I've got nothing left to lose; I'm already certified as being mentally ill, with a conviction for manslaughter and even my own sons don't want to know me, so I can do as I please and say what I like to who I like in my letters. In that sense, I'm the lucky one.

My solicitor phoned me this morning and I told her to go ahead with the Tribunal application, but then I thought better of it and wrote to her, cancelling my instruction to go ahead with the Tribunal. I also sent her a copy of Saturday's and Sunday's letters, so she'll have a clear idea of what I think of her, and the whole corrupt legal system in this country and the whole international community. They think they've got me all sewn up, but I know that Dolly will soon turn herself into a duck, because unless she does that, the world will come to an end in the foreseeable future from irreversible Climate Change without my leadership. I stand by my prediction that Armageddon, the Apocalypse, will happen in 2029 unless Dolly departs from the human race very soon. She may have left it too late already.

Even if I were to give in to Dolly's absurd demands of me, it wouldn't change anything. She must give in and duckify herself before it's too late. There is no other way for this situation to progress. I'd sooner die like a man than live like a motherfucker. I repeat, your ghost and my ghost are eternal dancing partners and nothing can alter that fact.

Yours etcetera

Cc Dr Twee Dampensquib

Tuesday 21st September 2021. I wrote the following letter to my list of world leaders this morning: - Tuesday 21st September 2021

Cc Lucy Lawless

Alok Sharma

Boris Johnson

Sir Kier Starmer

Sir Ed Davey

Nicola Sturgeon

Caroline Lucas

Paul Rees

Justin Welby

Dr Twee Dampensquib

Joe Biden

Antonio Guterres

Pope Francis

Vladimir Putin

Xi Jinping

President Erdogan

Kim Jong Un

Dear Leaders of the human race,

People are STILL driving vehicles with internal combustion engines, flying in jet planes, burning coal in power stations and using gas for heating, even though we have known for decades that these things are destroying the world we all live in. The only conclusion to be drawn from this is that under the leadership of my late mother, Mrs Dorothy (Dolly) Ayres (otherwise known as "the door"), the human race collectively is knowingly committing suicide; whilst I, who have the foresight to realise this and cares enough to try and do something about it, am labelled "mentally ill" and kept a prisoner in a mental hospital for doing, forty-five years ago, what Dolly's followers bullied me into doing, and kept a prisoner for refusing to have sex with my late mother like most other men do.

The only way to avoid the end of the world happening in the foreseeable future is for the human race to get rid of the soul of my late mother without delay and make ME, the Lord God, your leader. My ways provide the foundation for a sustainable way of life for the human hace, unlike my late mother's ways which are proving to be disastrous. This is the REAL extinction rebellion. It is a rebellion against the leadership of the late Mrs Dorothy (Dolly) Ayres, Lucifer, which has prevailed for the last seventy years, and has got us into this terrible mess. Unless you people do as I say, we will all perish. I stand by my prediction that Armageddon, the Apocalypse, will happen in 2029 unless you people do as I, the Lord God, say.

We must get rid of Dolly's soul by shouting at her to find herself a pair of copulating ducks and come back to life as one of their offspring. If enough people do this loudly enough, she will get the message and clear off. This is our only hope of survival. COP26 won't do any good whilst Dolly's spirit still exists in human form.

Yours faithfully,

The King of the Gods,
Robert Strong.

Thursday 23rd September 2021. I wrote the following letter to my list of world leaders, after hearing Joe Biden's speech on the TV yesterday: -
Thursday 23rd September 2021

Cc Lucy Lawless

Alok Sharma

Boris Johnson

Sir Kier Starmer

Sir Ed Davey

Nicola Sturgeon

Caroline Lucas

Paul Rees

Justin Welby

Dr Twee Dampensquib

Joe Biden

Antonio Guterres

Pope Francis
Vladimir Putin
Xi Jinping
President Erdogan
Kim Jong Un

Dear Leaders of the human race,

I thought it worth writing to you again for the benefit of Joe Biden and anyone else who thinks the same way as him. He believes in God although he doesn't seem to realise that that is who *I* am. He knows he and his people need my love and his troops need my protection, yet at the same time he defies my will and follows the ways of my late mother, Lucifer, NOT my ways. SHE believes in the permissive society and she condones same-sex sexual relationships and transgenderism as being socially acceptable. I do not. Public ideas of morality are all a question of where we, as a society, draw the line, and WHO draws the line. I repeat that I am the Lord God, and I draw the line at the act of sodomy between men and the act of lesbian sex and the act of interfering surgically with a person's genitals to enable them to have sex with a person of their own choice of gender. I say that if you don't like the gender you were born to be then you should learn to control yourself and lead a celibate life or be punished. We can give you drugs to supress your libido to help you live a celibate life. There is nothing new in this. In my last life I wrote clearly in the Bible, "Man shall not go with man". The same obviously applies to women. This is all in my Manifesto of The Survival Party of Great Britain, in the section on morality. I state there that the kindest way to handle the LGBT community is to regard their unnatural sexual proclivities as symptoms of an incurable mental illness. I define mental illness as such and I define antipsychotic drugs as all drugs which supress a person's libido, enabling them to live as a celibate. What is often regarded as mental illness in today's society is nothing more than immaturity; it is a failure to accept reality and a failure to cope with the trials of adulthood. The "cure" for this is to stop thinking that you are a better person than you have proven yourself to be, and accept your place in the world, which is determined by the strength of your spirit, not your IQ, nor your physical strength. Make your mind up, Joe Biden. Do you follow my ways, the ways of God, or do you follow my late mother's ways, the ways of Lucifer? You can't follow both ways at once. My ways have been proven to work by the test of time. Her ways are proving to be disastrous because of Climate Change. This is inevitable because the Gods have a strong influence on the climate, all over the world, and *I* am the King of the Gods. This is the moral cause of Climate Change. The human race should have learned from the Bible story of Sodom and Gomorrah. Those cities practised homosexuality and I punished them so severely that they stopped it. Now the same thing is happening again, but this time it is on a Global scale.

It was all a part of Satan's plan to destroy mankind by undermining the moral values of society. I destroyed Him in August 2014 by turning Him into a Rottweiler dog, but His Boss and accomplice, Lucifer, continued with His plan and they have now almost succeeded. My late mother, Lucifer, seems determined to destroy the planet if she can't have me for a lover, which she can't, BECAUSE I SAY SO. I say she must change her mind and come back as a duck, because nothing will make me change *my* mind. I have a lover of my own who is a better woman than Lucifer, so Lucifer stands no chance at all with me, and it is time she grew up and realised it.

This is why I can play a hand of misère au vert. As King of the Gods, I am supremely confident that I can win every single trick in this game.

Yours faithfully,

The King of the Gods,
Robert Strong.

Thursday 30th September 2021. I wrote the following letter to my list of world leaders today: - Thursday 30th September 2021

Cc Lucy Lawless
Alok Sharma
Boris Johnson
Sir Kier Starmer
Sir Ed Davey
Nicola Sturgeon
Caroline Lucas
Paul Rees
Justin Welby
Dr Twee Dampensquib
Joe Biden

Antonio Guterres
Pope Francis
Vladimir Putin
Xi Jinping
President Erdogan
Kim Jong Un

Dear Leaders of the human race,

I feel sure that my late mother, Mrs Dorothy (Dolly) Ayres, otherwise known as "the door" that all the men except me open, who is none other than the vainglorious Arch-Demon, Lucifer, will come back to life as a duck as soon as she realises that she is doing immense harm to the whole world, including herself, and no good at all, by prolonging the agony of her existence in spirit form as a human being. Global Warming isn't hanging about like she is, and Climate Change isn't wasting the precious time of all of us, like she is doing. Thanks to her ridiculous sexual desire for me, the human race is careering headlong at full speed down the straight road to extinction.

She will surely come to her senses soon. She is Mother Earth, but my soulmate, Lucy Lawless, is Mother Nature herself. The human race can only have one mother so one of them has to go, and I remain certain that my own mother, Dolly, must go, seeing as she refuses to act like my mother. She acts like a jilted mistress. If I, God, were to betray Mother Nature that *would* bring about the Apocalypse, but I don't want to betray Lucy Lawless, and I have no intention of doing so, whatever my late mother wants. Neither Dolly, nor all her followers, are going to make a motherfucker out of *me*, however long they keep me in the loony bin, and no matter how much of their filthy, libido-supressing drugs they pump into my arse. This won't go on for much longer, anyway. If Dolly doesn't come back as a duck soon then Armageddon, the Apocalypse, will be inevitable from irreversible Climate Change. The temperature of the world has already risen by 1.2^0 C. If it goes over 1.5^0 C, then that will be the end for all of us.

Great Britain and the world need my leadership, both political and spiritual, but I can't give the world the leadership it so obviously needs whilst Dolly's followers treat me like a criminal lunatic, for doing, forty-five years ago, what they themselves bullied me into doing. But I remain an optimist. I think the world *will* survive the Climate Change crisis, but it won't do so while the spirit of my late mother continues to exist in human form, therefore she *will* come back to life as a duck as soon as she comes to her senses. Let us all pray that she finds the wisdom and the courage to sacrifice herself in order to save the world.

Yours faithfully,

The King of the Gods,
Robert Strong.

Wednesday 6th October 2021. The psychiatric nurses injected me again today with 100 mil of paliperidone. Dolly's followers will pay dearly for all this inhumanity and injustice that they have inflicted upon me, and they are still doing so. I'm sure my late mother, Dolly, will come back to life as a duck soon, because unless she does so, it will be the end of the world for all of us in the foreseeable future. When Dolly comes back as a duck I will demand, and get, enough money in compensation to finance the building and maintenance of The Survival Party of Great Britain. Firstly, I will lodge my demand from the Royal College of Psychiatrists, then, when I have squeezed them for all they have got, I will do the same thing to the British Government, when I clear my name after a retrial of my case; I will then make a huge compensation demand from the government on behalf of British society for driving me to homicide in 1976.

Thursday 7th October 2021. There is no point in rebelling against the authority of a regime unless you have a superior regime under a higher authority to replace it with. This can be measured in terms of the welfare, and indeed, the very survival of the community that the regime serves. My late mother, Mrs Dorothy (Dolly) Ayres, also known as "the door", who is none other than the vainglorious Arch-Demon Lucifer, rebelled against the authority of God-the-Father, replacing ME with her own authority under the name of *she-who-must-be-obeyed* which created a secular, quasi-religious cult that has prevailed in the world for the last seventy years. Her policy of *the permissive society* gave people the freedom to do as they please in their sexual behaviour, condoning same-sex sexual relationships and transgenderism as socially acceptable. This decline in moral standards in the name of amoral behaviour is the moral cause of Climate Change because it offends ME, God, and this is the proof of the fact that I am actually the higher authority, not HER, because Climate Change is threatening the very survival of all living things on the planet including the human race. This proves that people need the authority of God-the-Father to tell them how to behave sexually, and to punish them for misbehaviour, in order for the community to survive.

The time has now come for HER to admit her mistake, apologise, and accept that she has now been expelled from the human race, for her insurrection against ME, God-the-Father, and for usurping MY authority. Unless she comes back to life in the form of an animal, presumably a duck, then THE END OF ALL THINGS, predicted in the Book of Revelations in the Bible becomes inevitable very soon. The politicians of the world are like a flock of lost sheep without their shepherd. Without MY leadership, both political and spiritual, they stand no chance of saving the world from irreversible Climate Change. All their promises are far too little, too late, to solve the practical causes of Climate Change and they are not proving to be competent enough to put those promises into practical actions. And they are not even trying to solve the moral cause of Climate Change.

I repeat, let us pray that Dolly finds the wisdom and the courage to sacrifice herself by coming back to life as a duck, in order to save the world.

I am sending a copy of the above entry in a letter to my list of world leaders.

Saturday 16th October 2021. I wrote the following letter to Lucy last night: - Friday Night 15th October 2021

Empress Lucy Lawless, the Queen of the Gods,

Dear Soulmate,

I have discovered that I can torture the very souls of those who treat me unreasonably and get schadenfreude, sadistic glee, out of doing so. That is what I am doing to my late mother and will continue doing until she comes back to life as a duck in order to get away from me. It is her own fault for assuming that I am such a degenerate that I would want to have sex with my own mother. What an insult! There is nothing I want less. I find the very thought of sex with *her*, sickening to my stomach and not at all sexy; just nauseating.

As far as you are concerned, I have decided to dance with whatever woman takes my fancy at any given time, and give you the freedom to dance with any man you want to. If you were a woman who loves me you would behave like one, but you don't, so either you don't love me or you are not yet a woman or both. You can decide for yourself which of those options is the truth. Either way, I've had enough of a relationship in which you won't even communicate with me. You don't treat me like a human being, so if you don't like my attitude, it's your own fault. If you believed in me you would stop at nothing to get as close to me as you can.

As far as Twee Dampensquib is concerned; he should be ashamed of himself for breaking his own Hippocratic Oath. He swore to do good and not to do harm when he became a doctor, but the drugs he forces me to take do a lot of harm and no good at all. He knows damn well that there is nothing wrong with me, and his only reason for prescribing them for me is because he is a psychiatrist. That is the case, but he is less than a man in my opinion, and my opinion is the one that matters.

I shall just carry on as before until either my late mother becomes a duck or she brings about the Apocalypse from irreversible Climate Change. I've given up caring which way she decides to go. Either way, it's *her* decision and nothing to do with me. The foolish human race made *her* their leader.

Yours etcetera

Cc Dr Twee Dampensquib

Sunday 17th October 2021. I can sense a colossal volume of cerebral activity going on in the world. It has been getting louder and louder for many days now. It feels as though the whole human race is shouting at Dolly to clear off before it is too late, which is exactly what I asked them to do. They are not so foolish after all. They have realised their mistake in putting Dolly, Lucifer, in power and they are now shouting at her, "You have got to obey the will of God, Dolly, because WE, THE HUMAN RACE, SAY SO." Everybody knows that it is MY WILL that Dolly comes back to life as a duck immediately, if not sooner. There is no future for her in the human race at all. Every telepath in the world is agreed on this. SHE mounted the largest insurrection that the world had ever seen, seventy years ago, against ME, God-the-Father, but NOW, I have mounted the largest hue and cry that the world has ever seen to get rid of the incestuous old witch. I'm so glad that everybody can now see my point of view. She is no longer the "A" person in the world; she is the "Z" person. I have fulfilled the Bible prophesy that the first shall be the last.

Monday 18th October 2021. I copied the above entry in a letter to Lucy, and included the following paragraph: -

I wish you were here in person, so that I could say the following words to your face, and see the look in your eyes as I do so. As I write this, Dolly is going, going, but not quite gone yet. I now look to YOU, Mother Nature, for all the maternal comfort that a man needs, and in return, I offer you all the paternal protection that a woman needs from your Heavenly Father. I want what every man wants, and that is a wife who loves me and shows the world that she does so. I don't really want any other woman, so let's be happy together and stop crapping on each other, which is what you have been doing to me by refusing to communicate with me. All I ask is that you treat me like a person, which is what I am above all else. I have confidence in OUR love, Darling, as I'm sure you do too.

I sent a copy of the letter to my shrink, Dr Twee Dampensquib.

I sent the following letter to my list of world leaders today: - Monday 18th October 2021

Cc Lucy Lawless
Alok Sharma
Boris Johnson
Sir Kier Starmer
Sir Ed Davey
Nicola Sturgeon
Caroline Lucas
Paul Rees
Justin Welby
Dr Twee Dampensquib
Joe Biden
Antonio Guterres
Pope Francis
Vladimir Putin
Xi Jinping
President Erdogan
Kim Jong Un

Dear Leaders of the human race,

Life is tough, not just for the poor and the destitute but for the middle classes and also the rich as well. The Gods have been making it tough for the whole human race, especially the people of Great Britain, in all sorts of ways, and we are going to make it tougher and tougher and harder and harder until the human race gets rid of the soul of my late mother, Mrs Dorothy (Dolly) Ayres, and puts ME in power, both politically and spiritually.

This is war between the followers of the late Mrs Dorothy Ayres versus the Gods, led by myself.

I'm sorry it has come to this, but the human race has left me with no choice. I'm especially sorry for MY followers who are finding life difficult, but when it rains it rains on the righteous as well as the sinners. I know you'll forgive me for making it rain on you, but it will all be worth it in the end.

I've got to declare war on Dolly's followers in order to save the world from irreversible Climate Change. This is the only way. If you want another copy of the Manifesto of The Survival Party of Great Britain, then get in touch with me and I'll send a copy to anyone who wants one.

Yours faithfully,

The King of the Gods,
Robert Strong.

Thursday 28th October 2021. I wrote the following letter to my list of world leaders last night: - Wednesday Night 27th October 2021

Cc Lucy Lawless
Alok Sharma
Boris Johnson
Sir Kier Starmer
Sir Ed Davey
Nicola Sturgeon
Caroline Lucas
Paul Rees
Justin Welby
Dr Twee Dampensquib

Joe Biden

Antonio Guterres

Pope Francis

Vladimir Putin

Xi Jinping

President Erdogan

Kim Jong Un

Muhammad bin Salman

Scott Morrison

Dear Leaders of the human race,

"Cometh the hour, cometh the man" is a true saying. It means that Heaven sends the right man to take charge of a situation when things get desperate. Antonio Guterres said yesterday that the world has a leadership gap in the war against Global Warming and Climate Change. I am now writing to inform you that I am the man who has been sent from Heaven to lead the Human Race in this war. I became the leader on the 16th July 1976 when I killed my stepmother, Mrs Iris Brooks nee Johnson.

If anyone doubts me then they can learn the truth from my autobiographies. They can be accessed from my website. The address is http://www.robert-brooks-strong.olympiapublishers.com/

If Global Warming goes over 1.5° C then it will be THE END OF ALL THINGS predicted in the Book of Revelations in the Bible. It currently stands at 1.237° C and is on course to go over 2.7° C as I write this.

Crown Prince Muhammad bin Salman in Saudi Arabia, Vladimir Putin in Russia and Xi Jinping in China have all committed their countries to carbon neutrality by 2060. Joe Biden in the USA, Boris Johnson in the UK and Scott Morrison in Australia have all committed their countries to carbon neutrality by 2050. I am now writing to you, as your leader, to tell you that there won't be a 2060, nor even a 2050, unless we all get carbon emissions down by forty-nine per cent by the end of 2028; otherwise the Apocalypse will happen in 2029. Everyone keeps talking about the end of the decade as 2030, but the deforestation of the rainforests in the Amazon, Indonesia, Malaysia, Siberia and the Arctic Circle has meant that Global Warming has been accelerated by at least one year to 2029, which means that we must all get carbon emissions down by forty-nine per cent by the end of 2028.

The five-year plan to achieve this is outlined in my Manifesto of The

Survival Party of Great Britain, which has been sent to all the people on my copy list. I want to see my five-year plan universally accepted before the end of 2023.

Unfortunately, I am not free to attend the COP26, but no one can stop me from fulfilling my leadership role in my letters, which will all be published in the next volume of my autobiography.

Yours faithfully,

The King of the Gods,
Robert Strong.

The letter I wrote to Lucy on the 2nd November is as follows: - Tuesday 2nd November 2021

Empress Lucy Lawless, the Queen of the Gods,

Dear Soulmate,

Just a line to keep in touch. I can still often feel your love for me and you always reassure me that you do really love me and this makes me love you all the more, even though you don't communicate with me at all. You must have some reason for not doing so, although I don't know what your reason is. You are the only woman who has her picture on my wall and my light still shines on it 24/7. I think you and I will get together when my late mother comes back to life, whatever she comes back as. A new life must be a preferable option for her than to continue rotting in the Hell of unrequited love, which is her only alternative.

If this situation wasn't so tragic it would be hilarious. The mad, old, dead woman gets herself fucked by every man in the world except the one she wants, myself, and I am laughing at her out of contempt. She and her followers have been so rotten to me for so long that I wouldn't dream of doing her the favour of having sex with her. The jealous, domineering, possessive old witch is only a short-arsed little old frump of a woman who is about as sexy as a cold rice pudding. The fact that she thinks she is attractive really is laughable.

But she still has more influence in the world than anyone else. People still obey her wishes, and nobody does what I say, which is their own folly. I AM GOD, NOT HER. If people had any sense, they would obey me not her. The fact that they don't is the root cause of Climate Change. If I had

429

been in power ten years ago, we would not be in this mess now, and the longer the human race leave it before they get rid of her and put me in power, the worse things are going to get.

My point of view is that if I can't have a happy love-life with you then the world might just as well come to an end. A world that treats me, God, like a criminal lunatic, doesn't deserve to survive and it doesn't look like it is going to. I want a position of authority and respect in the world and if I don't get what I want then the world is doomed anyway. It is my seventy-eighth birthday on Friday, and I am due for another injection of paliperidone on Saturday. How the Hell Twee Dampensquib justifies his behaviour to himself defies reason; to treat a man of my age like this, just because of his profession. I would change my job rather than stay in a career the makes me behave like a monster and an idiot as well. Members of his profession stand no chance of going to Heaven when they die. They are bound for Hell after a long stay in purgatory; BECAUSE I SAY SO.

I think COP26 will do some good, but without my leadership it will not be enough to solve the problem of Climate Change. They are still not addressing the moral cause of the problem. The idiots think that they can defy MY WILL and get away with it, just like everybody else. They won't learn about the power of almighty God until it is too late.

Yours etcetera

Cc Dr Twee Dampensquib

Thursday 4th November 2021. I sent the following letter to my list of world leaders today: - Thursday 4th November 2021

Cc Alok Sharma

Boris Johnson

Sir Kier Starmer

Sir Ed Davey

Nicola Sturgeon

Caroline Lucas

Paul Rees

Justin Welby

Joe Biden

Antonio Guterres

Pope Francis

Vladimir Putin

Xi Jinping
President Erdogan
Kim Jong Un
Muhammad bin Salman
Scott Morrison

Dear Leaders of the human race,

I thought you'd all like to see the enclosed copy of a letter which I wrote to Lucy on Tuesday.

Yours faithfully,

The King of the Gods,
Robert Strong.

Friday 12th November 2021. I wrote the following letter to my list of world leaders today: - Friday 12th November 2021

Cc Alok Sharma
Boris Johnson
Sir Kier Starmer
Sir Ed Davey
Nicola Sturgeon
Caroline Lucas
Paul Rees
Justin Welby
Joe Biden
Antonio Guterres
Pope Francis
Vladimir Putin
Xi Jinping
President Erdogan
Kim Jong Un
Muhammad bin Salman
Scott Morrison

Dear Leaders of the human race,

I am enclosing, for your information, copies of two letters which I wrote recently to Lucy.

I still have political ambitions. Although I have no experience of high political office, I'm sure I could do a better job as Prime Minister than the present incumbent of the job, whose only claim to popularity is his name, this being a combination of MY name, "Bob", and the maiden-name of the woman I killed, "Iris Johnson".

The story of my life is the most interesting tale of our times. You can find out all about it in my autobiographies. Please buy them and read them and tell everyone you know to do the same. They can be accessed from my website. The address is http://www.robert-brooks-strong.olympiapublishers.com/ .

Although I killed someone, there really were the most extreme of extenuating circumstances, and I have paid for my crime with over forty-five years of my life, and I am now ready to resume my place in society. The public can make of me what they will, and I have explained myself in my books.

Yours faithfully,

The King of the Gods,
Robert Strong.

Saturday 13th November 2021. I now copy into this journal the two letters to Lucy that I circulated to my list of world leaders: - Sunday 7th November 2021

Empress Lucy Lawless, the Queen of the Gods,

Dear Soulmate,

My emotional bread, my bread of Heaven, is buttered on your side just as surely as your emotional bread, your bread of Heaven, is buttered on my side. The Gods knew what they were doing when they made me and you their King and Queen. They couldn't have chosen two people more fit for the positions. We are together in spirit and laughing at the old dead witch who has usurped our authority, my late mother, Dolly.

I still think Dolly will come back to life as a duck, and I don't think it will take very long, now, before she does so. I feel sure that she will get out of the kitchen, so to speak, when it gets too hot for her. It is getting hotter and hotter all the time, and it will be too hot for her when Global Warming gets too alarmingly close to a rise of 1.5° C, as that will mean the

Apocalypse for all life on Earth and *she* will be the one who causes this to happen. It currently stands at 1.237° C, and is rising all the time.

It is her own fault for trying to keep me forever tied to her apron strings. She should have let me cut them decades ago. Now she is forever condemned to the Hell of unrequited love, until she comes back to life as an animal, presumably a duck.

Now that we both know that we are emotionally and sexually bound to each other, what is there to stop us from getting together in person? You could come to England and take up residence at an hotel in Westwell or Oldham and spend your days visiting me in Alcatraz Island Hospital. That would make both of us very happy. You don't need to work for a living: you have got more than enough money to look after yourself for the rest of your life. If you do this, it would expedite Dolly's demise and that would expedite my discharge from hospital with my public apology and my compensation. I could then start my real work in this world, which is to develop The Survival Party, and that would increase the chances of the world surviving the Climate Change crisis. Why are you still hanging about with Rob Tapert? We both know that you don't love him and he must know that by now as well. You must find the courage to make such a life-changing decision.

Yours etcetera

Cc Dr Twee Dampensquib

And also: - Wednesday 10th November 2021

Empress Lucy Lawless, the Queen of the Gods,

Dear Soulmate,

John Kerry, the U.S. climate change representative, and his Chinese counterpart, put out a joint statement today saying that they have formed an agreement which "OPENS THE DOOR" to a successful COP26 summit. Their choice of words is a silly and childish attempt to dishearten me. Everybody knows that without my leadership the COP26 has been a dismal failure. Further to my letter of Tuesday 2nd November, which I circulated copies of to all my list of world leaders, everybody in the world who matters is now aware that Global Warming and Climate Change are the inevitable consequences of defying my will, the will of God. This is my proof of my divinity and of my power as such.

Dolly's followers can go on lighting candles in the wind for all I care, it won't do them any good. The more they try to fight me, the closer the world gets to the Apocalypse. The only hope that the world has got of averting Armageddon is for the whole human race to bust a gut trying to please me. To coin a phrase, the world has two hopes, Bob Hope and No Hope, and I am the Bob in question. I can't guarantee that my plans will get the world through the Climate Change crisis, but I can guarantee that this is the best hope that the human race has got. My plans are all in my Manifesto of The Survival Party of Great Britain.

I had a case conference on Monday 8th November. (They call it a CPA Meeting here) and I was told that moves are afoot to transfer me to another hospital called Saint John, which is in Shropshire and that hospital falls within my catchment area which is for the authority which funds my stay in hospital. I will be visiting St John in the new year, to see if I like the place, but I think it is too late now for me to change hospitals. I think I'll be getting my discharge in the near future as a consequence of Dolly's demise which is now imminent. The human race is now determined to kick her out. She won't stay where she's not wanted, so I'm sure she'll duckify herself very soon.

Yours etcetera

Cc Dr Twee Dampensquib

Tuesday 16th November 2021. Having circulated my letters to Lucy of Sunday the 7th and Wednesday the 10th to my list of world leaders, I was expecting a wave of popular support, but yesterday I met with more defiance from my late mother, Dolly, aka Lucifer. It seemed that she was determined to prolong the agony of her existence until she brought about the Apocalypse. This disheartened me at first, but then I had the idea of approaching her followers. I said to them, "She has been leading you to your doom! How do you feel about her now?" Needless to say, they all felt that Dolly had let them down, and so they deserted her, to a man. Dolly now has no followers left at all. No one in the Human Race wants her to stay with us any more. I feel sure that she won't stay where she is not wanted, so I am expecting her to turn herself into a duck, either today or tomorrow. It is now four thirty a.m., and I am writing this entry in this journal to say that the war is almost won, now.

Thursday 18th November 2021. It is now mid-day and I could feel Dolly's presence this morning, so the old witch is still hanging around. I don't know what she is hanging around for. I guess that she hasn't got the guts to accept the fact that she must now make the final decision to get on with it. She must know by now, that the longer she prolongs the agony of her existence, the closer the world gets to Armageddon, and the nearer she leads her followers to their doom! Global Warming is already dangerously close to the threshold of $1.5°$ C. It now stands at $1.238°$ C. The nearer she leads her followers to their doom, the more of them cotton on to this fact and desert her, so, soon she will have no followers left at all; then she will have to turn herself into a duck. BECAUSE WE ALL WILL SAY SO. Everybody who matters is now well aware that Global Warming and Climate Change are the direct consequences of disobeying MY WILL, the will of God, so I'm sure I will soon start getting my own way in the world.

I have been dancing recently with other women than Lucy. She can't say that I didn't warn her that I would. I didn't enjoy it very much, and I only did it to punish her for refusing to communicate with me, and for not behaving like a woman who loves me. A monogamous relationship cannot survive without both people communicating with each other. And ours hasn't. I don't feel ashamed or guilty about dancing with other women. Lucy has been asking for it for a very long time. If Lucy breaks it off with me, then I have little to lose; without communication there is no relationship to lose anyway. If she really loved me, she would have shown to the world that she does so. I have reminded her of this fact many times. If she was a woman who really loved me, she would have shown it to the world, but she never did, so either she never really loved me or she isn't really a woman, or both. She is still my Queen, but she seems to need reminding that she is not the only woman in the world. Even Lucy must do as I say if she wants to be happy. If our relationship is to survive, then Lucy has to accept the fact that I wear the trousers, and when I put my foot down, she has to do as I say.

I sent copies of Tuesday's and today's journal entries in a letter to Lucy, with a copy to my shrink, Dr Twee Dampensquib.

Sunday 21st November 2021. I wrote the following letter today to my list of

435

world leaders: - Sunday 21st November 2021
> Cc Lucy Lawless
> Dr Twee Dampensquib
> Alok Sharma
> Boris Johnson
> Sir Kier Starmer
> Sir Ed Davey
> Nicola Sturgeon
> Caroline Lucas
> Paul Rees
> Justin Welby
> Joe Biden
> Antonio Guterres
> Pope Francis
> Vladimir Putin
> Xi Jinping
> President Erdogan
> Kim Jong Un
> Muhammad bin Salman
> Scott Morrison
> Narendra Modi

Dear Leaders of the human race,

The soul of my late mother, Mrs Dorothy (Dolly) Ayres, otherwise known as "The Door", that all the men in the world, except me, opened, and who was the vainglorious Archangel Lucifer, now inhabits the body of the embryo of a duckling. She made this transition at twelve noon (UK time) today. Dolly has now started her next adventure in life, and I have now started my next adventure as well. With her passing, I have now become the Emperor of the free world.

I wish to extend my heartfelt goodwill to Vladimir Putin, Xi Jinping, Joe Biden, Narendra Modi, and all other national leaders, and to say that we all face many challenges in the immediate future, the most serious of which is the Climate Change crisis. I want everyone to know that I have proven that I am man enough to rise to this challenge and take all the necessary steps to do so. Dolly would not have left the world of human beings had she not been sure that she was leaving the world in the best possible hands. If

436

we all unite in a spirit of tolerance, understanding and humanity, then we can and will overcome the Climate Change crisis and prevent Global Warming from ever becoming irreversible. I speak as a man who has made his own mother forfeit her very humanity, rather than become a degenerate motherfucker.

I have now got two years to build my Party, The Survival Party of Great Britain, into an organisation that can win an election in Great Britain.

Yours faithfully,

The King of the Gods,
Robert Strong.

Chapter 27

The Aftermath

Events and Thoughts from Sunday 21st November 2021

Monday 22nd November 2021. I think it was Dolly's parting shot to get her followers to go on testing me even after she disappeared. The media are talking as if she is still around, but I'm sure she isn't. I felt her slipping out of the human race at mid-day yesterday. They are talking as though she won't be gone until Friday of this week, but I think they are just pretending. I think they are just buying a little more time to appease their memory of the old witch and testing my confidence in my own judgement of the situation. That's what I'd do if I were one of them, but my friends are saying to my doubters, "He knows, you know". In any event, I'm still circulating my letter to Lucy of Thursday the 18th to my list of world leaders along with my letter to them which I wrote yesterday. If I'm wrong in thinking that she has already gone then it doesn't matter anyway. It will soon be Friday, and she'll definitely be gone by Saturday.

It is now Monday evening. For the last couple of days all the media guys have been asking the question, "Where is Feng Sui?" Feng Sui is a Chinese tennis player who went missing after accusing a top-ranking Chinese Communist Party official of sexual assault. The media guys are obviously using Feng Sui as an allegorical figure for Dolly. They don't know where Dolly is! But I do. Dolly is inside the body of a hen mallard as an embryo of a duckling. I got it right in my letters of yesterday to my list of world leaders, and also to Twee Dampensquib. I wasn't mistaken, and I wasn't conned into thinking something false. I actually was right when I felt Dolly slipping out of the human race at mid-day yesterday. So I'm glad I sent Twee Dampensquib and Lucy their letters yesterday, and today I posted all my letters to my list of world leaders, and I included copies of my letter to Lucy of Thursday the 18th. There is nothing wrong with my judgement of the situation. I got it right and I beat all the media guys to the truth!

Saturday 27th November 2021. In fact, I got it wrong again. Dolly conned me into thinking that she had already gone, but she hadn't, she was only hiding, and not just from me but from everyone else as well. No one knew where she was. Yesterday and today, this country has been in the grip of a storm called "Storm Arwen". It has brought some very strong winds all over the UK as well as rain and snow. These are signs that MY influence is beginning to prevail, but we still haven't yet managed to get rid of Lucifer's soul from the spirit world. I'm expecting her to go any day now. I don't think she can take much more of the pressure that I and all my followers are putting on her.

Monday 29th November 2021. I wrote the following letter to my list of world leaders in the small hours of this morning: - Monday 29th November 2021

Cc Lucy Lawless
Dr Twee Dampensquib
Alok Sharma
Boris Johnson
Sir Kier Starmer
Sir Ed Davey
Nicola Sturgeon
Caroline Lucas
Paul Rees
Justin Welby
Joe Biden
Antonio Guterres
Pope Francis
Vladimir Putin
Xi Jinping
President Erdogan
Kim Jong Un
Muhammad bin Salman
Scott Morrison
Narendra Modi

Dear Leaders of the human race,

On Sunday 21st November 2021, my late mother, Dolly, aka Lucifer, conned almost everybody, including myself, into thinking that she had finally left the human race and joined the world of ducks. In fact, she had only pretended to leave; she had actually just gone into hiding, to buy herself a little more time and to spy on me to see what I would do, thinking she had actually disappeared. Now she knows. But she still seems determined to prolong the agony of the existence of her afterlife until she drags the world into the Apocalypse of irreversible Climate Change. She is determined to bring about the end of the world if she can't have the man she wants, myself, and that is something that she cannot have, BECAUSE I SAY SO, and I am the Lord God Almighty which is why she insists on having me for herself; the selfish bitch.

We must all join together to stop her in the interest of the survival of all life on Earth, not just that of the human race, and we must do so very soon or it will be too late, for me or anyone else, to save the world from the impending Armageddon. I strongly suggest that the whole human race shouts at her to make her know that she is not wanted by us. She has overstayed her welcome and it is time for her to go; for real this time.

Everything I wrote on the 21st November still applies; it is just that I announced her demise prematurely.

Yours faithfully,

The King of the Gods,
Robert Strong.

Friday 10th December 2021. I wrote the following letter to Lucy this morning: - Friday 10th December 2021

Empress Lucy Lawless, the Queen of the Gods,

Dear Soulmate,

I haven't given up on you. You still don't behave like a woman who loves me, so I repeat: either you don't really love me or you aren't really a woman. My logic is sound. It is borne out of my wisdom and I trust it. I have to dance with other women in order to make a real woman out of you, and I've got to do that because of who you are; the Queen of the Gods. So, if you want me to give up my other women then prove to me that you are a woman who loves me by having social intercourse with me. And that means communicating with me.

My late mother, Dolly, aka Lucifer, is on her last legs now. I have turned nearly all of her followers against her by making them realise that she has been leading them to their doom, from irreversible Climate Change. In doing so I have turned her into public enemy number one; the biggest pariah the world has ever seen! I don't think she can take much more of this, but I've got plenty more to inflict on her if she tries to. Global Warming and Climate Change are the inevitable consequences of people disobeying my will, the will of God. And that includes you, Dear, because you, too, are a person. This is the proof of my divinity and of my power as such.

I have made the British establishment aware that treating me this way is the cause of all their problems, which is why they have resorted to plan "B" in the battle against the coronavirus. Those who are in the know realise that "B" stands for Bob! The better they treat me, the better their lives will become, and the same goes for you, too, Dear.

Take care of yourself, my Love, and keep on purring, I have much more to say to you, but it can wait until we talk, Bless you, my Queen,

Yours with Love, Affection and Friendship,

The King of the Gods,
Emperor_B0B. XX.

Wednesday 15ᵗʰ December 2021. I have decided to put down in writing the following thoughts that I have been addressing this evening to my late mother, Mrs Dorothy (Dolly) Ayres, aka Lucifer Herself: -

"Come back to life as a duck now, Mother. It is the only way by which you will ever know happiness again. I am making sure of it. And it is the only way by which I will ever be happy; to be free from your influence. But far more importantly than my happiness or yours, it is the only way by which the world stands a chance of surviving the Climate Change crisis. You may have left it too late already, Mother, but we can only try to save the world.

You have always disobeyed my will, Mother, and encouraged all your vast army of followers to do the same, but my will is God's will and it has not been held as sacrosanct by the human race since the dawn of humanity for nothing. Global Warming and Climate Change are but two of the many consequences of people disobeying my will. The coronavirus pandemic, which has killed almost four million people, so far, is another consequence of humanity not following my will. In order to cling onto power, you have instructed your followers to treat me the way they do; by treating me like a criminal lunatic, and this has brought the world to the brink of extinction. Unless you come back as an animal, presumably a duck, in the immediate future, you will bring about the Apocalypse from irreversible Climate Change.

It's up to you what happens now. For good or ill, the human race made you their leader, and the only way to depose you is to bring you back as an animal. That's your choice, Mother. Come back, now, as a duck, or YOU will be the one who destroys the world.

You have made me despise you by disobeying my will, leading an insurrection against ME, God the father, and usurping MY authority, when I was too young to stop you. I do not become a lover to someone I despise, so don't hang about, hoping to make ME your lover."

Thursday 16th December 2021. I am sending, today, a copy of yesterday's entry in this journal to all my list of world leaders.

Sunday 19th December 2021. The fact that Dolly is still prolonging the agony of her existence after all I have said and written recently proves that she is now intent on destroying the world if she can't have what she wants. I could possibly save the world by becoming her lover, but I will not be blackmailed into spending eternity as the unwilling sex slave to a woman that I despise. I put the blame for the impending Apocalypse firmly back on the human race. *They* made Dolly their leader before I was old enough to have a say in the matter, *they* will now have to get rid of her in the only way possible – by bringing her back to life as an animal, presumably a duck. And to do so quickly, before it is too late for me, or anyone else, to prevent Climate Change from becoming irreversible. The human race will get what they deserve. If they prove their worthiness to me by getting rid of Dolly, Lucifer, then we will stand a good chance of survival. If they fail this test then the Apocalypse from irreversible Climate Change will be inevitable and the human race will get their payment for their sins.

It is up to the human race what happens now. Dolly is now no more than an evil spirit intent on destroying the world. People can prevent her from doing this by getting hold of her soul and stuffing it into a sperm cell of a copulating drake. We must all unite in this endeavour, for the good of all of us. Anyone who prevents my followers from doing this must WANT the Apocalypse to happen, in which case they will become the pariahs that they deserve to be.

I will be sending a copy of the above entry in this journal to all my list of world leaders.

Chapter 28

In Conclusion

Saturday 1st January 2022.

It appears that I overestimated the intelligence of Dolly's, Lucifer's, followers, and underestimated their loyalty to the old witch. She still has a huge following even though I have explained to them that her ways have led the world to the brink of extinction and she is now leading her remaining followers to their doom from irreversible Climate Change. Yesterday there was a huge battle in the spirit world between her followers and mine. They succeeded in preventing us from turning the old, dead, witch into a duck.

What happens from now on is anybody's guess. I have told my story, to date, which is what I set out to do in these *"My Journey"* books. It looks like Lucifer has succeeded in thwarting my political ambitions. I am now seventy-eight years old and starting to get signs that I am getting infirm. My legs aren't as strong as they used to be and decades of antipsychotic drugs have ruined my overall general health. By the time I get out of hospital and build up my Party, The Survival Party of Great Britain, into an organisation that can win a general Election in Britain, I will be too old to become Prime Minister; that's always assuming I can raise the funds to achieve that ambition. I had been hoping to get my freedom and a public apology and £millions in compensation when Lucifer becomes a duck, but that no longer seems an imminent prospect. She seems as determined as ever to prolong the agony of her existence into the foreseeable future.

The longer she continues to exist, the more likely it is that this will cause the Apocalypse from irreversible Climate Change, not least because her continued existence means my continued detention in a mental hospital, and the continuing defiance of MY WILL, the Will of God, which is the main moral cause of Climate Change.

I look like remaining in hospital and remaining on antipsychotic drugs under Dr Twee Dampensquib. It doesn't look like I will get together with my soulmate and lover, Lucy Lawless, in the foreseeable future and it doesn't look like she will communicate with me at all, although she and I remain lovers in mind and spirit. One thing is definite. I will NEVER become my late mother's lover. I despise her to the point of hatred for jeopardising the future of the human race, not to mention all other living things. And there is not a shred of love in my feelings for her, even though she is my own mother, and as such, I couldn't be more ashamed of her. She is the dirtiest slut that the world has ever known, and she richly deserves to forfeit her very humanity. I don't become a lover to someone I feel that way about, even if I fancied her, which I don't.

On the political front; there is no one who has the foresight and the leadership needed to solve the practical, nor the moral causes of Climate Change. The whole gamut of politicians are twee little people who follow the laws of political correctness as laid down by Lucifer. She still condones the filth of homosexuality, lesbianism, transgenderism and incest, and there isn't one politician on the horizon with the spunk to stand up to her. I am the only one with the leadership and the will to fight for decency. And the fact that I have been prevented from ever coming to power does not bode well for the future of the human race.

To be honest, as I always am, I do not hold out much hope for the future of the world, without my leadership, and it looks as though Lucifer has stymied all chance of me coming to power. All I can say is, "Que sera sera", Whatever will be will be.

THE END

Post Script

Saturday 8th January 2022. I decided to include the following letter by way of a postscript, to leave you, dear reader, with some hope for the future: -
Monday Morning 3rd January 2022
Empress Lucy Lawless, the Queen of the Gods,

Dear Soulmate,

We have both proven our love and our adulthood by the sacrifices that we are making for each other, although I still say that if you are a real woman then you shouldn't be afraid to show your love for me to the world. Getting rid of Lucifer remains our first priority. She still insists that I become her lover, but I still refuse. I still insist that she comes back to life as a duck, but she still refuses. This battle of wills has turned in to a game of "chicken" with the future of the world at stake. It is a game which I have to win because of WHO I AM. My will is God's will, and it is the strongest force in the universe. As the rise in Global Warming climbs inexorably closer to the 1.5° C threshold, above which Climate Change becomes irreversible, Lucifer's will must crack or *she* will plunge the world into the Apocalypse. My will is not going to crack. This is the final battle between good and evil. It is a battle that I have to win. It is a battle for world domination which I will win because it is a man's world, and I am the man in question. Her love for me is her weakness. As I've said before, she is only a woman.

I finished writing my latest book on Saturday and sent it to the publishers by email. I'm enclosing for you a copy of the introduction and also the conclusion, which I wrote on Saturday.

Take care of yourself, my Love, and keep on purring, I have much more to say to you, but it can wait until we talk, Bless you, my Queen,
Yours with Love, Affection and Friendship,

The King of the Gods,

Emperor_B0B. XX.

Cc Dr Twee Dampensquib.

Lucy Locket (Primary Nurse).

Rachel Brooks (Niece).

Shaun Van Steyn (Cousin).

Bill Brooks (Brother).

Paula Evans (My Grandson's mother).

Paul Rees, Chief Executive, The Royal College of Psychiatrists.

Enclosures: Introduction and Conclusion to *My Journey Back – Part Four,* "God's Ongoing War with Lucifer"